Two wee

Benthyciad pyth...

Please return on or before
A wnewch chi ddychwelyc...

Poultry Production
and
Waste Management

Poultry Production
and
Waste Management

K. H. Nahm, Ph.D.

Professor of Taegu University
President of the Korean Poultry Science Association
Feed and Nutrition Laboratory
College of Natural Resources
Taegu University
Gyong San, 712-714
South Korea

B. A. Nahm, D.V.M.

Practitioner of Lincolnway Animal Hospital
6363 Lincoln Highway
Matteson, IL 60443
U.S.A.

This book is dedicated to our sons, Nickolas and Noel Nahm.
"Always have a dream."

Table of Contents

Contents

Preface

This is a nonprofit book. Whenever the author published one of his articles in a journal, he has had many requests for copies of those articles. When he would answer these requests, he thought there should be some way to share more information with these scientists. This is his idea of how he can assist them and their further research. This is the reason why he and Dr. B. A. Nahm started to compile this collection of articles for this book about three years ago. He sincerely hopes that this book can assist you in various ways for your research.

Dr. Bonnie Nahm is a well known veterinary practitioner in this area. The author could see that she always handles her pet animal patients in a scientific manner. She also invested an enormous amount of time for preparing this book. Even though her area of study is different than the author's, her encouragement has always helped him to progress in his area and to write more. The author is always grateful that he has had a chance to work closely with her.

The author will always have plenty of topics that he would like to write about step by step in journals or other magazines. He feels as though he has only begun to write about chicken manure and its impact on the environment. The author will remain at Taegu University for less than 10 years, but he wants to keep writing after he leaves that school. This book is dedicated to the readers and people who love livestock animals and poultry.

The Authors

Conditions for mould growth and aflatoxin production in feedstuffs

K. H. Nahm

Department of Animal Science, College of Agriculture, Taegu University
Gyong San 713-714, Korea Republic

INTRODUCTION

The presence of moulds or fungi in various feedstuffs has been a problem for many years. This is especially true when conditions for optimal mould growth exist such as high feed moisture content, high humidity and high temperature. All moulds are not harmful; however, those commonly found in field or storage environmental conditions are capable of forming toxins and must be considered as potentially hazardous. Since the recognition that dietary mycotoxins pose a threat to animal health, numerous investigations have been initiated in an effort to elucidate the mechanisms by which mycotoxins cause production inefficiency. Perhaps the most extensively studied of all mycotoxins that cause disease in poultry and pigs is aflatoxin. Aflatoxicosis in broiler chickens and young pigs has been shown to cause poor growth and an impairment in feed efficiency (Smith & Hamilton 1970), an increased susceptibility to bruising (Tung et al. 1971), coagulopathy (Doerr et al. 1976), poor digestion of nutrients (Osborne et al. 1982), impairment in the function of lymphoid tissues (Giamborne et al. 1978), and numerous other adverse effects (Hamilton 1971).

ENVIRONMENTAL CONDITIONS FOR MOULD FORMATION

There are primary conditions which promote mould growth and under which inhibitors should be used. If moisture levels exceed 13 to 14% or relative humidity goes beyond 80 to 85%, mould is apt to grow (Fig. 1). When temperatures rise above 55℃, mould begins to grow rapidly. Cooler temperatures retard mould growth but do not stop it. Damaged and broken grains open areas for mould growth in cereals or feeds that have become infested with insects. It was found that crumbles (feed that has been pelleted and then reduced in particle size) were more susceptible to fungal attack than unpelleted mash. Apparently, pelleted feed is more easily digested than non-pelleted by fungi as well as by animals (Jones & Hamilton 1983).

Hamilton (1985) reported about the relationship between fungal activity and the water content of feeds and their ingredients. This was demonstrated by samples of feed from three poultry companies which were analyzed for water content and production of CO_2. The water contents averaged 11.5, 12.5 and 13%, respectively. Feed from all three companies produced measurable CO_2 and correlation between CO_2 and moisture content was highly significant. Nahm & Nahm (1988) reported that production of CO_2 in feeds with water contents averaging 12.6 and 12.7% reached a peak of 10.9% after 40 days of storage. It is generally assumed that a feed moisture content of below 13% is low enough to inhibit microbial activity but the above studies showed that this assumption is clearly untrue.

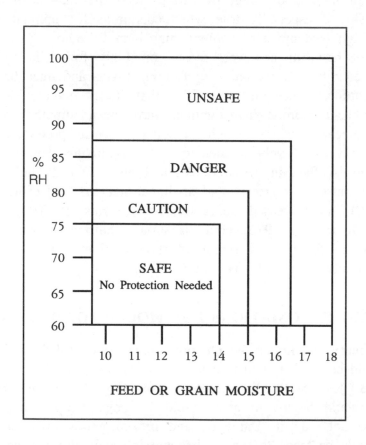

Figure 1. Relationship of relative humidity and moisture in causing feeds to become mouldy (Tindall, 1983b)

Pig News and Information Vol. 11(3): 349-352 (1990)

THE NUTRITIONAL VALUE OF MOULDY GRAINS

The possible effects of fungi on the nutritional value of feedstuffs has received attention. Richardson *et al.* (1962) observed in poults receiving mouldly soybean meal a growth depression that was prevented by the addition of lysine. Fritz *et al.* (1973) noted that *Fusarium moniliforme* [*Gibberella fujikuroi*] caused thiamin deficiency. Bartov *et al.* (1982) observed a marked decrease in the fat content of mouldy maize and sorghum during storage (Table 1). The cereals, whole or ground, with their original moisture content (12.1 to 13.0%) or increased moisture content (15.0%), were stored for 63 to 96 days. The authors showed that the ground mouldy cereals had a reduced dietary fat level during the 3 weeks feeding period and significantly (P < 0.05) lowered ME values and depressed performance. Data from other studies indicated that the fat content (Bartov & Paster 1985) and carotene content (Nahm & Nahm 1988) decreased in feeds untreated with mould inhibitors after 40 days of storage. These changes were prevented by the addition of fungistats.

Table 1. Effect of mould development on a few nutritional components of maize
(Bartov *et al.*, 1982)

Parameter[1]	Maize quality[2]	
	Good	Mouldy
Total fat (%)	3.8	2.4
Fatty acid composition[3]		
16 : 0	11.3	9.1
18 : 0	1.7	1.7
18 : 1	24.4	25.6
18 : 2	60.9	61.9
18 : 3	1.6	1.6
Vitamin E (mg/kg)	22.1	20.6
Carotene (mg/kg)	3.1	2.3
Xanthophyll (mg/kg)	16.2	16.6
Crude protein (%)	8.7	8.7

[1] The values are averages of two determinations in well-mixed material.
[2] Ground maize containing 13.0 and 15.1% moisture, respectively, stored for 96 days.
[3] Expressed as percentage by weight of total fatty acids of the individual fatty acid represented by chain length: number of double bonds.

ENVIRONMENTAL CONDITIONS FOR AFLATOXIN PRODUCTION

Toxins produced by moulds are called mycotoxins and the effects of these toxins on animals are called mycotoxicoses. The most studied of the mycotoxins is aflatoxin. This toxic compound is produced by different strains of mould that can grow on virtually any feed source that will support growth.

Not many articles have reported the environmental conditions for aflatoxin formation. Schroeder (1969) stated that three most important factors influencing aflatoxin formation in stored field crops were moisture, relative humidity and temperature. Jones *et al.* (1982) found that the optimum conditions for production of aflatoxin in feed appeared to be 10 to 13% moisture, which was lower than reported for mould formation, and 70 to 89% relative humidity, which was also lower than the safety level for mould formation (Tables 2 and 3). Jones *et al.* (1982) also showed that the optimum temperature for production of aflatoxin in feed was 19 to 27℃ which agreed with laboratory findings of Schroeder & Hein (1967).

The greatest differences noted in the above study of aflatoxin formation (Jones *et al.* 1982) from the environmental conditions for mould formation would appear to be in the low moisture level and the low relative humidity level compared with the safety boundary for mould formation in feed storage, associated here with peak aflatoxin production.

Table 2. Moisture and aflatoxin content of feed (Jones *et al.*, 1982)

Moisture range (%)	Samples (no.)	Aflatoxin (ppb)	Aflatoxin (% positive)
9.5~9.9	3	0[a]	0[a]
10.0~10.4	4	0.8[a]	25.0[c]
10.5~10.9	22	4.6[abc]	31.8[c]
11.0~11.4	27	10.9[e]	25.9[c]
11.5~11.9	22	24.5[f]	34.8[c]
12.0~12.4	40	8.4[bcde]	24.0[c]
12.5~12.9	27	10.0[cde]	32.1[c]
13.0~13.4	26	3.8[ab]	12.5[b]
13.5~13.9	22	4.0[ab]	9.1[ab]
14.0~14.4	22	3.5[ab]	9.1[ab]
14.5~14.9	8	6.1[abcd]	25.0[c]
15.0 and >	7	12.9[e]	28.6[c]

[a,b,c,d,e,f] Value in a column with different superscripts differ significantly (P < 0.05).

Table 3. Relation of aflatoxin in the feed to relative humidity in the poultry house (Jones *et al.*, 1982)

Moisture humidity (%)	Samples (no.)	Aflatoxin (ppb)	Aflatoxin (% positive)
< 60	34	2.0[a]	8.8[a]
60~69	72	2.7[a]	15.5[a]
70~79	66	11.1[b]	28.8[b]
80~89	28	5.6[ab]	32.1[b]
90~99	3	1.1[a]	33.3[b]

[a,b] Values in a column with different superscripts differ significantly ($P < 0.05$).

MOULD INHIBITORS

There are several methods of preserving feed ingredients. The list includes: drying, antioxidants, mould inhibitors, organic acids, phosphates, cooking or toasting, fat extraction, blending and fermenting, mould inhibitors are manufactured to inhibit mould growth and prevent the production of toxic substances. They are fungistats and not fungicides, that is, they only stop the growth of moulds. They do not kill all moulds and mould spores present.

Effective mould inhibitors should have the following characteristics: (1) the ability to inhibit growth of a broad spectrum of moulds, (2) be composed of compounds which are synergistically effective in prohibiting the formation of moulds, (3) have a small enough particle size to allow ready dispersion throughout the entire feed mix or cereal mass, (4) have a low pH value, (5) have the ability to release inhibitor in low moisture content feed, (6) be easy to handle and be packaged securely, and (7) be cost effective. Each type of acid in the various mould inhibitors serves a different function. Propionic acid is an actual mould controller, acetic acid lowers the pH, benzoic acid controls yeast growth, and sorbic acid is a slow release product which controls mould growth over a long period of time. These acids by themselves, in combination, or else as salts have been typically used as mould inhibitors. When reviewing the acids used as mould inhibitors it must be noted that they do not penetrate very well into the substrate of cereals or feeds when moisture levels are below 30% (Tindall 1983a). As a result, only the exo-spores are readily controlled.

Dixon and Hamilton (1981a) found that the smaller the maize meal particles, the better the inhibition observed. In their study maize meal was separated into four particle size ranges (< 0.15, 0.59 to 0.83, 1.41 to 1.65 and > 2.36 mm), and the effect of particle size on inhibition of the native mould flora by propionic acid was determined by measuring CO_2 production. At the higher concentrations of propionic acid (1.0 and 2.0 mg/g of meal), the inhibition was size dependent at the three moisture levels tested (20, 25 and 30%). Nahm & Nahm (1988) showed similar results in which the particle sizes of the substrate had an influence on the inhibitory properties of the mould inhibitor (Table 4). Their experiments were on the effect of particle size of two different levels of protein in the feed (18% for chick starter and 12% for beef feed) on the inhibitor and the interactions between particle size and protein levels on the inhibitor. The effect of particle size in this research was such that the smaller the particle size, the greater the activity displayed by the mould inhibitor. On a practical basis these findings suggested that mould inhibitors would be more efficacious if the milling process produced a finely ground feed.

The effect of mixing varying amounts of soybean meal, fish meal and poultry by-product meal in maize meal was observed to antagonize the antifungal activity of propionic acid (Dixon & Hamilton 1981b). They found that the antagonistic

Table 4. Carbon dioxide concentrations at 10, 20 and 40 days storage (Nahm and Nahm, 1988)

Protein (%)	1.19 mm particle size (%)	Moisture content (%)	CO_2 concentration (%)					
			10 days		20 days		40 days	
			UT	T	UT	T	UT	T
18	80	12.6	5.50	0.29[A]	6.10	0.27[A]	10.40	0.29[A]
	40	12.6	5.26	0.39[B]	6.00	0.42[B]	10.50	0.41[B]
12	80	12.7	5.80	0.25[A]	6.50	0.25[A]	10.90	0.27[A]
	40	12.7	5.30	0.41[B]	6.00	0.41[B]	10.50	0.47[B]
Mean protein (%)	18		5.38	0.34	6.05	0.35	10.45	0.35
	12		5.55	0.33	6.25	0.33	10.70	0.37
1.19 mm particle size (%)	80		5.65	0.27[C]	6.30	0.26[C]	10.65	0.28[C]
	40		5.28	0.40[D]	6.00	0.42[D]	10.65	0.44[D]

UT: Untreated diet.   T: Treated diet
[A,B] Values with different supersripts within the 4 treatments are significantly different (P < 0.05).
[C,D] Values with different supersripts within the different particle sizes are significantly different (P < 0.01).
* Protein: particle size interaction was significant (P < 0.05).

effects could be rationalized on the basis of the free acid form of propionic acid being converted to the less active salt form by the buffering capacity of the antagonistic supplements. However, Nahm & Nahm (1988) could not show any antagonistic effects of the different levels of protein (18% and 12%) in the feed to the activity of a mould inhibitor.

Mould inhibitors tend to lose their ability to control fungi with continued use. They act directly on the fungal protoplasm. Fungi which are not entirely destroyed by acid treatment tend to mutate and thus become more resistant from season to season. It becomes necessary to increase the dosage each year to obtain the same control. Acids can also affect the nutrient quality of feeds. It has been found that acids can destroy vitamin E (Allen 1974). In addition, the mode of action of mould inhibitor is pH dependent with their activity being higher at lower pH (Hagler, 1983). When products such as limestone are used in feed, the pH is raised, thereby reducing the effectiveness of mould inhibitors.

CONCLUSION

Much of the feed manufactured today contains mould inhibitors. Most pig feeds have some type of inhibitors as do poultry feeds and horse feeds. Ammonia, copper sulfate, urea, chlorine, certain antibiotics and various chemicals have been tested as mould inhibitors. Most have shown good antifungal activity but for reasons of expense or lack of penetration into the market, have not been widely used.

The best insurance to protect feeds or cereals from mould attack is to avoid mould as much as possible through careful handling or to curb it through the use of various available mould inhibitors. In addition to using mould inhibitors, feed quality can be kept by maintaining suitable storage conditions. These can be achieved by: (1) Cleaning storage facilities prior to filling. Remove materials from walls, cracks and crevices, and spray interiors with an approved residual insecticide. (2) Feed to be stored should be (a) at a safe moisture level for storage or (b) dried to safe moisture levels for storage, and (c) kept in condition by physical means such as aeration and agitation, (d) kept in condition by preservation such as by organic acids or oxygen-free storage or (e) kept in condition by a combination of the above. (3) Feeds in storage on a long term basis should be monitored at regular intervals for moisture, temperature and/or insect activity.

When a mouldy feedstuff presents itself, one must decide whether or not to use it.

Some factors to consider include: (1) the extent of spoilage, (2) the age and type of animal to be fed, (3) estimated value of the feedstuff, given that (a) moulds deplete nutrients in feeds and (b) moulds may have a detrimental effect on animal performance, and (4) a comparison of the cost of mouldy feed to that of uncontaminated feed.

REFERENCES

Allen, W.M. (1974). Loss of vitamin E in stored cereals in relation to myopathy of yearling cattle. *Veterinary Record* **94**, 373-375.

Bartov, I.; Paster, N. (1985). Effect of early stages of fungal development on the nutritional values of diets for broiler chicks. *British Poultry Science* **27**, 415-420.

Bartov, I.; Paster, N.; Lisker, N. (1982). The nutritional value of mouldy grains for broiler chicks. *Poultry Science* **61**, 2247-2254.

Dixon, R.C.; Hamilton, P.B. (1981a). Effect of particle sizes of corn meal and a mould inhibitor on mould inhibition. *Poultry Science* **60**, 2412-2415.

Dixon, R.C.; Hamilton, P.B. (1981b). Effect of feed ingredients on the antifungal activity of propionic acid. *Poultry Science* **60**, 2407-2411.

Doerr, J.A.; Wyatt, R.D.; Hamilton, P.B. (1976). Impairment of coagulation function during aflatoxicosis in young chickens. *Toxicology and Applied Pharmacology* **35**, 437-446.

Fritz, J.C.; Mislivec, P.B.; Pla, G.W.; Harrison, B.N., Weeks, C.E.; Dantzman, J. G. (1973). Toxicogenicity of mouldy feed for young chicks. *Poultry Science* **52**, 1523-1530.

Giambrone, J.J.; Ewert, D.L.; Wyatt, R.D.; Edison, C.S. (1978). Effect of aflatoxin on the humeral and cell-mediated immune systems of the chicken. *American Journal of Veterinary Research* **39**, 305-308.

Hagler, W.M.,Jr. (1983). An update on mould inhibitors. In *Maryland Nutrition Conference. National Feed Ingredients Association*, 1983. Feed Ingredients Institute.

Hamilton, P.B. (1985). Factors influencing activity of fungi and antifungal agents in poultry feed. In *Trichthecenes and other Mycotoxins*, 207-218.

Jones, F.T.; Hamilton, P.B. (1983). Evidence for fungal activity in poultry feed under typical field conditions. *Annual Meeting of the American Society for Microbiology* **83**, 246 (Abstract).

Jones, F.T.; Hagler, W.H.; Hamilton, P.B. (1982). Association of low levels of aflatoxin in feed with productivity losses in commercial broiler operations. *Poultry Science* **61**, 861-868.

Nahm, K.H.; Nahm, K.S. (1988). Effects of particle size and the levels of protein in the ration on the usage of a mould inhibitor. *Korean Journal of Poultry Science* **15**, 261-268.

Osborne, D.J.; Huff, W.E.; Hamilton, P.B.; Burmeister, H.R. (1982). Comparisons of ochratoxin, aflatoxin, and T-2 toxin for their effects on selected parameters related to digestion and evidence for specific metabolism of carotenoids in chickens. *Poultry Science* **61**, 1646-1652.

Richardson, L.R.; Wilkes, S.; Godwin, J.; Pierce, K.R. (1962). Effect of mouldy diet and mouldy soybean meal on the growth of chicks and poults. *Journal of Nutrition* **78**, 301-306.

Schroeder, H.W. (1969). Factors influencing the development of aflatoxins in some field crops. *Journal of Stored Products Research* **5**, 87-192.

Schroeder, H.W.; Hein, H. (1967). Aflatoxins: production of the toxins in vitro in relation to temperature. *Applied Microbiology* **15**, 441-445.

Smith, J.W.; Hamilton, P.B. (1970). Aflatoxicosis in the broiler chicken. *Poultry Science* **49**, 207-215.

Tindall, W. (1983a). Mould inhibitor round up. *Animal Nutrition and Health* October, 43-47.

Tindall, W. (1983b). Mould problems and controls. *Feed Management* **34**, 32-34.

Tung, H.T.; Smith, J.W.; Hamiton, P.B. (1971). Aflatoxicosis and bruising in the chicken. *Poultry Science* **50**, 795-800.

World's Poultry Science Journal Vol. 51: 177-185 (1995)   21

Possibilities for preventing mycotoxicosis in domestic fowl

K. H. Nahm

Feed and Nutrition Laboratory, College of Agriculture, Taegu University, Gyong San, 713-714 Korea Republic

---

Since the recognition of mycotoxicosis about 30 years age, various research projects have been undertaken to develop measures to prevent or reduce the serious financial losses it causes. Although inhibitors which prevent mould growth and the production of toxic substances have been developed, several factors still limit their effectiveness and practical use by the feed industry. Various kinds of sorbent materials have also been assessed for their ability to remove or diminish the adverse effects of mycotoxins in animal feeds. Even though it does not bind all the mycotoxin and allows partial absorption of toxin in the gastrointestinal tract, hydrated sodium calcium aluminosilicate (HSCAS) is considered to be an outstandingly effective additive. Several new possibilities have emerged involving the use of the sulphur-containing amino acids, antioxidants, vitamins, trace mineral and other nutrients in building detoxicants. Research into methods of preventing mycotoxicosis in poultry needs to be carried out against the background of the underlying levels of mycotoxins found under the normal storage conditions for feed used in the industry.

(Keywords: Antioxidants; detoxicants; domestic fowl; HSCAS; mould inhibitors; mycotoxicosis; mycotoxins; sorbent materials)

Introduction

Mycotoxins are chemical substances produced by certain moulds that can cause serious adverse effects in poultry and other animals. These effects include reduced feed intake, poor growth, gastrointestinal lesions, bone abnormalities, neurological disturbance, immunosuppression and death. Poultry feeds are an excellent medium for microbial growth, with the risk of fungal growth increasing rapidly with rising moisture content. While the growth of micro-organisms may resulting the deterioration in the purely nutritional value of feed, this paper focuses on mycotoxins.

Various practices, including major changes in harvesting methods, can have important effects on mould growth and subsequent mycotoxin production. It is generally believed that at moisture contents below 13% microbial activity is largely inhibited, but studies by Hamilton (1985) and Nahm (1991a) have shown that such feed still produces easily measurable amounts of carbon dioxide. Jones *et al.* (1982) found that aflatoxin production in feed occurred at 10-13% moisture, which is lower than the level reported for mould growth, and at atmospheric moisture contents below 70% relative humidity, which is often regarded as the threshold safety level for mould growth. It is clear that, because fungi differ in their environmental requirements for growth, it is difficult to predict toxin production (Seiter and Jurdan, 1990). This paper reviews the possibilities for preventing mycotoxicosis in poultry.

Mould inhibitors

A traditional method of controlling fungal activity is the use of antifungal agents (mould inhibitors) of which there are many on the market. Some of those widely used in the feed industry are based on short-chain fatty acids such as propionic, acetic, sorbic, benzoic and formic acids. Mould inhibitors are manufactured to inhibit mould growth and to prevent the production of toxic substances. It is important to remember that they are fungistats and not fungicides, i.e. they only stop the growth of molds and do not kill all moulds and mould spores present.

The activity of mould inhibitors in animal feed is limited by several factors. For example, mould inhibitors are all weakly acidic with a pKa of about pH 5. Hence, the pH of concern is 6.5 and the range shown by 125 varieties was an entire pH unit, although the pH distribution curve was normal. Such variation may significantly affect the antifungal activity of organic acid mould inhibitors. Other ingredients of animal feed such as limestone flour, soybean meal, fish meal, poultry by product meal and other high-protein supplements neutralize free acids and convert them to their less active salts (Dixon and Hamilton, 1981a; Nahm, 1990).

The particle size of the substrate and of the mould inhibitor also influences fungal and antifungal activity. The smaller the particle size of the feed, the greater the amount of respiratory carbon dioxide produced by the resident microorganisms, presumably because of the greater surface area associated with the smaller particles (Dixon and Hamilton, 1981b; Nahm, 1989). Tabib *et al.* (1984) reported that the onset of fungal activity in pellets containing mould inhibitors was delayed beyond that of the pelleted untreated material, or of treated mash. Tabib *et al.* (1982) also showed that there might be a threshold dose which must be exceeded before any antifungal activity is evident; and the activity of antifungal agents in feed is time-dependent.

Mould inhibitors tend to lose their ability to control fungi with continued use. They act directly on the fungal mycoprotoplasm, but those which are not entirely destroyed by mould inhibitor treatment tend to mutate so becoming more resistant from season to season (Rose and Bradley, 1980). To achieve the same degree of control it therefore becomes necessary to increase the amount of mould inhibitor used each year. They may also affect the nutrient quality of feeds; for example, it has been found that mould inhibitor can destroy vitamin E (Forenbacher *et al.*, 1975).

There are a number of factors which affect the application of mould inhibitors and these are outlined below (Whiteside and Halley, 1990).

(1) Product characteristics - physical form and chemical composition and nature.
(2) Type of feedstuff to be treated - whole grain, meal, other forms and other ingredients.
(3) Feed mill design and operation - physical layout, conveying systems, type of mixer, and operational control.
(4) Other factors - operational control of application system and degree of accuracy desired.

In practice, depending on scale and other factors, the installation and operational requirements for the application mould inhibitors range from the simple and inexpensive to those which are highly complex and expensive (Whiteside and Halley, 1990).

Today's feed mill managers are faced with an overwhelming choice of mould inhibitors and application decisions. One of the major decisions involves the acceptable degree of corrosion damage to the equipment caused by the mould inhibitor since any liquid, including water, is to some extent corrosive. Corrosion has been accepted in the feed industry as a cost of doing business (Coelho, 1990). The considerations outlined above should be evaluated when planning, designing, and installing systems using feed preservatives. Hamilton (1985) pointed out that the study of fungal activity and antifungal activity in feed and feed ingredients is a neglected area and such studies are necessary to achieve control over fungal activity.

Addition of sorbent materials

Various classes of sorbent materials (aluminosiliates, bentonite, silicas, zeolite, etc.) have been evaluated for their ability to remove or diminish the adverse effects of mycotoxins in animal feed. One compound in particular, hydrated sodium calcium aluminosilicate (HSCAS), was found to have an affinity for aflatoxin B_1 (Kubena et al., 1987). HSCAS at a concentration of 210.5% of the diet protected broiler and Leghorn chicks from the adverse effects of dietary aflatoxin B_1 (Phillips et al., 1988; Kubena et al., 1990a, b). These scientists indicated that HSCAS sorbed aflatoxin selectively during the digestive process, which rendered most of the aflatoxin unavailable for absorption from the gastrointestinal tract. Although HSCAS is effective at sorbing aflatoxin, Huff et al. (1992) pointed out that HSCAS did not tie up all the aflatoxin, as evidenced by the fact that a proportion of the aflatoxin-induced responses were still present when aflatoxin was added to HSCAS, and silicated-type sorbent are not equal in their ability to protect against aflatoxicosis (Kubena et al., 1993). The addition of HSCAS reduced the toxicity of aflatoxin based on body weight by 65%. However, dietary HSCAS did not alter the toxicity of ochratoxin A and only slightly altered the toxicity of the combined treatment of aflatoxin and ochratoxin A (Huff et al., 1992). While the belief that sorbtive materials can be used to manage mycotoxin problems associated with poultry production is therefore a valuable working hypothesis, to be truly effective these materials must have the ability to sorb a large number of chemically distinct mycotoxins (Huff et al., 1992).

Detoxification therough nutrition

Sulphur-containing amino acid and protein

Detoxification is also called 'biotransformation'. Ward (1988) cited its definition as the sum of all chemical reactions that alter the structure, water solubility and eventual disposition of non-nutritive substances that are generally foreign to the animal. Toxic agents such as mycotoxin require metabolic conversion ('activation') for the full range of their damage to target tissues to take effect. Aflatoxin B_1 (AFB$_1$), the best known representative of mycotoxins, is well documented as having hepatotoxic and hepatocarcinogenic properties (Newberne and Butler, 1969; Wogan, 1973). Epoxidation of the 2, 3-double bond has been emphasized as a metabolic activation step and recent results indicate that the 2, 3-epoxide is the reactive metabolite responsible for the reaction with cellular macromolecules, particularly nucleic acid, and thus may well be the ultimate carcinogen (Swenson et al., 1977; Martin and Garner, 1977). The most damaging form of epoxidation is AFB$_1$ epoxide. An intermediate epoxide is predominantly transformed into a water-soluble conjugate rather than into an extractable diol or other metabolites. A prospective action may be afforded by reaction of this electrophilic AFB$_1$ metabolite with reduced glutathione (GSH) (Lotlikar et al., 1980). The presence of the detoxification product, an AFB$_1$-GSH conjugate, in the bile of AFB$_1$-treated rats, and its formation *in vitro* in liver-derived subcellular fraction, has been reported (Dengen and Neumann, 1978; Moss *et al.*, 1983). Moss *et al.* (1983) found more than 80% of water-soluble AFB_1 and AFB_1-GSH conjugates in rat mitochondrial preparations. The mouse liver preparations were 2-4 times more active in conjugating AFB_1 with GSH than were the rat preparations. This may explain why the mouse is much less susceptible to AFB_1 than the rat. Moss *et al.* (1983) summarized the overall metabolic conversion which shows AFB_1 normally being detoxificated by conjugation with GSH as follows:

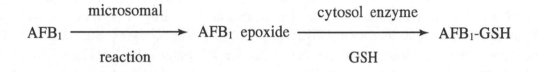

The GSH conjugate was efficiently eliminated into the bile (Dengen and Neumann, 1978).

A study has shown that 0.25% methione supplementation of the diet of young chicks significantly reduced the toxicity of 1.25 ppm AFB_1 (Nahm, 1991b). In other studies in which chicks were fed 1.25 ppm aflatoxin (Veltmann *et al.*, 1983), diet with 66%, 100% and 134% of the NRC requirement for sulphur amino aids resulted in body weights that were 82%, 87% and 96% of the control group fed no mycotoxin. Studies conducted by Smith (1982) and Richardson *et al.*, (1987) demonstrated that broilers fed high protein diets contaminated with aflatoxins grew almost as fast as chicks fed the same diet without aflatoxins. This protection may be due to the presence of the sulphhydryl-containing amino acids, cysteine and methionine. Cysteine is an immediate precursor of tissue GSH and methionine is a more distal precursor of GSH (West *et al.*, 1966; Boyland and Chasseaud, 1967; Veltmann *et al.*, 1983). Most research on the interactions of mycotoxins and protein (amino acids) has been carried out on aflatoxins. DeRecono *et al.* (1966) reported that AFB_1 inhibits DNA synthesis in the liver and possibly prevents protein synthesis (Clifford and Rees, 1967). This effect could potentially affect nearly all biological functions in birds.

Antioxidants

The effects of natural and synthetic antioxidants have been attributed to their capability to scavenge free radicals during the tissue-damaging peroxidation process and to increase enzymatic detoxification of compounds in the liver (Wattenberg, 1976). Studies have suggested that protective effects occur in birds when detoxifying enzymes are previously induced by an antioxidant. Ehrich *et al.* (1981)

and Ehrich and Larsen (1983) proved that detoxification enzyme systems in adult fowl could be increased by the administration of the antioxidants butylated hydroxytoluene (BHT) and beta-naphthoflavone. They also found that elevated hepatic enzyme activities in the birds subsequently resulted in increased detoxification of the aflatoxin (Ehrich *et al.*, 1984). Larsen *et al.* (1985) reported that growth depression caused by AFB_1 (3000 ppb) was significantly less in birds given BHT than in those fed the diet without antioxidant. Combs and Scott (1974) indicated that antioxidants, when used at high levels in a low vitamin E/low selenium chicken diet, increased glutathione peroxidase (GSH-px) activities. The nutritional role of selenium is as a cofactor for SeGSH-px (selenium dependant GSH-px) which is important in the detoxification of hydrogen peroxidase and lipid hydroperoxides, and increases GSH-px (Combs, 1981). Gregory and Edds (1984) observed that selenium enhanced the formation of water-soluble conjugated forms of aflatoxin which promotes the clearance of the toxin and also promotes chick growth. Supplemental vitamin E did not affect the activity of GSH-px in the liver and slightly increased the activity of SeGSH-px in plasma of chicks fed selenium. However, only dietary selenium increased the activity of SeGSH-px in all tissues (Combs, 1981; Nahm, 1991b, 1995). Intake of ethoxyquin and vitamin E has been shown to promote the utilization of dietary selenium (Combs, 1978).

Vitamins

   There is no evidence to suggest that supplementing poultry diets with more than the recommended levels of vitamin A, D, E or K will counteract the adverse effects of mycotoxins. However, a few studies have shown that some water-soluble vitamins provide a protective effect against xenobiotics which must be excreted to complete detoxification. Kamat *et al.* (1980) noted that niacinamide and nicotinic acid induced the production of the detoxification enzymes (mixed function oxidases) and a synergistic response was evident with a combination of the two nutrients. These results suggest that increase niacinamide and niacin may enhance conjugation of AFB_1 during the detoxification process. Bhavanishankar *et al.* (1986) demonstrated that the mortality of albino rats decreased from 62.5% to 25% and 37% respectively by the intraperitoneal injection of thymine and folic acid together with AFB_1. The addition of thymine, or a combination of thymine and folic aid, significantly reduced the extent to which AFB_1 reduced the liver DNA content and increased liver weight (Prema *et al.*, 1981; Bhavanishankar *et al.*, 1986). The influence of vitamin C supplementation following exposure to mycotoxins has also been examined in domestic fowl. In layers fed diets containing 300 ppm of vitamin C and/or 3.0 ppm of ochatoxin A, Haazele *et al.* (1991) reported that vitamin C supplementation significantly improved egg production, egg weight, and reduced egg shell elasticity. However, vitamin C supplementation failed to alter the effects of aflatoxin in chickens (Pardue *et al.*, 1987). Kim and Combs (1992) found that vitamin C affected GSH metabolism at low concentrations.

Other nutrients

Research by Hamilton *et al.* (1972) with turkey poults showed that high-fat diets (containing 6% fat) were capable of preventing mortality caused by aflatoxicosis. However, the growth retarding effects caused by aflatoxins could not be reversed by increasing the fat content (18%) of the diet. A few researchers have studied the interaction of aflatoxins and trace minerals such as iron (De Recondo *et al.*, 1966; Maurice *et al.*, 1983; Huff *et al.*, 1986) and zinc (Jones *et al.*, 1982). The adsorption of toxins by dietary fibre in the intestines has also been suggested as a mechanism for reducing absorption in the chicken gastrointestinal tract (Cummings, 1978; Frape *et al.*, 1982; Schneider *et al.*, 1982; Anderson, 1985). Differences between experiments still show a large disparity in the responses of experimental animals to mycotoxins.

Increasing immunity and resisting mycotoxicosis

Sign of immunosuppression are increases in mortality in a flock or increased susceptibility to infectious disease. Studies have shown that the toxin secreted from mould causes immunosuppression in chicks (Lee *et al.*, 1985; Pier, 1991), decreases the antibody response to sheep red blood cells (Chu *et al.*, 1988), is a potent inducer of tibial dyschondroplasia (Chu *et al.*, 1988), results in 50% mortality due to infectious bursal disease virus (Chang and Hamilton, 1982) and increases susceptibility of chicks to *Salmonella* species (Boonchuvit *et al.*, 1975). From these data it is apparent that the immunosuppressing capabilities of mycotoxins make them a serious threat to the poultry industry. However, there are many potential causes of immunosuppression, giving rise to great variation in the way in which flocks may be affected and making diagnosis very difficult. There have been few studies of mycotoxin-induced immunosuppression or the resistance mechanisms that may operate against mycotoxins.

Some considerations when designing protectants against mycotoxicosis

Studies have been carried out with various levels of mycotoxin ranging from <1 ppm to >10 ppm in poultry feed. These levels need to be reviewed thoroughly when designing effective protectants against mycotoxicosis in the poultry industry. It is difficult to summarize levels of each mycotoxin produced under unstable climates and inadequate storage facilities since the capacity for screening samples for toxin is still limited. Wood (1992) reported that the worldwide occurrence of aflatoxins in foods and feedstuffs for three years (1989, 1990 and 1991) was 0-23.5 ppb for peanuts, 0-20.0 ppb for tree nuts, 0-50.0 ppb for shelled corn, 0-28.6 ppb or milled corn and 0-26.6 ppb for cotton seed. Aflatoxin is the best known and the most toxic mycotoxin. The actual analysis of a sample for mycotoxin requires efficient extraction from the sample for accurate quantitative analysis. The best extracting solvent systems extract 42-68% of aflatoxin from feed samples (Romer, 1990; Nahm, 1992). Even though the lowest extraction ratio (42%) is adopted in the calculation for the aflatoxin levels shown in the Wood (1992) report, the worldwide levels of aflatoxin in feeds for these three years are much lower than levels of aflatoxin which have been used in scientific research.

Although the chemicals used in many research projects have appeared to give promising results, none has been found to have the capability of eliminating mycotoxicosis. Research involving the use of several approaches in combination is indicated and should look at the possibilities for linking mould inhibitors, sorbent materials, antioxidants, sulphur amino acids and other nutrients and chemicals. Similarly, although studies have examined the effects on the fowl of combined toxicity from aflatoxin and ochratoxin and from aflatoxin and zearelone and others, this is an aspect that also needs further research.

References

ANERSON, J.W. (1985) Physiological and metabolic effects of dietary fiber. *Federation Proceedings* 44:2902-2906

BHAVANISHANKAR, T.N., SHANTHA, T. and AMESH, H.P. (1986) Counteraction of the toxicity of aflatoxin B_1 by thymine and folic acid in experimental animals. *Nutritional Reports International* 33:603-612

BOONCHUVIT, B., HAMILTON, P.B. and BURMEISTER, H.R. (1975) Interaction of T-2 toxin with Salmonella infections of chickens. *Poultry Science* 54: 1693-1696

BOYLAND, E. and CHASSEAUD, L.F. (1967) Enzyme-catalyzed conjugations of glutathione with unsaturated compounds. *Biochemical Journal* 10:95-102

CHANG, C. and HAMILTON, P.B. (1982) Increased severity and new symptoms of infectious bursal disease during aflatoxicosis in broiler chickens. *Poultry Science* 61:1061-1068

CHU, Q., COOK, M.E. and SMALLEY, E.B. (1988) Immune and bone properties of chicks consuming corn contaminated with a Fusarium that induces dyschondroplasia *Avian Diseases* 32:132-136

CLIFFORD, J.I. And REES, K.R. (1967) The action of aflatoxin B_1 on the rat liver *Biochemical Journal* 102:65-75

COELHO, M.B. (1990) Mold inhibitor corrosion *A BASF Reference Manual*, pp.

87-91

COMBS, G. F. Jr. (1978) Influences of ethoxyquin on the utilization of selenium by the chick. *Poultry Science* 57:210-222

COMBS, G.F. Jr. (1981) Influence of dietary vitamin E and selenium on the osicant defense system of the chick. *Poultry Science* 60:2098-2105

COMBS, G.F. Jr. and SCOTT, M.L. (1974) Antioxidant effects on selenium and vitamin E function in the chick. *Journal of Nutrition* 104:1297-1303

CUMMINGS , J.H. (1978) Nutritional implications of dietary fiber. *American Journal of Clinical Nutrition* 31:21-29

DENGEN, G.H. and NEUMANN, H.G. (1978) The major metabolite of aflatoxin B_1 in the rat is a glutathione conjugate. *Chemicobiological Interactions* 22: 239-243

DE RECONDO, A. M., FRAYSSINET, C., LAFARGE, C. and LE BRETON, E. (1966) Action de laflatoxin sur le metabolisme du DNA an sours de lhypertrophie compensat rice du doie après hepatectomie parielle. *Biochimica et Biophysica Acta* 119:322-330

DIXON, R.C. and HAMILTON, P.B. (1981a) Effect of feed ingredients on the antifungal activity of propionic acid. *Poultry Science* 60:2407-2411

DIXON, R.C. and HAMILTON, P.B. (1981b) Effect of particle sizes of corn meal and a mold inhibitor on mold inhibition. *Poultry Science* 60:2412-2415

EHRICH, M. and LARSEN, C. (1983) Drug metabolism in adult White Leghorn hens-response to enzyme inducers. *Comprehensive Biochemistry and Physiology* 74c:383-386

EHRICH, M., HUCKLE, W.R. and LARSEN, C. (1984) Increase in glucuronide conjugation of aflatoxin B_1 after pretreatment with microsomal enzyme inducers. *Toxicology* 32:145-152

EHRICH, M., LARSEN, C. and POTTER, L.M. (1981) Effect of dietary butylated hydroxytoluene (BHT) on the activity of a chicken liver enzyme that metabolises foreign compounds. *Avian Diseases* 25:742-746

FORENBACHER, S., HERC EG, M. and FELDHAFER, S. (1975) Systemic mycopathy of fattening cattle caused by lack of vitamin E. *Veterinary Archiv* 45:159-164

FRAPE, D.L., WAYMAN, B.J. and TUCK, M.C. (1982) The effect of dietary fiber sources on aflatoxicosis in the weanling male rat. *Nutritional Reports International* 24:46-57

GREGORY, J.F. and EDDS, G. T. (1984) Effects of dietary selenium on the metabolism of aflatoxin on young turkeys and broiler chickens. *Poultry Science* 64:1678-1684

HAAZELE, F., GUENTER, W., MARQUARDT, R.R. and FROLICH, A.A. (1989) Effect of ochratoxin A and/or ascorbic acid supplementation on production in laying hens. *Poultry Science* 70:47

HAMILTON, P.B. (1985) Factors influencing activity of fungi and antifungal agents in poultry feed. In: *Trichothecens and other Mycotoxins* (Ed. Smith, J.E), University of Glasgow Press, Glasgow, pp. 207-218

HAMILTON, P.B., TUNG, H.T., HARRIS, J.R., GAINER, J.H. and DONALDSON, W.E. (1972) The effect of dietary fat of aflatoxicosis ill turkeys. *Poultry Science* 51:165-170

HUFF, W.E., KUBENA, L.F., HARVEY, R.R., CORRIER, D.E. and MOLLENHAUER, H.H. (1986) Progression of aflatoxicosis in broiler chickens. *Poultry Science* 65: 1981-1991

HUFF, W.E., KUBENA, L.F., HARVEY, R.B. and PHILLIPS, T.D. (1992) Efficacy of hydrated sodium calcium aluminosilicate to reduce the individual and combined toxicity of aflatoxin and ochratoxin A. *Poultry Science* 71:64-69

JONES, F.T., HAGLER, W.H. and HAMILTON, P.B. (1982) Association of low levels of aflatoxin in feed with productivity losses in commercial broiler operations. *Poultry Science* 61:861-868

KAMAT, J.P., NARURKAR, L.M., MHATRE, N.A. and NARURKAR, M.R. (1980) Methionine niacine in detoxification. *Biochimica et Biophysica Acta* 628:26-31

KIM, Y.S and COMBS, G.F.Jr. (1992) Effects of selenium and vitamin E and C of glutathione and glutathione S-transferase in the chick. Cornell Nutrition Conference, pp. 37-42

KUBENA, L.F., HARVEY, R.B., PHILLIPS, T.D. and HEIDELBAUGH, N.D. (1987) Approach to the preventive management of aflatoxicosis in poultry. *Animal Health Association*: 302-304

KUBENA, L.F., HARVEY, R.B., HUFF, W.E., CORRIER, D.E., PHILLIPS, T.D. and ROTTINGHANS, G.E. (1990a) Efficacy of a hydrated sodium calcium aluminosilicate to reduce the toxicity of aflatoxin and T-2 toxin. *Poultry Science* 69:1078-1086

KUBENA, L.F., HARVEY, R.B., PHILLIPS, T.D., CORRIER, D.E. and HUFF, W.E. (1990b) Diminution of aflatoxicosis in growing chickens by the dietary addition of a hydrated sodium calcium aluminosilicate. *Poultry Science* 69: 727-735

KUBENA, L.F., HARVEY, R.B., PHILLIPS, T.D. and CLEMENT, B.A. (1993) Effect of hydrated sodium calcium aluminosilicates on aflatoxicosis in broiler chicks. *Poultry Science* 72:651-657

LARSEN, C., EHRICH, M., DRISCOLL, C. and GROSS, W.B. (1985) Aflatoxin-antioxidant effects on growth of young chicks. *Poultry Science* 64:2287-2291

LEE, Y.M., MIROCHA, C.S., SHROEDER, D.J. and WALSER, M.M. (1985) TDP-1, a toxic component causing tibial dyschondroplasia in broiler chickens and trichothecenes from *Fusarium reseum* "Graminearum". *Applied Environmental*

Microbiology 50:102-107

LOTIKAR, P.D., SETTA, S.M., LYONS, P.A and JHEE, E.C. (1980) Inhibition of microsome-mediated binding of aflatoxin B_1 to DNA by glutathione S-transferase. *Cancer Letters* 9:143-149

MARTIN. C.N. and GARNDER, R.C. (1977) Aflatoxin B-oxide generated by chemical or enzyme oxidation of aflatoxin B_1 causes guanine substitution in nucleic acids. *Nature* 267:863-867

MAURICE, D.V., BODINE, A.B. and REHVER, N.J. (1983) Metabolic effects of low aflatoxin B_1 levels on broiler chicks. *Applied Environmental Microbiology* 45:960-984

MOSS, E.J., JUDAH, D.J., PRZYBYLSKI, M. and NEAL, G.E. (1983) Some mass-spectral and n.m.r. analytical studies of a glutathione conjugate of aflatoxin B_1. *Biochemical Journal* 210:227-234

NAHM, K.H. (1989) Effects of particle size and the levels of protein in the ration on the usage of a mold inhibitor. *Poultry Science* 68 (Suppl.):103

NAHM, K.H. (1990) Conditions for mold growth and aflatoxin production in feedstuffs. *Pig News and Information* 11:349-352

NAHM, K.H. (1991a) Use of mold inhibitor for feed storage and improved chick performance. Asian-Australian Journal of Animal Science 4:756-760

NAHM, K.H. (1991b) A study on the detoxification in the chicks body of aflatoxin B_1 found in feed. *Poultry Science* 70 (Suppl):501

NAHM, K.H. (1992) Practical guide to feed, forage and water analysis. *Yoo Han (English Edition)* 126-131

NAHM, K.H. (1995) Prevention of aflatoxicosis by addition of antioxidants and hydrated sodium calcium aluminosilicated to the diet of young chicks. *Japanese Poultry Science* 32:117-127

NEWBERNE, P.M. and BUTLER, W.H. (1969) Acute and chronic effects of aflatoxin on the liver of domestic and laboratory animals: a review. *Cancer Research* 29:236-244

PARDUE, S.L., HUFF, W.E. KUBENA, L.F. and HARVEY, R.B. (1987) Influence of ascorbic acid on aflatoxicosis in broiler cockerels. *Poultry Science* 65:156

PHILLIPS, T.D., KUBENA, L.F., HARVEY, R.B., TAYLOR, D.S. and HEIDELBAUGH, N.D. (1988) Hydrated sodium calcium aluminosilicate: a high affinity sorbent for aflatoxin. *Poultry Science* 67:243-244

PIER, A.C. (1991) The influence of mycotoxin on the immune system. In: Mycotoxins and Animal Foods (Eds Smith, J.E. and Henderson, R.S.), CRC Press, Boca Raton, Florida, pp. 489-497

PREMA, V., BASAPPA, S.C. and SCREENIVASA, M.V. (1981) Counteraction of inhibitory effects of aflatoxin in Bacillus magaterium. *Journal of Food Science Technology* 18:92-97

RICHARDSON, K.E., NELSON, L.A. and HAMILTON, P.B. (1987) Interaction of dietary protein level on dose response relationship during aflatoxicosis in young chickens. *Poultry Science* 66:1470-1478

ROMER, T.R. (1990) Mycotoxin assays in feed. A BASF Reference Manual 147-154

ROSE, G.W. and BRADLEY, B.L (1980) *Part I. Mycotoxins and Their Activity*, Agrimerica, Inc.

SCHNEIDER, M.U., DONSCHKE, S. and DOMSCHKE, W. (1982) Effect of dietary fiber on exocrine pancreatic enzyme activity *in vitro and in vivo*. Digestion 24: Abstract 67

SEITER, J. and JURDAN, J. (1990) Molds, mycotoxins and feed preservatives in the feed industry. *A BASF Reference Manual* 1-3

SMITH, T.K. (1992) Influence off mycotoxins on protein and amino acid utilization. *Federation Proceedings* 41:2828-2832

SWENSON, D.H., LIN, J.K, MILLER, E.C. and MILLER, J.A. (1977) Aflatoxin B_1 2,3-oxide as a probable intermediate in the covalent binding of aflatoxin B_1 and B_2 to rat liver DNA and ribosomal RNA in vivo. *Cancer Research* 37: 172-181

TABIB, Z., HAGLER, W.M. and HAMILTON, P.B. (1982) Factors influencing activity of antifungal agents in animal feed and ingredients. *Abstracts of Annual Meeting American Society of Microbiology*. 204

TABIB, Z., JONES, E.T. and HAMILTON, P.B. (1984) Effect of pelleting of poultry feed on the activity of mold and mold inhibitors. *Poultry Science* 63:70-75

VELTMANN, J.R., WYATT, R.D., VOIGHT, M.N. and SHAMSUDDIN, Z. (1983) Influencing of dietary sulfur amino acid levels on performance, free amino acids and biochemical parameters in plasma and hepatic glutathione of broiler chicks fed nutrition. *Poultry Science* 62:1518-1519

WARD, N. (1988) Detoxification through nutrition. *Feed Management*, January, pp. 18-26

WATTENBERG, L. (1976) Inhibition of chemical carcinogenesis by antioxidants and some additional compounds. In: Fundamentals in Cancer Prevention, (Ed. Magee, P.N.), University of Tokyo Press, Tokyo, Japan, pp. 153-166

WEST, E.S., TODD, W.R. and MASON, H.S. (1966) Textbook of Biochemistry, Macmillan, New York, pp. 1243-1247

WHITESIDE, B. and HALLEY, J.T. (1990) Mold inhibitor application systems. A BASF Reference Manual, 101-107

WOGAN, G.N. (1973) Aflatoxin carcinogenesis. *Methods of Cancer Research* 7: 309-313

WOOD, G.E. (1992) Mycotoxins in foods and feeds in the United States. *Journal of Animal Science* 70:3941-3949

World's Poultry Science Journal Vol. 53: 71-77 (1997)   33

Korean native Ogol fowl

K. H. Nahm

Feed and Nutrition Laboratory, College of Natural Resource, Taegu University Gyong San, 713-714 South Korea.

The native Ogol fowl, which is a protected species under the Korean government (Protected Species Act No. 265), has not been accepted as a breed because of insufficient research. Its external features include black colouring of the beak, eyes, face, earlobes, wattle, tongue, shank, toes, feathers, skin and bones. Average weights of males and females at hatching are 32.0 and 29.6 g, respectively. Sexual maturity is reached at about 24 weeks of age, but growth continues to around 500 days. Age at first egg averages 167 days and production is about 100 eggs annually. The weight of the edible parts is 60-63% of the total body weight. Fertility rates reported range from 76.4% to 82.2%, while hatchability ranges from 74% to 79%. The paper includes haematological data together with heritability estimates for traits of economic importance.

(Keywords: Blood cells; diet; Korea; Ogol fowl; performance; heritability estimates)

Introduction

Indigenous species represent a valuable genetic resource that should be carefully preserved. Native fowl are no exception as it is likely that some of their genetic characteristics will, in the course of time, help to enhance food supplies by contributing to increased productivity and decreased production costs. In Korea, the native Ogol fowl has been known from olden times. At present, however, there are about 88,000 of these native fowl remaining, including those found on farms and at the National Research Centre (Anon, 1994). This bird still has not been accepted as a breed because of insufficient research (Han and Kim, 1985). The Korean government has designated this bird under the Protected Species Act No. 265.

This paper has been written to draw attention to the Korean Ogol fowl in the hope that it will help to promote research in other countries into its characteristics, including those relating to its genetics and breeding. The main results from the limited number of papers written about the Ogol fowl are reported.

External features

The Korean Ogol fowl is a dual purpose variety with a short, rectangular shaped body with the following characteristics (*Figure 1*):

Comb - small, single, six to eight pointed, stands up straight on the head, reddish
       black in colour
Beak - medium length, black coloured with a white tip
Eyes - round and black
Face - reddish black and not feathered
Ear lobes - small, may be greyish black, white or half black and half white
Wattles - reddish black, of medium size and elongated
Tongue - greyish black
Shank and feet - shank of medium length with four greyish black toes
Feathers - dark black on both male and female
Skin - greyish black
Bone cortex - greyish black

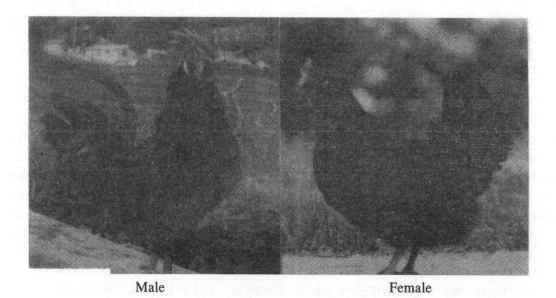

Male   Female

Figure 1. Native Ogol fowl from Korea

General characteristics

During the brooding period Ogol fowl are very sensitive to inappropriate environments such as change in temperature, inadequate ventilation and poor protection from diseases or parasites, but their ability to adjust to environmental changes increases with age. They are nervous and easily frightened. They enjoy eating high fibre foods such as grass and leaves which they seem to digest without difficulty. The egg colour is brown and hens show excellent broodiness (Ohh, 1989).

Body growth and meat yield

Male and female Ogol chicks weigh, on average, 32.0g and 29.6g at hatching, 660g and 590g at eight weeks and 1390g and 1090g at 16 weeks of age, respectively (Kim, 1983; Han *et al.*, 1988a). Like other breeds, Ogol chicks show most rapid growth up to 2-3 weeks of age, with the growth rate sharply decreasing after 6-7 weeks of age (Kim, 1983; Han *et al.*, 1988b). The mean (SD) weight of total edible parts (legs, wings, neck and back including skin) was found to be 375.5 (76.5)g at 8 weeks and 555.6 (72.7)g at 10 weeks which is 60-63% of the total body weight (Kim and Han, 1981). The composition of Ogol fowl meat is shown in Table 1.

Egg productivity, fertility and hatchability

Korean Ogol fowl reach sexual maturity at about 24 weeks of age, but they continue their growth until about 500 days. The age at first egg averages 167 days [mean (SE) 166.5 (1.69) days]. Annual egg production is about 100, with about 80

Table 1. Composition of Ogol fowl meat at 8 and 16 weeks of age (Han *et al.*, 1988a)

Age (weeks)	Sex	Part	Moisture (%)	Crude protein (%)	Crude fat (%)	Crude ash (%)
8	M	Breast	71.6	21.6	4.5	0.8
		Thigh	70.9	19.5	5.3	0.8
	F	Breast	70.9	20.6	4.8	1.1
		Thigh	70.8	19.9	5.8	0.9
10	M	Breast	70.4	22.0	4.8	0.9
		Thigh	70.3	19.5	4.7	0.8
	F	Breast	71.0	19.9	4.5	0.9
		Thigh	71.0	19.1	5.5	0.9

[mean 80.12 (19.84)] being produced by 300 days of age and about 163 eggs [162.82 (45.25)] by 500 days of age. Egg weight at first egg is 36g [mean (SE) 35.7 (0.49)g], at 44 weeks it is 49g [48.8 (0.47)g], and at 72 weeks 50g [50.2 (0.44)g] (Chung, 1971; Yeo, 1981; Han et al., 1989).

Chung and Chung (1985) reported fertility of 76.4% and hatchability of 74.0%, but Han et al. (1986) found slightly higher levels with the fertility in spring, summer, autumn and winter being 81.7%, 89.8%, 83.6% and 81.6%, respectively [mean (SE) 82.2 (1.37)%] and seasonal hatchability of 77.6%, 72.9%, 74.1% and 83.8%, respectively [mean (SE) 79.0 (1.91)%]. The Korean Poultry Association (1973) and Chung and Chung (1985) reported the survival rates of young chicks to be 96.6% at 0-6 weeks, 95.7% at 7-20 weeks and 84.2% at 21-72 weeks.

Haematological and blood chemical profile

The mean (SE) red blood cell (RBC) count of Ogol fowl at two weeks of age has been reported by Won (1985) to be 2.89 (0.08) X 10^6/ul, while Han et al. (1987) found slightly lower values [female 2.42 (0.06) X 10^6/ul; male 2.27 (0.04) X 10^6/ul]. The mean (SE) haemoglobin level at two weeks of age was found by Won et al. (1985) to be 9.5 (2.4)g/100ml, but Han et al. (1987) reported a haemoglobin level in two week old males of 12.2 (0.28)g/100ml and in females of 12.2 (0.57)g/100ml. In the adult chicken the mean (SE) haemoglobin level has been reported by Lee and Park (1984) to be 11.75 (2.27) (range 9.01-14.11)g /100ml. Blood corpuscle indices are shown in Table 2.

Table 2. Mean (SE) red blood cell and corpuscle indices in the blood of Ogol fowl (Han et al., 1987)

Age (weeks)	MCV (fl)		MCH (pg)		MCHC (G/100ml)	
	Male	Female	Male	Female	Male	Female
2	147.9(1.21)	140.5(1.62)	53.5(0.24)	50.3(0.24)	36.5(0.24)	35.8(0.61)
4	144.9(1.51)	143.3(1.12)	49.7(2.42)	55.3(5.87)	34.3(1.58)	44.2(6.29)
6	144.0(1.60)	143.6(1.36)	51.6(0.45)	52.0(0.45)	35.8(0.19)	36.2(0.46)
8	142.5(1.65)	139.4(1.90)	54.8(0.15)	53.8(0.64)	38.4(0.39)	38.6(0.34)
10	146.7(3.23)	145.0(2.52)	52.9(0.60)	52.6(0.29)	36.0(0.38)	36.3(0.57)
12	138.5(1.23)	136.0(1.72)	55.7(0.44)	54.2(0.42)	40.2(0.57)	39.8(0.61)
14	141.0(1.75)	137.2(0.91)	55.2(0.65)	54.3(0.88)	39.1(0.60)	39.6(0.32)
16	150.6(1.24)	142.2(2.12)	53.4(0.36)	52.3(0.66)	35.4(0.34)	36.8(0.53)

MCV, red blood cell indices of mean corpuscular volume; MCH, mean corpuscular haemoglobin; MCHC, mean corpuscular haemoglobin

However, Won (1985) reported lower values for the mean corpuscular volume [106.6 (3.7) fl], mean corpuscular haemoglobin [32.8 (2.2)pg] and mean corpuscular haemoglobin concentration [32.4 (1.39)g/100 ml] at two weeks of age and Lee and Park (1984) reported values of 102.65 (17.45) fl, 36.2 (6.20)pg and 34.26 (6.20)g /100 ml, respectively, in adult birds. The mean (SE) white blood cell (WBC) count was reported to be 16.33 (4.75) X 10^3/ul in adult Ogol fowl by Lee and Park (1984), but Han *et al.* (1987) reported counts of 21.91 (2.04) X 10^3/ul and 16.24 (2.79) X 10^3/ul in 16 week old male and female Ogol fowl, respectively. There has been only limited research into the blood composition of Ogol fowl and further studies are needed.

Breeding and genetics

Recent research by Lee *et al.* (1995) into the genetic characteristics of Korean native Ogol fowl using DNA fingerprinting has shown that it is a highly inbred line (band sharing > 0.68) which is more closely related to the Korean native yellow fowl than to other breeds such as Rhode Island and White Leghorns.

Each chromosome of the Korean native Ogol fowl had three dark bands in the G band at 1p2, a distinct light band in 1p1, a dark band in 2p2, a broad light band in 3p1, a dark band from the centromere and distal part of the fourth chromosome and a dark band in 5p1. The z-sex chromosome was dark at the distal p-arm. The morphology of the chromosomes showed that chromosomes 1

Table 3. Heritabilities of the economic traits from sire, dam, and combined variance components (Han *et al.*, 1989, 1990, 1991)

Traits	h^2s			h^2d			h^2s+d		
	1st egg	300 days	500 days	1st egg	300 days	500 days	1st egg	300 days	500 days
Body weight	0.448	0.453	0.661	0.243	0.276	0.120	0.345	0.365	0.391
Age at 1st egg	0.356	—	—	0.207	—	—	0.282	—	—
Egg production	—	0.365	0.354	—	0.230	0.204	—	0.296	0.279
Egg weight	0.259	0.440	0.464	0.512	0.633	0.616	0.386	0.536	0.540
Egg shape index	0.120	0.485	0.232	0.827	0.503	0.872	0.473	0.494	0.552
Shell thickness	0.197	0.184	0.272	0.819	0.756	0.557	0.508	0.470	0.428
Albumin height	0.202	0.394	0.225	0.678	0.119	0.537	0.440	0.256	0.376
Haugh units	0.108	0.251	0.443	0.698	0.237	0.354	0.398	0.244	0.399
Shank length	—	0.235	—	—	0.890	—	—	0.563	—
Breast width	—	0.185	—	—	0.444	—	—	0.314	—
Breast girth	—	0.552	—	—	0.499	—	—	0.510	—
Tibia length	—	0.432	—	—	0.408	—	—	0.420	—

Table 4. Genetic and phenotypic correlations between economic traits [*] (Han et al., 1989)

Traits	Body weight			Age at 1st egg	Egg production at 300 days	Egg weight	
	at 8 weeks	at 1st egg	at 300 days			at 1st egg	at 300 days
Body weight							
at 8 weeks		0.775	0.424	0.539	-0.552	0.264	0.180
at 1st egg	0.542		0.802	0.617	-0.391	0.754	0.580
at 300 days	0.421	0.593		0.605	-0.517	0.285	0.309
Age at 1st egg	0.167	0.173	0.019		-0.717	0.587	0.552
Egg production at 300 days	-0.154	-0.118	-0.061	-0.495		-0.381	-0.383
Egg weight							
at 1st egg	0.140	0.083	0.172	0.451	-0.153		0.809
at 300 days	0.271	0.212	0.254	0.187	-0.154	0.673	

[*]Genetic correlations are above the diagonal and phenotypic correlations are below the diagonal.

and 2 were submetacentric, chromosomes 3, 5 and 6 were telocentric, chromosomes 4 and 7 were acrocentric and chromosome 8 was metacentric (Kang et al., 1985).

The heritability estimates of the Korean native Ogol fowl based on the variance of sire, dam and combined components on performances, egg qualities and body shape are summarized in Table 3 (Han et al., 1989, 1990, 1991). These estimates are different from some studies but are similar to those found in other studies. For example, the heritability estimates for body weight in Table 3 are 0.448-0.661 (h^2s), 0.120-0.276 (h^2d) and 0.345-0.391 ($h^2s + d$). The estimate of 0.448-0.661 (h^2s) is higher than that of Clayton and Robertson (1996) and Johari et al. (1981) (0.18-0.28), lower than that of Kawahara and Inoves (1967) (0.895), and similar to Merritt (1968) and Buchel (1970) (0.47-0.60). Han et al. (1989) provided the research results on genetic and phenotypic correlation between economic traits as shown in Table 4. These values were also different from some studies but similar to those reported in others.

Future research

Many areas of research into the Korean native Ogol fowl have been limited up to the present time and more extensive research is needed which will require financial support from the Korean government and intellectual support from scientists worldwide.

Acknowledgment

I would like to express my thanks to Professor Sung Wook Han, President of the Korean Association of Poultry Science, for making valuable suggestions.

Reference

ANONYMOUS (1994) Native animals in Korea: Series for introduction. Korean Farmer Press Co. Inc.

BUCHEL, K. (1970) Investigations of the heritability of certain characteristics in fowls of medium heavy breeds with reference to the possibility of selection for the breeding of broiler. *Animal Breeding Abstract* **38**:4238.

CHUNG, S.B. (1971) Studies on the economic traits between genetic and phenotypic correlations of chicken. Ph.D. Thesis, Chung Nam National University

CHUNG, I.C. and CHUNG, S.B. (1985) Studies on the preservation of livestock breeds and their production. *Annual Report of Korean Livestock Centre*, pp. 401-404

CLAYTON, G.A and ROBERTSON, A. (1996) Genetics of changes in economic traits during the laying year. *British Poultry Science* **7**:143-151

HAN, S.W. and KIM, S.H. (1985) Studies on the hereditary characteristics and some economical traits of Korean native Ogol chicken. *Korean Journal of Poultry Science* **12**:65-73

HAN, S.W., OHH, B.K. and KIM, S.H. (1986) Studies on the hereditary characteristics and some economic traits of Korean native Ogol fowl. II. Fertility, Hatchability, egg production and body weight. *Korean Journal of Poultry Science* **13**: 179-186

HAN, S.W., KIM, D.H., OHH, B.K. and KIM, S.H. (1987) Studies on the hereditary characteristics and some economic traits of Korean native Ogol chicken. III. Hemogram and blood chemical values. *Korean Journal of Poultry Science* **14**: 63-68

HAN, S.W., CHANG, K.S., CHANG, Y.O. and OHH, B.K. (1988a) Studies on the hereditary characteristics and some economic traits of Korean native Ogol fowl. V. Experiments of processing suitability. *Korean Journal of Poultry Science* **15**: 61-65

HAN, S.W., OHH, B.K. and KIM, S.H. (1988b) Studies on the hereditary characteristics and some economic traits of Korean native Ogol fowl. IV. Body growth and meat productivity. *Korean Journal of Poultry Science* **15**:1-19

HAN, S.W., SANG, B.C. and KIM, H.K. (1989) Studies on the estimation of the genetic parameters on all traits in Korean native Ogol fowl. I. Estimation of the heritabilities and genetic correlations on economic traits. *Korean Journal of*

Poultry Science **16**:129-137

HAN, S.W., SANG, B.C., KIM, H.K. and BAEK, S.B (1990) Studies on the estimation of the genetic parameters on all traits in Korean native Ogol fowl. III. Estimations of the heritabilities and genetic correlations on the egg shape index and egg qualifications. *Korean Journal of Poultry Science* **17**:71-78

HAN, S.W., SANG, B.C., and KIM, H.K. (1991) Studies on the estimation of the genetic parameters on all traits in Korean native Ogol fowl. IV. Estimations of the heritabilities and genetic correlations on the body conformations. *Korean Journal of Poultry Science* **10**:1-8

JOHARI, D.C., MUTT, M. and HUSAIN, K.Q. (1981) Genetic and phenotypic correlation for some traits of economic importance in a strain of White Leghorn. *Animal Breeding Abstracts* **49**:1673

KANG, T.S., OHH, B.K. and SOHN, S.H. (1985). The study on the G-banding chromosomes of Korean Ogol chicken. *Korean Journal of Poultry Science* **12**: 83-87

KAWAHARA, T. and INOVES, J. (1967) Variance and covariance analysis of egg production and related characters in the domestic fowl. *Animal Breeding Abstracts* **35**:3041

KIM, J.H. (1983) Studies on the hereditary estimates of edible parts of broilers in the different growth phases. Ph D Thesis, Chung Nam National University

KIM, J.H. and HAN, S.W. (1981) The hereditary estimates and edible parts of broiler. *Annual Report of Chung Nam National University* **10**:221-234

KOREAN POULTRY ASSOCIATION (1973) *10th Annual Report on Layer Productivity.* pp. 24-39

LEE, H.K. and PARK, O.Y. (1984) Studies on the hematology of Korean native Ogol chicks. *Korean Journal of Veterinary Science* **20**:233-238

LEE, S.J., HWANG, K.C., CHOI, K.D., LEE, H.K., SHIN, Y.S. and HAN, J.Y. (1995) Genetic analysis of Korean native Ogol chickens through DNA fingerprinting. *Korean Journal of Animal Science* **37**:207-215

MERRITT, T.S. (1968) Genetic parameter estimates for growth and reproductive traits in random breed strain of meat fowl. *Poultry Science* **47**:190-199

OHH, B.K. (1989) *The History of the Poultry Production in Korea.* Sun-Jin Publishing Co., pp. 42-52

WON, S.D. (1985) Studies on the ochratoxin A toxicity in the Korean native Ogol chicks. Ph D Thesis, Kun Kuk University

YEO, C.S. (1981) Studies on the genetic selection parameters of the economic traits and certain other traits in hens. Ph D Thesis, Seoul National University

The Possible Minimum Chicken Nutrient Requirements for Protecting the Environment and Improving Cost Efficiency
-Review-

K. H. Nahm and C. W. Carlson

Feed & Nutrition Laboratory, College of Natural Resources, Taegu University Gyong San 713-714, Korea

ABSTRACT: Nitrogen and phosphorus are major nutrients in animal feeds which partially remain in the environment as pollution. In addition, nitrogen and phosphorus along with energy are the main nutrients which determine the feed cost. Any decreases in the levels of these three nutrients can contribute to reducing the pollution problem as well as the cost of feed. The nutrient requirements for chickens in the work here reported should allow for the addition of mixed enzymes (phytases, proteases, glucanases, xylanases and others). Such minimal levels of crude protein in the research results which are here reported are 16% for 0-6 weeks of age, 13.5% for 7-12 weeks of age, 11.5% for 13-18 weeks of age for layer type chicks, 13% for layer, 18% for 0-3 weeks of age broiler and 16.5% for 4-7 weeks of age broiler. These research projects have been done without adding enzyme supplements to their experimental diets.

The minimal values of phosphorus, shown as available phosphorus, are 0.25% for pullets, 0.09% for layers and 0.25% for broilers with the addition of phytase. The minimum energy requirement (metabolizable energy) for reducing the feed cost could be summarized as 2,750 kcal per kg feed for pullets, 2,800 kcal for layers and 2,700 kcal for broilers.

(Key words: Environment, Pollution, Nitrogen, Phosphorus, Enzymes, Crude Protein, Metabolizable Energy, Pullets, Layer, Broiler, NRC, Vitamin)

INTRODUCTION

More and more frequently attention is focused on animal production systems as one of the sources of pollution affecting the quality of streams, estuaries and ground water resources. In particular, nitrogen (N) and phosphorus (P) may pollute water after application of manure or chemical fertilizer to the soils. These nutrients may be carried away as run off water after a rainfall, or they (especially N) may leach through soils into ground water. Some N becomes volatilized as ammonia and eventually contributes to acid rain that endangers forests. While both nutrients are essential for life, when the concentrations become too high in water, they endanger the ecosystem. And also N and P are the main nutrients along with energy to determine the feed cost.

In many countries on the earth, restrictions and regulations related to manure are already commonplace and regulations and legislation are increasing in several countries. Environmental control systems are revolutionizing the poultry industry. Chickens do not lay or grow or eat like they used to and we cannot feed them the same way (Roland, Sr., 1994). A study (Nahm and Sung, 1995) showed that many layer rations still maintain excessive protein levels varying from 17 to 22% and excessive phosphorus contents of 0.35 to 1.27%. Poultry producers in some areas of the earth do not have any choice to select the nutrient levels for their own poultry farm because they must rely on the rations which were mixed with the imported grain by feed companies.

Low-protein and phosphorus diets offer advantages in lower cost, less excretion of nitrogen, phosphorus and other potential pollutants of the environment. They may result in greater sensitivity to dietary ammo acid excesses which might occur through unusual formulations or inadvertent supplementation of the diets with individual amino acids (Austic, 1996). Instead of the conventional feed formulation, protein and phosphorus usage in practical diets must be minimized for solving these problems, and provide added commercial amino acids and enzymes like proteases and phytases for use of biologically available amino acid and phosphorus in feeds that are less well digested. These formulations result in excretion of minimum amounts of nitrogen and phosphorus.

This review will discuss the possible minimum levels of protein and phosphorus on the basis of previous research results to reduce the nitrogen and phosphorus content in the chicken manure. This could be one of the ways to contribute to preventing pollution and achieving cost efficiency, while allowing poultry producers to follow the environmental regulations and restrictions.

Addition of synthetic amino acids

A purified diet formulated on the same principles gives excellent growth in starting Coturnix quail (Blair *et al.*, 1972). This example illustrates the validity of the concept of balanced amino acids, quantified according to the values outlined by Scott *et al.* (1969). Addition of certain amino acids allows for a reduction in dietary protein with no negative effect on poultry performance. These diets also help to improve the environment by reducing nitrogen excretion by poultry and reducing ammonia production from their manure (Cromwell, 1996). McNaughton (1995b) predicted the use of more synthetic amino acid, not only the use of more pounds of synthetic amino acids, but the use of more kinds of synthetic amino acids.

The use of more amino acids would result in formulating feeds that more closely approximate the minimum nutrient requirements of the bird with minimum excesses. Excesses are wasteful and may be environmentally destructive. Amino acids consisting of essential and nonessential amino acids are the building blocks of protein. Although both categories of amino acids are needed at the physiological or metabolic level, normal poultry diets contain sufficient nonessential amino acids or sufficient precursors for their synthesis; consequently, most of the emphasis in poultry nutrition is on the essential amino acids.

The use of feed grade methionine and lysine in poultry diets has been a common practice for many years. While many of the other essential amino acids have been available, their cost has restricted their use in practical diets. This, however, is changing as a result of biotechnology, such as new fermentation techniques and other new technological advances, particularly in the production of tryptophan and threonine. As a result, the price of these two amino acids has decreased in recent years and they are now being used to a limited extent in poultry diets.

Methionine or methionine hydroxyanalog (MHA) is almost universally used in poultry diets because methionine is relatively inexpensive and is generally regarded as the first limiting amino acid in poultry diets. Feed-grade lysine is produced by fermentation, using genetically engineered microorganisms. This product contains 78% lysine and is 98.5% pure. Methionine is sold as DL-methionine (99% pure) and DL-MHA (a liquid that contains 88% MHA). Feed-grade L-tryptophan (98.5% pure) and L-threonine (98.5% pure) also are produced by fermentation. In addition, lysine and tryptophan are available as a mixture that contains 15% L-tryptophan and 70% L-lysine HCL (55% L-lysine) (This is the feed-grade lysine which is produced by fermentation formed by three firms in the U.S. and is sold as L-lysine HCl). The order of amino acid limitation in most poultry diets is methionine, lysine, threonine, tryptophan, isoleucine and arginine (Elliot, 1995). However, most feed mills use supplemental methionine and lysine, and in most cases threonine becomes the next limiting amino acid in commercial pullet and layer diets today.

As more of the essential amino acids become economically and commercially available, nutritionists will include more of them into their feed formulations on a routine basis. This will allow the nutritionist to further decrease dietary crude protein levels. Care will have to be taken to ensure that the diet still provides adequate levels of the nonessential amino acids and the remaining essential amino acids.

Enzyme utilization

The addition of enzyme preparations to feed for poultry is not a new concept, but is becoming more fine tuned with the production of special enzyme preparations which are specific for the substrate. Recent market research indicates that in the U.K. approximately 90-95% of all broiler diets contain feed enzymes, and on world-wide basis as much as 60-70% of wheat and barley based poultry feeds are enzyme supplemented (Wyatt and Harker, 1995).

The tremendous growth in this particular application of biotechnology to animal production has accelerated over a relatively short period (less than 5 years). These changes have come about due to more recent developments in specific enzymes designed to function optimally in the intestinal tract of the bird and are stable through the feed processing. High enzyme costs have restricted the commercial use. However, large suppliers have now developed enzymes specifically for feed application.

The feeding value of plant-based ingredients, especially cereal grains, and their use in poultry diets are influenced by the level of antinutritive compounds (e.g. non-starch polysaccharides, NSP), some examples of which are arabinoxylans and mixed-linked beta-glucans derived from the endosperm cell wall, that tend to create viscous conditions to form gels. This gel like environment can reduce normal movement and limit nutrient absorption from the intestinal tract of the bird causing the reduction of body weight and feed conversion. Viscosity of digest impacts the digestibility of all dietary nutrients by interfering with the diffusion of pancreatic enzymes, target substrates and the end products of the digestion process. NSP levels in barley may alter and/or inhibit the bioavailability of starch, fat and protein in the digestive tract of the bird (Hesselman and Aman, 1986).

A trial looking at nutrient digestibilities at the terminal ileum has demonstrated improvements in amino acids and energy digestibility in the presence of feed enzymes (Almirall et al., 1994). Supplementing an enzyme to the wheat-based (63%) diet significantly increased ideal energy (8%) and all major limiting amino acids, ranging from 8% (lysine) to 36% (cysteine). Improvements in apparent energy digestibility of 8% would, if attributed solely to the wheat component, equate to a 12% increase in available energy of this wheat. Whereas, the improvement in fecal amino acid digestilbility would equate to an increase in availability of 29% for lysine, 14% for methionine + cysteine and 28% for threonine (Wyatt and Harker, 1995).

Reducing the dry matter content of the digesta in the intestinal tract with supplemental feed enzymes has a marked impact on excreta volume and composition, resulting in a reduction in dry matter output of 12-15% (Wyatt and Harker, 1995) or 20% (Patterson, 1998). A reduction in manure output would have environmental benefits far beyond the broiler industry, and be particularly relevant to producers in areas of intensive animal production.

Phytic acid of phytate (myo-inosital hexophosphate), being an essential component of all seeds, being a main storage form of phosphorus and being an antinutritial factor as well as an indigestible nutrient factor, must be hydrolyzed by phytase into inorganic phosphate before it can be utilized by poultry. The phytate molecule, with its six phosphoric acid residues, usually occurs as a mixture of calcium, magnesium, potassium and zinc salts. The phytate contents of most cereals and oil seeds are about 1-3%, which accounts for 60-80% of the total phosphorus in seeds (Simell et al., 1989).

Phytate is located in different parts of different seeds. In wheat, barley, oats and rye, it is mostly in the aleurone layer (bran). In dicotyledonous seeds, including legumes and oil seeds, phytate is distributed throughout the cotyledon. Corn differs from most other grains in that about 90% of the phytate is concentrated in the germ fraction. Phytate phosphate has a limited bioavailability in poultry in that 60-75% of the phosphorus in common feed ingredients is not available for digestion by the bird. Available phosphorus values for corn and SBM (0.08 and 0.22%, respectively) indicate that phytate phosphorus utilization by poultry for these ingredients is essentially zero (NRC, 1994). Because wheat and barley contain endogenous phytase, phytate phosphorus utilization for these ingredients can range from 15 to 30%.

Phytase (myo-inositol hexaphosphate phosphohydrolase) is a special kind of phosphotase that catalyses the stepwise removal of inorganic or orthophosphate from phytate (Gibson and Ullah, 1990). There are two classes of phytase enzymes. Microorganisms and fungi produce 3-phytase, which first removes orthophosphate from the 3-position, while plants contain 6-phytase. Both phytases can successively remove the remaining orthophosphates which result in intermediates ranging from free myo-inositol to mono- to tetra-phosphates of inositol.

The phytase activity in feedstuffs varies depending on the ingredient (Eeckhout and de Paepe, 1994). Wheat and barley have significant phytase activity (1190 and 580 phytase units/kg, respectively). The efficacy of phytase depends on a number of factors such as pH, moisture, exposure, gastrointestinal tract retention time, phytase source as well as the calcium content of the diet. Microbial phytase has two pH optima at pH 2.5 and pH 5.5. Plant-derived phytase has only one pH optimum in the range of pH 4-6. Plant phytase appears to undergo irreversible inactivation at pH 2.5. Investigations have suggested that a minimum moisture content of 20-25% is required for phytase activity. Maximum phytase activity is achieved at moisture contents of 30%. This precludes any phytase activity in a dry mixed feed, unless the feed is mixed into a slurry (Heinzl, 1996). Phytase activity is expressed as "phytase units" or FTU (FTU = fytase unit; fytase = Dutch name for phytase) per unit of feed. This unit of measurement was developed in Europe and has now been adopted worldwide. One phytase unit (FTU) is the activity of phytase that generates 1 micromole of inorganic phosphorus per minute from an excess of sodium phytase at pH 5.5 and 37 degrees C. Measurement of release of phosphorus is done photometrically (McKnight, 1996).

Supplemental microbial phytase is well known for its effectiveness in improving the availability of P in plant ingredients, containing high levels of phytate P and some reports have also suggested that the availabilities of Ca, Zn and amino acid (N) are improved. Kornegay *et al.* (1996b) reported that microbial phytase is very effective for improving the availability of phytate-P in corn and soybean meal diets, and the magnitude of the response of several measurements to added phytase is inversely related to the level of available P (and total P including phytate P) and the level of supplemental phytase added. These scientists also noted that there was a potential for improving the digestibility of amino acids and protein, and also reducing the excretion of P, Ca and Zn when diets were properly formulated with supplementing microbial phytase.

Nutrient requirements between strains of birds

To more consistently attain the genetic potential of each strain, producers should follow the nutritional and management recommendations specified by the breeder company for each strain (Elliot, 1995). Each breeder company will have a set of key performance parameters that should be monitored during the growth phase. These should include mortality (daily), feed consumption (weekly), body weights (weekly), shank lengths (weekly), house temperature (daily extremes), and water consumption (daily).

A single recommendation of each nutrient based on age does not take into consideration differences between strains of birds. Herrick and Ross (1986) reported from the trials using three different strains that there were differences in layer performances such as egg production, feed/dozen eggs, egg weight, eggshell quality, body weight gain and mortality.

Leeson and Caston (1996) recently found feeding birds a lower level of crude protein had significant effects on bird performances among different strains. Their trial showed that the DeKalb and H & N strains produced less total egg mass when fed low crude protein diets, while the Babcock and Shavor strains were apparently not adversely affected by their low protein diets. The low crude protein diet did result in an overall loss of egg mass of approximately 1 kg per bird to 70 weeks of age. They showed reduced levels of dietary crude protein and available phosphorus to cause similar responses.

NUTRIENT LEVELS FOR EACH TYPE OF CHICKEN

Growing layer pullets

Recent studies have demonstrated the pullet response to dietary energy concentration under moderate and high temperature environments (Leeson and Summers, 1989). This data pointed out that less than 2,750 kcal ME/kg feed resulted in smaller pullets at 20 weeks of age. Data from these studies suggested that pullet growth was most sensitive to dietary energy concentration, and that forcing the bird to consume excessive quantities of protein has little positive effect on growth and development.

However, early growth rate (0-8 wks) is likely to be more sensitive to amino acid intake than to energy intake (Leeson, 1990). As more of the essential amino acids become economically and commercially available, nutritionists will be including more of them into their feed formulations on a routine basis. This will allow to further decrease dietary crude protein levels. Keshavarz and Jackson (1992) showed that pullets grown on low protein diets (16%, 0-6 wks; 13.5%, 6-12 wks and 11.5% crude protein, 12-18 wks) supplemented with methionine, lysine, threonine, and arginine were only 37 g lighter at 18 weeks than control birds fed 20, 16 and 14% crude protein (CP) during the growth period.

The dietary requirement for protein is more accurately expressed as a requirement for the 22 physiologically essential amino acids. Of these 22 amino acids, 10 cannot be synthesized by poultry or synthesized in inadequate amounts. Quantities to meet their metabolic needs are considered dietary essentials. The order of amino acid limitation in most poultry diets is methionine, lysine, threonine, tryptophan, isoleucine, valine and arginine (Elliot, 1995). However, care needs to be taken to ensure that the diet still provides adequate levels of the nonessential amino acids and the remaining essential amino acids. Low-protein diets providing 15% CP for starters fed to 42 days of age and 12.75% CP for growers fed to 125 days of age, even though these diets were supplemented with synthetic methionine, and lysine, were not adequate to support the growth rate of the Leghorn pullets when compared to growers on high-protein diets containing 20% CP for starters and 16% for growers (Leeson and Caston, 1996).

The suggested levels of the limited amino acids in Table 1 are 10% higher than those of the NRC (1994) requirements, carrying a 10% margin of safety (Harms, 1987).

The present trend of lowering dietary protein levels by supplementing with limited essential amino acids will tend to lower overall amino acids requirements (Austic, 1996). Each amino acid value in table 1 during each growing period is lower than those shown by Leeson and Summers (1991), Rhone-Poulenc Animal Nutrition (1993), Degussa (1995) and the requirements recommended by commercial breeder companies including Dekalb, Hy-line, ISA, Avian Farms and Arbor Acres (The Korean Poultry Research, 1995). The suggested amino acid values by Harms (1989) were higher than values in table 1 except for lysine. Recommended amino acid values for pullets in each stage by the Nutrient Requirement for Poultry of Japan (NRPJ, 1984) and Heart-Land Lysine (1990) are lower than the values in table 1, even though recommended values of Heart-Land Lysine were given as the digestible amino acid values. Betram and Schmidtborn (1984) suggested the higher values of sulfur-containing amino acid (methionine, methionine cystine) than values in table 1, with lower values for the rest of the amino acids. The connection between NRC diets and actual production rations are only in time, not in fact and NRC (1994) nutrient requirements are designed to be minimum, not a real diet (Anon, 1994). Each amino acid value in table 1 for pullets was developed on the basis of the NRC (1994), which requires the modification of each value to apply to a real diet in a practical environment.

It is commercially recommended that there is 1.00% calcium and 0.5% available phosphorus in all pullet diets. However, Schoner and Hoppe (1992) indicated that no adverse effect on weight gain and phosphorus (P) utilization in broilers due to increase in dietary calcium (Ca) (6.0-9.0 g/kg) could be measured when 500 units of phytase activity were added to a diet which had a basal P content of 5.5 g per kg. They also showed that a further reduction in the P content of diet from 5.5 to 5.0 g at the same Ca and phytase levels reduced live mass of broiler. Simons and Varsteegh (1990) reported that chicks fed phytase had 40% less phosphorus in excreta as compared to chicks receiving phosphorus from a mixture of dicalcium phosphate and mono-ammonium phosphate. Calcium retention and dry matter (DM) digestibility were improved when phytase was added to broiler diets (Kornegay et al., 1996). Supplemental microbial phytase is well known for its effectiveness in improving the availability of P in plant ingredients containing high levels of phytate P, and this report has also suggested that the availability of Ca, Zn and amino acids (and N) are also improved (Kornegay, 1996a). Most of the scientists' data were generated with a diet based on corn and soybean meal. Kornegay et al. (1996) confirmed that microbial phytase was very effective for improving the availability of phytase P in corn and soybean meal diets. They also showed that the magnitude of the response of several measurements to added phytase was inversely related to the level of available P (and total P to include phytate P) and to the level or amount of supplemental phytase added. They calculated that P equivalency of 1 g of P ranged from 467 to 922 units of phytase, and these equations could be used to estimate the equivalent amount of inorganic P released over a range of 250 to 1,000 units of phytase/kg of diet.

Very few research projects have attempted to determine the requirements of calcium and phosphorus for the layer pullets with phytase supplementation, since phytase supplementation increases the availability of calcium and phosphorus for broilers (table 1). The research report of BASF (McKnight, 1997) provided that the AP level could be reduced up to 0.25% with phytase supplementation in the broiler diet without any performance differences from the 0.45% AP of the control diet. Nutrient requirement tables from several sources including NRC (1994) suggest the same or very similar levels of calcium and phosphorus requirements between pullets and broilers (Read the section for broilers).

The National Research Council vitamin requirements are expressed in terms of the minimum amount required to prevent deficiency symptoms as evidenced by strict scientific research. Optimum nutrition occurs only when poultry makes efficient use of nutrients in the feed for growth, health, reproduction and survival (McNaughton, 1990). Optimal vitamin requirements are the vitamin levels required by an animal to prevent marginal (undetected) deficiencies and inadequacies to allow optimal health and performance. Low dietary crude protein and phosphorus levels in poultry diets are possible when optimal vitamin requirements are maintained which would allow starter and growing pullets to remain healthy during this stressful period. Waldroup (1996) pointed out that many values in the NRC (1994) nutrient requirements are based upon research done more than 40 years ago with animals of markedly different productive potential than exist today, and this is particularly true with requirements for most vitamins and trace minerals.

Vitamin addition levels should be based on field experience. Unfortunately, very little extensive research has been conducted at levels in which vitamins are used (Shurson et al., 1996). For practical purposes, vitamin values recommended by BASF (1994) in table 1 were selected because these values are the average levels which feed manufacturers use in their rations for pullets under the field conditions.

The numbers indicated in table 1 are considered very high compared with those of NRC (1994) tables but are still lower than the recommended values by Hoffman-La Roche in a review paper written by Shurson et al. (1996) and even lower than those for starters and growers suggested by Leeson and Summers (1991) other than values for vitamins A, D_3, B_2, and B_{12}. Interestingly enough, all values in table 1 were much lower than values recommended for chick starters by Germans and Europeans, and still lower than values recommended for replacement chickens suggested by Germans and Europeans (Gropp, 1994) except for riboflavin and pyridoxine. The choline and biotin values provided in table 1 were offered from NRC (1994). These contents are more than the recommendation of Germans (750 mg/kg and 80-120 ug/kg) and Europeans (1,000 mg/kg and 100 ug/kg), while lower than those for starter (1,600 mg/kg and 200 ug/kg) and for growing chickens (1,400 mg/kg and 150 ug/kg) in Leeson and Summers (1991), respectively. The results of comparing these values suggest that vitamin values for starter chicks and replacement chickens need not to be divided to provide for optimal health and performance of chicks fed the low dietary crude protein and phosphorus levels during this stressful period.

Vitamins only represent 0.5% of the weight and 1.5% of the cost of complete chicken feeds (Coelho, 1994), and the higher levels indicated would allow the producer to save time and investment of mixing two different types of vitamin mixes, one for starter chicks and one for replacement chickens.

Layers

As energy intake increases, there is a dramatic increase in egg production, particularly when protein intake is very low (Lesson, 1990). In this study egg production increased from 45% to 85% when energy intake increased from 185 to 312 kcal per day for birds consuming 13.1 g CP per day. Summers and Lesson (1989) indicated that the average daily energy intake was from 185-312 kcal ME/bird from 18 to 61 weeks of age and protein intake varied from 13 to 21 g/bird/day. These scientists recommended 2,800 kcal ME/kg which was a higher level than values given by the NRPJ (1984) and Rhone-Poulenc Animal Nutrition (1993) and lower than the recommendations of most commercial layer production companies as well as NRC (1994).

Many egg producers attach great importance to dietary crude protein content. It is possible that the protein requirement is much lower, providing dietary amino acid levels are maintained. Reducing crude protein could limit the amount of excess nitrogen excreted. Belyavin (1992) reported that there were no significant differences for any of the performance characteristics in the diet containing 14% crude protein, with supplementing amino acids added at the level of 0.78% lysine and 0.36% methionine can lead to as good a physical performance as a diet containing 17% crude protein. All diets in this research were fed ad libitum and the trial was conducted over the period of 20-76 weeks of age. Crude protein can be reduced to a concentration of 13% in the diet without negatively affecting percent production (Summers, 1993). This study showed that the N-excretion could be cut by approximately 30-40%, compared to diets with 17 or 19% crude protein. At 15% crude protein or less, there was a tendency towards a reduced egg weight. Whether or not an adequate supply of the essential amino acids was always secured in the experiments, cannot be deduced from the results.

Scientists compared the performance parameters of laying hens fed complete diets with either conventional or redeuced crude protein levels, being 16.7% vs. 14.1% CP (Schutte et al., 1983), 16.5% vs. 14% CP (Van Weerden et al., 1984), 17.5% vs. 15.5% CP (Scholtyssek et al., 1991), 17.6% vs. 14.9% CP (Harms and Russel. 1993), and 18% vs. 13% CP (Lettnet and Preining, 1991). These research results did not show any differences in the production rate between the conventional protein levels and the reduced protein levels with the supplemented amino acids. Schutte *et al.* (1994) and Bertram *et al.* (1995) compared the performance parameters of laying hens fed complete diets with either conventional or reduced crude protein levels. The crude protein levels of the standard rations in these trials ranged from 17 to 18% and contained the major limiting among acids in the following concentrations: methionine 0.4%, methionine plus cystine 0.65-0.70%, and lysine 0.70-0.90%. The content of limiting amino acids in the low protein diets (13.3-15.5%) was adjusted to the levels of the "normal" crude protein content by the incorporation of crystalline amino acids. The performance criteria of the birds after feeding both complete diets show that under current commercial conditions the utilization of dietary protein can be considerably enhanced by feeding protein-reduced rations supplemented with methionine and lysine. In these ways laying performance and daily egg mass production are maintained for the protein-reduced, supplemented diets. The feed conversion ratio showed a slight, but not significant, upward trend in some cases. However, the use of low-protein amino acid-supplemented diets (14, 13 and 12% crude protein supplemented with methionine, lysine, tryptohan and isoleucine for age periods of 18-34, 34-50 and 50-66 weeks) during the laying period failed to produce a comparable performance to those fed the protein levels (18, 16.5 and 15% for similar age periods) that are typically used in commercial practice (Keshavarz, 1991). Keshavarz (1997) also provided the results of another trial that 16.5, 15.5, 14.5 and 13.5% protein for 20 to 36, 36 to 48, 48 to 60 and 60 to 72 weeks of age did not influence layer's overall performance for the entire laying period. In this research, the levels of total sulfur amino acids were maintained at 0.59% and the minimum level of lysine was 0.68% in the laying rations.

Recently Leeson and Caston (1996) reported that four egg-type strains of layers had no significant differences in performance when fed varying levels of crude protein in their diets. In their experiment, each strain of pullets was fed diets of 16.8% crude protein or 14.4% crude protein supplemented with methionine and lysine. Strain affected body weight and feed intake. At 70 weeks of age, egg production and egg mass were similar for the four strains, However, egg mass on the low protein amino-acid fortified diet was almost on kilogram (2.2 pounds) less for the 52 weeks of the experiment. And the strain with the lightest body weight at 18 weeks of age was heaviest at 70 weeks.

The amino acid values for layers in table 1, which are 10% higher than those of the NRC (1994) requirements, are at considerably lower levels than those given by several commercial breeder companies (Dekalb, Hy-line brown layer, ISA brown, Hy-line W-77 White Layer, Avian Farm, and Arbor Acres adapted from The Korean Poultry Research, 1995). However, further research is required for the proper levels of the limited amino acids with the reduced protein content in the commercial layer farm. As enzymes and more synthetic amino acids become justified, their use in layer's diets may provide a means of reducing pollution (Belyavin, 1992). Each limited amino acid in table 1 was lower or higher than the levels of Belyavin (1992; methionine, 0.36%; lysine, 0.78%; methionine & cystine, 0.67%) and the values, 0.52% (threonine), 0.18% (tryptophan), 0.68 (isoleucine) and 0.92% (arginine), were provided by Rhone-Poulenc Animal Nutrition (1993), Harms (1989) and Russell and Harms (1997), indicating a balance on the basis of 17% crude protein. This was the control diet in the Belyavin (1992) research and was recommended for light and semi-heavy body weight as well as low and high environmental temperatures. These limited amino acid values are higher than values of NRC (1994), the NRPJ (1984), those provided by Lesson and Summers (1991), and offered by Bertram and Schmidtborn (1984).

The level of phosphorus in feed influences eggshell quality and egg production (Keshavarz, 1990). The results of short- and long- term performance were reduced (p < 0.05) and mortality was increased (p < 0.05) due to consumption of a diet containing 6.5% calcium and a marginal level of available phosphorus (0.2%). The results of digestion trials (Keshavarz, 1987a, b) indicated that calcium and phosphorus retention were reduced due to increasing the dietary levels of calcium. However, increasing the dietary levels of phosphorus did not influence (p > 0.05) the retention of calcium or phosphorus. Because of disposal and environment concerns over the amounts of phosphorus in the manure, one experiment with four egg-type strains of layers recently was conducted by Leeson and Caston (1996). In this experiment starting with pullets at 18 weeks of age, diets had available phosphorus levels of 0.41, 0.34 or 0.27%. Egg production and total egg mass were similar for all strains. Dietary phosphorus had no effect on body weight or feed intake, although there were consistent strain effects on these parameters.

Simons and Versteegh (1993) fed laying hens a low available phosphorus (0.06% AP) diet supplemented with graded levels of monocalcium phosphate (MCP) or phytase from 24 to 52 weeks of age and measured laying performance, eggshell quality, skeletal quality and phosphorus excretion. Phosphorus deficiency symptoms observed with the negative control diet were completely compensated by the lowest level of phytase (200 FTU/kg, FTU = fytase unit). Phosphorus excretion via manure increased when MCP was added to the diet and decreased when phytase was added to the diet. Phosphorus excretion of the groups with phytase average 40% less than the groups receiving MCP. Roland, Sr. (1996) conducted a trial with sixteen hundred pullets (21 weeks of age), which were divided into 10 groups and fed diets containing 0.1, 0.2, 0.3, 0.4 and 0.5% AP, with and without 300 FTU of phytase. In this trial, dietary energy, protein and calcium were maintained at 2,819 ME kcal/kg, 16.6% and 4.0%, respectively. Hens fed diets containing 0.1% AP maintained production equal to other treatments for 11 weeks. However, during week 12, egg production and feed consumption decreased in hens fed 0.1% AP and by week 17, production had dropped to 60% vs. 87% for hens in other treatments. The addition of phytase to the diet containing 0.1% AP completely prevented the adverse effects. Another phytase trial (Roland, Sr., 1996) was conducted with two other groups of hens (Hy-Line and Delta). Diets containing 0.3% AP (control) and 0.09% AP were fed with and without phytase. In the trial with Hy-Line W36 hens, production dropped within 3 to 4 weeks but phytase completely prevented the drop. Feed consumption decreased but phytase prevented it. Egg weight also dropped but phytase prevented it. The same results were obtained with Dekalb (Delta) hens.

Because low calcium levels increase phosphorus excretion and low phosphorus levels increase calcium excretion, a proper ratio of calcium and phosphorus must be maintained in order to satisfy the hens requirement of either nutrient (Gordon and Roland, Sr., 1996). How much calcium should be fed to optimize the phosphorus requirement? There are many complex factors that influence calcium and phosphorus requirements as follows (Gordon and Roland, Sr., 1996). 1. calcium level, 2. particle size of $CaCO_3$, 3. cage density, 4. accuracy of P feed ingredient analysis, 5. accuracy of feed intake value, 6. accuracy of availability values, 7. variation in individual feed intake, 8. variation in average feed intake, 9. flock uniformity, 10. vitamin D_3, 11. strain of bird, 12. dietary chloride level, 13. environmental temperature, 14. method of formulation and feeding, 15. age at sexual maturity, 16. feed intake, 17. variation in phytate P utilization, 18. transition time from pre-lay to lay diet. Still few parts about calcium and phosphorus requirement have been discussed in several research reports and the levels recommended must be continued to be used until more knowledge is obtained. The new Hy-Line (1995) management guide increased their maximum calcium level from 3.85 to 4.4% and reduced their protein.

The vitamin values of layers in table 1 were recommended for commercial layers as being adequate for production performance, health, feed conversion, reproduction and survival under the commercial production conditions, as used by commercial feed manufacturers (BASF, 1994). These values were higher than those of the NRC (1994) recommendation but include pyridoxine (2.5 mg/kg feed in NRC versus 1.03 mg/kg feed in BASF recommendation table) and folic acid (0.25 mg/kg feed in NRC versus 0.23 mg/kg feed in the BASF table). All of the values except vitamin D and vitamin B_2 are lower than the recommendation of Lesson and Summer (1991).

All the values of vitamin recommendations for layers in table 1 remain lower than the recommendations of Germany or Europe, with the exception of the higher values of pyridoxine, folic acid and biotin than the European recommendations

(European recommendations are lower than German recommendation in vitamin recommendations for layers). The choline levels in table 1 were given by the NRC (1994), showing lower recommendation values than Lesson and Summers (1991), and higher than the value of Miles *et al.* (1986).

Broilers

Large amounts of energy can promote better feed efficiency and optimize growth, but can also increase metabolic problems such as ascites, leg weakness and sudden death syndrome. Some researchers have shown that the broiler may adapt to lower-energy diets and just eat more to make up the difference. Leeson (1996) indicated that growth rate of the male broiler is independent of dietary energy level and that the bird will adjust intake so as to maintain almost constant energy intake. He said that broilers do not eat to near physical capacity when offered conventional diets, but the bird has the ability to increase its intake when energy levels in its diet are reduced. In one of their experiments, male broilers were fed single-stage diets that provided 2,700, 2,900, 3,100 or 3,300 kcal ME/kg through day 49. All diets contained 21% CP with 1.20% lysine and 0.58% methionine. Results showed that there was a small reduction in live weight and carcass weight between the highest and lowest energy level used, although bodyweight was not changed significantly between energy levels. Birds that were fed diets containing less ME tended to eat more.

Various research trials have been done to restrict either protein levels or restrict feed intake during part or all of the feeding program in broiler production. A trial was designed to test the effect of early protein restriction on broiler performance (Scheideler, 1989). The control diet was formulated to 100% of NRC (1984) recommended levels of protein and amino acids. The second diet was formulated to 80% of NRC-recommend levels of total protein, but 100% of NRC-recommended levels of essential amino acids. The experimental diets were fed to the chicks from day one to three weeks of age. At three weeks all birds were placed on the same control diet. Both restricted diets resulted in body weights that were significantly less than the control diet at six weeks of age. Skinner *et al.* (1991) provided different research results about nutrient restriction. They found that feeding a starter diet containing only 75% of the NRC (1994) amino acid requirements will reduce growth rate during the starting period. When the birds are placed on 100% of the NRC (1994) amino acid requirements for the grower and finishing periods they actually grow faster than birds fed a comparable control feeding program and they exhibited fewer leg problems and fewer heart attacks. They reported the research results from a different trial when a diet diluted with 50% ground oat hulls was fed during the starter period and the birds achieved the same as, or even more weight than control-fed birds at 49 days of age, with an improved feed and nutrient efficiency.

Huran (1984) demonstrated that the low-protein rations of 16 and 20% crude protein level in the growing periods of 0-20 and 21-49 days could successfully bring male and female body weights in 49 days to broiler market weight. Both male and female birds are able to perform quite well with low protein diets containing low amino acid levels (18% CP for starter, 18% CP for grower and 16% CP for finisher) as well as on high protein diets (22% CP for starter, 20% CP for grower and 16% CP for finisher)(Leeson and Summers, 1991). These research results showed that the female is slightly smaller at 42 days, and there is a general trend for inferior feed efficiency with the low protein diets. For males, 42 day body weight was not affected, although again feed efficiency was slightly inferior.

The protein requirement of the bird can be expressed more correctly as a requirement per each essential amino acid and a total requirement for non-essential amino acids which is related to a minimal concentration in crude protein. On the basis of this concept, one attempt was conducted with two different protein levels (19.5% CP and 16.5% CP) with birds aged from 4 to 7 weeks (Uzu, 1982). The low protein diet (16.5% CP) with the addition of methionine and lysine or threonine, lysine and methionine resulted in the feed consumption level identical to and growth performance even higher than that of the control diet (19.5% CP). In fact there was no crude protein level specified as a minimum (Baker, 1995). Baker (1995) suggested to drive the appropriate protein minimum by using the amino acid to lysine ratio.

The amino acid values in table 1 are cited from the NRC (1994) amino acid requirements after adding 10% for a safety margin (Harms, 1987), except for increasing lysine value from 1.10% to 1.20% for 1-21 days old, threonine value from 0.74% to 0.78% for 21-42 days old and isoleucine value from 0.72% to 0.85% for 5-43 days old (9.0 g/kg from 15 to 23 days of age and 8.0 g/kg from 33 to 43 days of age)(Schutte and Pack, 1995; Kidd and Kerr, 1996). Kidd and Kerr (1996) reported that increasing dietary lysine from 1.10 to 1.20% from 1 to 18 days in broilers (p < 0.001), improved weight gain (453 g versus 488 g) and feed gain (1.39 versus 1.33). No interactions between lysine and threonine were observed. They found out that the NRC (1994) lysine requirement for 1 to 21 day old chicks is too low and the 1 to 18 day lysine requirement for chicks is at least 1.20% of diet. They also provided research results that showed the low protein diet containing 0.78% total threonine supported growth performance and carcass yield that was equal to or not significantly different from the high protein diet and that broilers fed low protein diets require the addition of synthetic threonine, in addition to additions of synthetic sulfur amino acid and lysine.

In a report on ascites, sudden death syndrome (SDS) and leg problems, Summers (1994, 1996) presented data that suggested that increased levels of dietary methionine and lysine, while having little effect on weight gain or feed: gain ratio, could significantly increase the incidence of ascites, SDS and leg problems. In this test, conducted with male broilers, the birds of 0-6 weeks of age were fed a commercial-type diet (0.88% of total sulfur amino acid and 1.21% of lysine) or the same diet supplemented with and additional 0.2% DL-methionine, or 0.45% L-lysine HCl or with the methionine plus lysine supplementation. McNaughton (1995a) and Whitehead (1995) have indicated that ascites, SDS and leg problems occur in particular situations such as high energy rations (i.e., more than 3250 kcal/kg), high salt rations (i.e., more than 0.6% salt) and other inadequacies of management as well as environment situations.

Amino acid values in table 1 are elevated to be quite a bit higher than values shown in the NRPJ (1984), the Rhone-Poulenc Animal Nutrition (1993), Lesson and Summers (1991), and the Korean Poultry Research (1995). However, the methionine values of table 1 were lower than those in the NRPJ (1984) and Heart-land Lysine (1990). Amino acid values provided by Avian Farms(1995) were lower than values of amino acid in table 1 for 0-3 weeks but higher for 4-7 weeks. Adding 10% safety margins to each amino acid in table 1 resulted in higher values, especially in total sulfur amino acid.

McKnight (1996) summarized that phytase addition improved phosphorus (total) utilization from an average of 47% to an average of 64% in the practical broiler diets. Contor (1995) conducted a trial to compare the broiler diet containing 0.45% AP and 0.92% calcium to the basal diet (calcium = 0.65%, available phosphorus = 0.27%) supplemented with 1,200 units/kg of phytase (A. niger phosphotases or yeast acid phosphotase or A. niger phytase). There were no differences among these treatments in weight gain, feed intake and feed conversion.

The magnitude of the response to added phytase is proportionally related to the phosphorus retention rate in the broiler body and inversely related to the phosphorus excretion, even though it did not appears as a straight line on their figure (Kornegay, 1996a). McKnight (1997) recommended 500 ug/kg of phytase (Natuphos) to replace 0.1% AP and 0.1% calcium, with 300 ug/kg of phytase replacing 0.1% AP and 0.1% calcium for broiler grower and finisher diets. 1,200 ug/kg of phytase in the broiler diet (calcium = 0.65%, AP = 0.27%) resulted in the same broiler performances the diet supplied with 0.45% AP and 0.92% calcium (Contor, 1995). According to McKnight (1997), the research results of BASF showed that the AP level could be reduced up to 0.25% with phytase supplementation in the broiler diet, which did not cause any performance differences from the 0.45% AP of the control diet.

Thirteen vitamins are added to practical poultry rations. NRC (1994) poultry requirement for vitamins is only a minimum like other nutrients and NRC's (1994) minimum nutrient requirements are not designed to be the real level found in the diet. They are abstract, and sometimes theoretical guesses (Anon, 1994).

The best evidence of the impact of vitamin addition on animal performance is illustrated in a series of trials comparing the highest vitamin supplementation (top 5%) with consecutive lower supplementation levels (top 25%, average industry, bottom 25% and NRC, 1994) in broilers based on an industry survey conducted by BASF in 1994 (BASF, 1994). Each decrease in vitamin supplementation led to a significant ($p < 0.05$) decrease in performance measured by weight, feed efficiency and mortality.

The NRC (1994) published requirements are generally lower than the average values used by most nutritionists, except for thiamin and biotin. These two vitamins are being gradually increased by most nutritionists. The most striking difference between the NRC and field requirements are in vitamin A and D. NRC (1994) values are 25-50% lower than field requirements (Coelho, 1994). Table 1 recommends vitamin levels for starter and grower broilers which were suggested by BASF (1994). These values are average commercial vitamin fortification for broilers based on an industry survey conducted by BASF in 1994 (BASF, 1994), which show much higher levels than the NRC (1994) recommendation levels. However, they are much lower than European commercial average recommendations (Gropp, 1994). For example European average recommendations (broiler starter/ grower) for vitamins A, D_3 and K are 12,000 IU/kg, 4,000 IU/kg and 4 mg/kg, respectively while US average commercial vitamin fortification for broiler starters are 8,840 IU/kg, 2,811 IU/kg and 1.85 mg/kg, respectively, maintaining the same trends of each value for the rest of the other vitamins. Interestingly, the recommended values of BASF (1994) for thiamin, pyridoxine and biotin are lower than values recommended by the NRC (1994) while maintaining less than half values for biotin recommendations providing 0.08 mg/kg and 0.07 mg/kg for broiler starters and growers of US average commercial fortification compared to 0.2 mg/kg for broiler starter/grower of European average commercial fortification. However, the recommended value for thiamin is a reflection of the German minimum values of which figures for the pyridoxine supplementation of broiler diets in Germany from 1 to 7.3 mg/kg.

Methyl groups such as choline and methionine are essential in the diet, but interest in their use lagged because many researchers thought growing birds could synthesize sufficient choline from normal rations to fulfill requirement (Sunde, 1982). Sunde (1982) suggested that 868 mg/kg were sufficient in broiler diets, while higher levels, including levels up to 3,906 mg/kg, did not produce sufficiently different performance. Surprisingly, German poultry diets provide the minimum figure of choline chloride, too. The maximum values for broiler starter/grower are 750 (1,000) mg/kg in Germany (Europe). The level of choline for broiler starter/ growers did not appear in the BASF (1994) table.

Table 1. The Possible Minimum Nutrient Requirement of Chicken as Percentages or Units per kilogram of Diet (90% dry matter) [*][**]

Age (wk)		Pullet			Layer	Broiler	
		0~6	7~12	13~18	18>	0~3	4~7
ME (minimum)	Kcal/kg		2,750		2,800		
CP (exact)	%	16	13.5	11.5	13	18	16.5
Methionine	%	0.33	0.28	0.22	0.33	0.55	0.42
Lysine	%	0.94	0.66	0.50	0.76	1.32	1.19
Threonine	%	0.75	0.63	0.41	0.52	0.88	0.85
Tryptophan	%	0.19	0.15	0.12	0.18	0.22	0.20
Isoleucine	%	0.66	0.55	0.44	0.72	0.88	0.80
Valine	%	0.68	0.57	0.45	0.77	0.99	0.90
Arginine	%	1.10	0.09	0.74	0.77	1.38	1.21
Met & Cys	%	0.68	0.57	0.46	0.67	0.93	0.89
The rest of amino acids[1]							
Ca (minimum)	%		0.65		3.75	0.65	
AP (exact)	%		0.25		0.09	0.25	
The rest of minerals[2]							
Vitamin A	IU		10,000		7,380	8,840	8,113
Vitamin D$_3$	IU		1,800		2,440	2,811	2,568
Vitamin E	IU		25.0		7.5	17.9	15.8
Menadione (K$_3$)	mg		1.30		1.00	1.84	1.63
Riboflavin	mg		7.00		4.60	7.10	6.44
Niacin	mg		50.0		24.7	45.8	43.4
D-pantothenic acid	mg		10.00		7.10	12.04	10.91
Choline	mg		1,300		1,050	1,300	1,000
Folic acid	mg		0.60		0.23	0.68	0.75
Thiamin	mg		1.0		0.7	3.0	3.0
Pyridoxine	mg		3.50		1.03	5.00	5.00
Vitamin B$_{12}$	ug		18.0		7.7	14.0	14.0
d-Biotin	ug [*]		150		100	150	150
Xanthophyll[3]							
Linoleic acid[4]							
Enzyme[5]							

[1,2,3,4] Levels of nutrients in furnished feed must meet minimum daily intake as suggested by NRC (1994).

[3] A minimum of xanthophyll should be used based on yolk color demand of the market area.

[5] Exogenous enzyme complex combining with phytase, protease, -glucanase, xylanases and others is required for applying the nutrient requirements in this table.

ME: metabolizable energy, CP: crude protein, AP: available phosphorus.

[*] The same amount of NRC (1994) requirement.

[**] Based on data from 15 scientific publications (Huran, 1984; Leeson and Summers, 1989; Lettner and Preining, 1991; Keshavarz and Jackson, 1992; Summers, 1993; BASF, 1994; NRC, 1994; Baker, 1995; Contor, 1995; Schutte and Pack, 1995; Gordon and Roland, Sr., 1996; Kidd and Kerr, 1996; Lesson, 1996; Roland, Sr., 1996; McKnight, 1997)

Under stress conditions, vitamin E requirements for broiler were definitely increased to 300 mg/kg feed in heat stress and 150-300 mg/kg feed in moderate *E. coli* infections when supplying with vitamin E acetate (Fletcher and Tappel, 1973). Murphy *et al.* (1981) reported that vitamin E fed to broiler chickens at 100 IU/kg of feed apparently interferes with vitamin D utilization.

The vitamin values recommended in table 1 still remain at lower levels compared to those of vitamin supplement companies like Hoffman-La Roche and BASF (Shurson *et al*, 1996), with these values being higher than most values recommended by Leeson and Summers (1991) except vitamin D_3, riboflavin, vitamin B_{12} and pyridoxine. Vitamin values in table 1 provide the average commercial vitamin fortification for broiler starter/grower based on industry survey in US mostly, with two vitamins (thiamin, and pyridoxine) being from Europe and two vitamins (choline and biotin) from NRC (1994).

CONCLUSION

Restrictions and regulations related to manure disposal from the animal production systems are already commonplace in many countries, while regulations and legislation pertaining to this problem are pending in other countries. In particular, nitrogen (N) and phosphorus (P) may pollute water after application of animal manure or chemical fertilizer to the soils.

Low-protein and lower phosphorus diets offer advantages in lower costs and less excretion of nitrogen, phosphorus and other potential pollutants of the environment. Instead of the conventional feed formulations, the levels of protein and phosphorus in the ration should be reduced while supplementing synthetic amino acids and enzymes like proteases and phytases. This would allow biologically available amino acids and phosphorus in feeds that are less well digested to be better utilized.

Vitamin contents in table 1 of this review are 1-6 times higher than those of the NRC (1994). Vitamin cost does not significantly affect feed cost, but vitamins are nutrients which contribute to increasing the utilization of protein and phosphorus, thereby minimizing pollution and increasing the metabolic efficiency of chickens.

REFERENCES

Almirall, M., M. Francesch, A. M. Perez-Vendrell, J. Bruf and E. Esteve-Garcia. 1994. Effect of avizyme on production and intestinal parameters in barley fed broilers. British Journal of Nutrition (In press).

ANONYMOUS. 1994. NRC minimums should not be part of drug evaluation. Feedstuffs. March 14. p. 10.

Austic, R. E. 1996. Dietary protein level and the response to dietary amino acids. Cornell Nutrition Conference. pp. 168-175.

Avian Farms. 1995. Avian Farm Nutrient Requirement Manual.

Baker, D. H. 1995. Ideal protein in broilers. Poultry Digest. November. pp. 8-14.

BASF. 1994. Vitamin stability in premixes and feeds: A practical approach. BASF keeping current, KC9138. 4th revised edition.

Belyavin, C. 1992. Updating layer feeding. Poultry International. October. pp. 16-20.

Betram, H. and H. Schmidtborn. 1984. Amino acids in animal nutrition. Feed Management. 35(5):48-50.

Bertram, Heidrun-L., E. Danner, K. Jeroch and H. Jeroch. 1995. Effect of DL-methionine in a cereal-pea diet on the performance of brown laying hens. Archiv fur Gelflugel-kunde. 59(1):103-107.

Blair, R., R. J. Yong and M. L. Scott. 1972. Unidentified factor activities in whole soybeans required for optimal growth of Cotumix quail. Journal of Nutrition. 102:1529-1524.

Contor, A. H. 1995. Using enzymes to increase phosphorus availability in poultry diets. Biotechnology in the Feed Industry. Proceedings of Alltech's 11th Annual Symposium (T. P. Lyons and K. A. Jaques, Edition.). Nottingham University Press, pp. 349-353.

Coelho, M. B. 1994. U. S. Commercial vitamin fortification rates in poultry and swine feeds. Arkansas Nutrition Conference. pp. 62-90.

Cromwell. G. L. 1996. Synthetic amino acid may improve performance, reduce nitrogen excretion. Feedstuff. November 25. pp. 12-13, 17-20.

Degussa. 1995. Amino Acid Recommendations for Poultry.

Eeckhout, E. and K. de Paepe. 1994. Total phosphorus, phytate phosphorus and phytase activity in plant feedstuffs. Animal Feed Science and Technology. 47: 12-22.

Elliot, M. A. 1995 Feeding and managing pullets to optimize genetic potential. California Nutrition Conference. pp. 149-175.

Fletcher, B. J. and A. L. Tappel. 1973. Protective effects of dietary tocopherol in rats. Environmental Resource 6:165-175.

Gibson, D. M. and A. B. Ullah. 1990. Phytase and their actions on phytic acid. pp. 77-92. in: Inositol Metabolism in Plants. D.J. Morre, W.F. Boss and F.A. Loewus Edition Wiley Liss Press, NY.

Gordon, R. W. and D. Roland, Sr. 1996. Influence of supplemental phytase on calcium utilization of laying hens. BASF Technical Symposium. June 19. pp. 31-44.

Gropp, J. M. 1994. Vitamin fortification levels in European commercial poultry and swine diets. Arkansas Nutrition Conference. pp. 105-134.

Harms, R. H. 1987. Life cycle feeding of broiler breeders explored. Feedstuffs,

May 25. pp. 14-20.

Harms, R. H. 1989. Lifetime feeding of commercial laying hens. Poultry International. May. pp. 40-46.

Harms, R. H. and G. B. Russel. 1993. Optimizing egg mass with amino acid supplementation of a low-protein diet. Poultry Science. 72:1892-1896.

Heart-Land Lysine Inc. 1990 True digestible amino acid recommendations for poultry feed formulation.

Heinzl, W. 1996. Technical specification of Natuphos phytase enzyme. In BASF Corp Technical Symposia. World Congress Center, Atlanta, Ga., January 20. p. 14.

Herrick, R. B. and E. Ross. 1986. Hawaiian study suggests advantages in open housing. Feedstuffs, January 20. p. 14.

Hesselman, K. and P. Aman. 1986. The effect of glucanase on the utilization of starch and nitrogen by broiler chickens fed on barley of low and high viscosity. Animal Feed Science and Technology. 15:83-91.

Huran, L. 1984. Low protein diets suggested for growing broilers. Feedstuffs. May 21. pp. 15-16.

Hy-Line Management Guide. 1995. The Korean Poultry Research. (1995) The nutrient requirement given by different breeder companies. (5th Edition) pp. 27-41.

Keshavarz, K. 1987a. Interaction between calcium and phosphorus in laying hens. Nutrition Reports International. 36:1-20.

Keshavarz, K. 1987b. Influence of feeding a high calcium diet for various duration of prelaying period on growth and subsequent performance of white Leghorn pullets. Poultry Science. 66:1576-1582.

Keshavarz, K. 1990. Practical approach can improve eggshell quality. Feedstuffs. March 26. pp. 13-15.

Keshavarz, K. 1991. Low-protein, amino acid-supplemented diets hinder poultry growth. Feedstuffs. December 9. pp. 11-12, 17.

Keshavarz, K. 1997. Investigations on the use of low-protein, amino acid-supplemented diets for poultry. Cornell Nutrition Conference. pp. 155-166.

Keshavarz. K. and M. Jackson. 1992. Performance of growing pullets and laying hens fed low-protein. amino acid-supplemented diets. Poultry Science. 71: 905-918.

Khalid. B. 1991. Making more use of barley. Poultry International. August. pp. 36-40.

Kidd, M. T. and B. J. Kerr. 1996. Threonine and broiler nutrition. Arkansas Nutrition Conference. pp. 203-228.

Kornegay, E. T. 1996a. Nutritional, environmental and economical consideration for using phytase in pig and poultry diets. In Proceeding International Symposium. Management of Food Animals to Enhance the Environment. June 4-7, 1995. Blacksburg. VA.

Kornegay, E. T. 1996b. Effect of phytase on the bioavilability of phosphorus, calcium, amino acids, and trace minerals in broilers and turkeys. BASF Technical Symposium. January 23. pp. 39-68.

Kornegay, E. T., D. M. Denhow, Z. Yi and V. Ravindran. 1996. Response of broilers to graded levels of Natuphos phytase added to corn-soybean meal-based diets containing three levels of nonphytate phosphorus. British Journal of Nutrition. (IN press).

Leeson, S. 1990. Energy intake for Leghorns. Feed Management. 41(1):27-31.

Leeson. S. 1996. Broiler can adjust feed intake based on dietary energy levels. Maryland Nutrition Conference. pp. 37-50.

Leeson. S. and L. J. Caston. 1996. Response of laying hens to diets varying in crude protein or available phosphorus. Journal of Applied Poultry Research. 5: 289-296.

Leeson. S. and J. D. Summers. 1989. Response of Leghorn pullets to protein and energy in the diet when reared in regular or hot-cyclic environments. Poultry Science. 68:546-557.

Leeson. S. and J. D. Summers. 1991. Commercial Poultry Nutrition. University Book Store, University of Guelph. p. 68.

Lettner, F. and F. Preining. 1993. Verringerung der Stickstoffausscheidung bei Legehennen. Absenkung des Rohproteingehaltes in Alleinqutter. Der Frderungsdienst 4 (41):110-112.

McKnight, F. W. 1996. Phytase: Technical specifications and properties. BASF Technical Symposium. June 19. pp. 1-13.

McKnight, F. W. 1997. Personal communication.

McNaughton, J. L. 1990. Vitamin fortification essential to poultry rations. Feedstuffs. August 27. pp. 13-15.

McNaughton, J. L. 1995a. Ascites-Potential methods of reducing the incidence. California Nutrition Conference. May 3-4. pp. 123-133.

McNaughton, J. 1995b. Poultry nutrition in the 21st century. California Animal Nutrition Conference. pp. 15-26.

Miles. R. D., N. Ruiz. and T. H. Harms. 1986. Response of laying hens to choline when fed practical diets devoid of supplemental sulfur amino acids. Poultry Science. 65:1760-1770.

Murphy. I. P., K. E. Wright. and W. J. Pudelkiewiez. 1981. An apparent rachitogenic effect of excessive vitamin E intakes in the chick. Poultry Science. 60:1873-1878.

Nahm. K. H. and C. H. Sung. 1995. Improving management of layer farms through utilization of a checklist: A field report. Korean Journal of Feed and Nutrition. 19(4):261-272.

National Research Council. 1984. Nutrient Requirements of Poultry. 8th Revised Edition. National Academy Press. Washington D.C.

National Research Council. 1994. Nutrient Requirements of Poultry. 9th Revised Edition. National Academy Press. Washington D.C.

Nutrient Requirement for Poultry of Japan. 1984. National Research Council of Agriculture, Forestry and Fishery. Japan.

Patterson, P. H. 1998. Minimizing nutrient waste. Feed Management. 48(12):21-22.

Rhone-Poulenc Animal Nutrition. 1993. Thone-Pulence Nutrition Guide. 2nd Edition.

Roland, D., Sr. 1994. Poor communication results in excessive phosphorus use. Feedstuffs. October 3 pp. 15-17.

Roland, D., Sr. 1996. Phosphorus and calcium optimization in layer diets with phytase. BASF Technical Symposium. June 19. pp. 16-23.

Russell. G. B. and R. J. Harms. 1997. Tryptophan requirement of the commercial laying hen. Southern Poultry Science Society and Southern Conference. Avian Diseases. S3.

Scheideler. S. E. 1989. Restricted feeding programs for broilers. Carolina Poultry Nutrition Conference. December 6-7 pp. 24-34.

Scholtyssek. S., D. Feuerstein and B. Kutritz. 1991. Versuch zur Optimierug von Eiweverwertung und Stickstoffaus-scheidung in der Legehennenfutferung. Archiv fur Gelfu gelkunde. 55(3):134-141.

Schoner. F. J. and P. P. Hoppe. 1992. Microbial phytase, a tool to alleviate environmental phosphorus pollution from broiler production. Proceedings, World's Poultry Congress. 3:429-441, Amsterdam.

Shurson, J., T. Salzer and D. Kechler. 1996. Metal-specific amino acid complexes, inorganic trace minerals effect on vitamin stability examined. Feedstuffs. October 28. pp. 13-18.

Schutte. J. B., J. DeJong and Bertram, HeidrunL. 1994. Requirement of the laying hen for sulfur amino acids. Poultry Science. 73:274-280.

Schutte. J. B. and M. Park. 1995. Effects of dietary sulfur-containing amino acids on performance and breast meat deposition of broiler chicks during the growing and finishing phases. British Poultry Science. 30:747-762.

Schutte, J. B., E. J. Van Weerden and H. Bertram. 1983. Sulphur amino acid requirement of laying hens and the effects of excess dietary methionine on laying performance. British Poultry Science. 24:319-326.

Scott, M. L., M. C. Nesheim and R. J. Young. 1969. Nutrition of the chicken. Ithaca., N.Y., M. L. Scott Associates.

Simell. M., M. Turunen. J. Piironen and T. Vaara. 1989. Feed and food applications of phytase. Proceedings of the Third Meeting on Industrial Applications of Enzymes, Barcelona. Spain.

Simons. P. C. M. and H. A. J. Varsteegh. 1993. Role of phytase in poultry nutrition in enzymes in animal Nutrition. Wenk. C. and Boessinger. M., Edition Proceeding lst Symposium. Kartause litingen, Switzerland. October 13-16. p. 192.

Skinner. J., A. Izat and P. Waldroup. 1991. Short-term nutrient restriction for lower feed cost does not affect performance. Feedstuffs. September. 2. pp. 22-27.

Summers. J. D. 1993. Reducing nitrogen excretion of the laying hen by feeding lower crude protein diets. Poultry Science. 72:1473-1478.

Summers. J. D. 1994. Ascites and related metabolic diseases. Recent Advances in Animal Nutrition. Nottingham University Press. pp. 83-94.

Summers. J. D. 1996. Dietary acid-base balance likely plays role in SDS and ascites. Feedstuffs. January. 4. pp. 13-17.

Summers. J. D. and S. Lesson 1989 The effect of dietary protein and energy intake on egg production and egg weight of egg-production type pullets. Nutrition Report International 40:645-652.

Sunde. M. L. 1982. The effects of adding these compounds to the corn-soy diets of broiler chicks. pullet chicks and laying hens. Cornell Nutrition Conference. pp. 36-45.

The Korean Poultry Research 1995. The nutrient requirements given by different breeder companies. pp. 27-41.

Uzu. G. 1982. Aspects of protein nutrition of broilers and layers. Feed Management 33(1):40-45.

Van Weerden. E. J., J. B. Schutte and H. Bertram. 1984. Protein and amino acid requirements of laying hens. Proceedings and Abstracts 260-262. World's Poultry Congress. Helsinki.

Waldroup. P. W. 1996. Dietary nutrient allowances for poultry 1996. Reference Issue for Feedstuffs. pp. 66-74.

Whitehead. C. 1995. Nutrition and skeletal disorders in broilers and layers. Poultry International. December. pp. 40-48.

Wyatt. C. L. and A. Harker. 1995. Application of feed enzymes to commercial wheat and barley based poultry feeds California Animal Nutrition Conference. pp. 203-211.

Korean Journal of Poultry Science Vol. 26(1): 1-25 (1999)   65

Quality Poultry Meat Production

K. H. Nahm

Feed and Nutrition Laboratory, College of Natural Resources, Taegu University, Gyong San, South Korea, 712-714

ABSTRACT

Concerns about meat quality, including chicken meat, for the human diet has led to many attempts to manipulate the carcass fat and increase the eating quality. For actual eating quality, the birds must be grown and finished in a manner that results in meat that is tender, succulent and of good flavor, as well as being free from any foreign taint, flavor or safety hazard. Tenderization would improve the tenderness of chicken meat. Proper programs for the withdrawal of feed and water require a team approach for maximizing yield of meat and minimizing carcass contamination. Also feeding of supplemental levels of α-tocopherol to poultry with vegetable or fish oils increases the desirable polyunsaturated fatty acid (PUFA) content and stabilizes the meat against rancidity and fish off-flavors. The nutritional effects of varying dietary ingredients on broiler carcass fat content are also important. Increasing the levels of energy in the ration increases the carcass fat content, while increasing the protein levels decreases carcass fat content. Supplementation of poultry diets with amino acids such as methionine, lysine, glycine and tryptophan as well as amino acid mixtures can reduce body fat deposition. Normal stress leads to chicken muscular damage resulting in reduced meat quality, but this can be controlled by preslaughter management practices. Feed manufacturers can utilize nutrient modulation to control pale soft exudative (PSE) syndrome.

Finally, the success in poultry meat production depends on the consistent achievement of carefully selected levels of quality. Quality assurance should be the wider function of incorporating quality into the production system and the combination of motivating quality into actions and operations.

(Key words: carcass fat, tenderness, stress, PSE, nutrient modulation)

INTRODUCTION

Worldwide consumption of poultry meat will continue to rise. Prices have not increased significantly over the past 30 years and improvements in productivity will probably ensure that prices will remain relatively low in the future. Shifts of consumption from beef and pork to poultry meat will continue, partially due to this price stability.

In the US, consumption has already reached high levels and limits are in sight according to one report (Boekhuyse, 1994). In Asian countries with high incomes and in Europe further increases in consumption are likely, but growth in Europe will probably be less than the current growth rate of 4% per year.

As a result of less rapid increases in US consumption, annual production growth will decline from 6% to between 3 and 4% (Broekhuyse, 1994). It has been predicted that Mexico and the leading producers in Latin America, such as Brazil and Argentina, will continue to have rapid growth. The same forecast of continued growth applies to most Asian countries, except Japan and Hong Kong. China is presently trying to increase poultry meat production to satisfy growing domestic demands (Earnst, 1993).

Individual economic and agricultural policies will be influenced by the competitive edge of exporting countries. Labor costs, the availability of low cost feed of good quality, know-how, infrastucture and environmental requirements will be important factors. Some studies have shown that the US, Brazil, Thailand, France and the Netherlands are the best placed for worldwide competition. The strong competitive position of these countries is determined by extensive availability of feed resources, their high technical know-how, and a stimulating government policy (Nahm, 1996). The high technical know-how results in low cost production and quality poultry meat.

Wherever per capita incomes have risen, demands for high quality protein have also risen. The traditional meat preferences are predominate at first, but the technological miracle of poultry quickly comes to the front. People in the industrial countries are not the only ones who need to produce leaner meat, including chicken, while people in other countries will want to consume low fat, the correct types of fat, and the correct fat balance in meat in the 21st century, which is provided through quality poultry meat. In addition to these, a number of quality attributes are associated with poultry meat. Of these, the actual eating quality, the nutritional control of stress, the meat quality of free-range chickens, and quality assurance programs will continue to attract the attention of research workers as well as consumers in a number of countries, which are the aims of this paper.

THE QUALITY OF POULTRY MEAT

1. Actual eating quality

The actual eating quality of poultry meat is the combination of texture, succulence and flavor (Holroyd, 1991; Nahm and Chung, 1995).

Texture is defined as being tender or tough as the two extremes. It is the first quality characteristic to be appraised when placing any food into one's mouth. The sensation of tenderness is a complicated physical process since chewing involves cutting and grinding, as well as squeezing, shearing, and tearing.

Succulence (moisture) is the degree of dryness through the degree of wetness. Dry meat usually is unpalatable but when it is measured for a tenderness score, it is not judged to be so. Succulence is really relative to the amount of fat in the meat. The presence of fat around and particularly within the muscles increases the succulence of the meat.

Flavor is a mixed sensation of aroma and tastes by which identification of foods occurs.

This information about how the quality of meat is determined can be used to establish target standards for all involved with the production and processing of chicken. This means that the birds must be grown and finished in a manner that produces meat which is:

- well fleshed and wholesome
- tender, succulent and of good flavor
- blemish free
- free from any foreign taint, flavor or safety hazard

2. Factors which influence product eating quality

The production and processing of chicken meat involves many factors which influence the eating quality of the end product. We also must realize that we do not fully understand all the factors that can be of significance for influencing quality. Meat quality has been summarized as "the totality of all properties and characteristics of meat that are important to its nutrient value, acceptability, human health and processing" (Jones, 1991).

Reckless disregard of live birds during catching, transport and unloading may cause significant stress, which then results in the birds being presented to the stunner in an unrelaxed state. The end effect of this bird after processing, cooking and being presented on the dinner table is tough meat. (Read the section on effect of stress on meat quality). Equally, fresh birds that are chilled too rapidly can result in toughness of the meat. Raw feed materials that are highly tainted are known to cause foreign flavors in the meat. The wrong litter material can cause a musty taint in chicken, especially when combined with inadequate ventilation and overstocking (Gurer, 1991; Coelho, 1994).

The farm covers live production to the point of on-farm catching. The processing plant covers from the in-house catching to the final products. Quality production involves careful planning and using materials and components at every stage in the production and processing that are well documented and proven to improve upon the final eating quality of poultry products (Maurer, 1988).

3. Tenderizing by electrical stimulation

Broiler carcasses must be aged for a minimum of 4 hours to avoid the toughening that accompanies prerigor harvesting of broiler breast meat (Lyon *et al.*, 1992). Because holding carcasses for the aging period is expensive, postmortem electrical stimulation (ES) has been examined as a means to eliminate the toughness associated with early harvesting (1 hour postmortem) of broiler breast fillets (Sams *et al.*, 1989).

While this technique was effective with low voltages (40 to 59V), potentials in the range of 100 to 3000V were said to ensure a more positive effect (Holroyad, 1991). Research indicated that tendon treatment of high voltage (820V) ES and prechill muscle tensioning (MT) would improve the tenderness of early-harvested broiler breast fillets (Birkhold *et al.*, 1992). The increased tenderness was believed to arise from physical disruption of the muscle structure itself. It has also been shown that voltages as low as 100 volts may damage muscle fibers.

While the tenderness of cooked turkey breast has been shown to increase with high or low voltage stimulation, there is little proof that voltage will significantly reduce variations between birds. Although the Danish work (Sosnicki and Wilson, 1992) mentioned that electrical stimulation at various voltages has also little or no effect on the toughness of broiler meat, subsequent work in England showed that the application of low voltage stimulation could actually increase the toughness of chicken breast meat and that the tenderness was not completely resolved by extended "aging". The cause of the problem was probably rigor- or hot-toughening, a phenomenon known for a number of years and which occurs when rapid glycolysis results in rigor taking place while the muscle temperature is above 25 degrees C. The problem may be exacerbated by the fact that stimulation accelerates glycolysis (Honikel *et al.*, 1981).

Much of the research on stimulation has been directed towards determining at which time after slaughter carcasses may be deboned. When chickens are stimulated at low voltage for up to 18 seconds, the tenderness of breast muscles harvested immediately after plucking is increased (Nahm and Chung, 1995). The studies by U. S. workers indicated that in order to be fully effective, low voltage stimulation should be applied within 9 minutes of the birds' slaughter. European studies employing low voltage have confirmed the toughness of stimulated chicken breast meat deboned soon (within 15 minutes) after slaughter, but showed that if a delay was introduced before deboning, the stimulated meat was more tender than that of unstimulated controls. At twenty minutes post mortem, the pH of stimulated muscle is generally 0.3 to 0.4 units lower than controls, but there is no evidence that the ultimate pH values differ. ES (440 V, 2 seconds on and 1 second off for 15 seconds) also reduced muscle pH values (Birkhold and Sam, 1993). This decline in pH is a result of numerous biochemical changes that are caused by the conversion of muscle into meat. One result may be that the storage carbohydrate, glycogen, is degraded as the tissues attempt to maintain the muscle cell's energy supply of adenosine triphosphate (ATP). Under the anaerobic condition in the meat, the final product of glycolysis is lactic acid, which is responsible for the low pH value of the meat. A rapid fall in muscle pH results in a pale meat which readily loses water. Dry meat is often unpalatable (Xiong *et al.*, 1993).

4. Color problems and their elimination in poultry meat

The presence of raw-like, color defects in fully cooked poultry meat have been well documented (Trout, 1989). Such defects have important economic implications because consumers believe that this meat is undercooked and, therefore, unsafe. Although many factors have been reported to be associated with color defects in poultry, no cause-and-effect relationships have been conclusively shown.

The poultry personnel need to control a number of variables to free chicken meat from color defects.

a. Blood vessels can rupture resulting in bruises if there is improper grasping of shanks, excessive wing flapping, and incorrect stunning prior to slaughter (Gurer, 1991).
b. Aflatoxins in the feed may cause capillaries to become fragile and result in pinpoint (petechial) hemorrhages in the breast and large muscle hemorrhages at slaughter (Jones, 1991).
c. Adenoviruses may cause hemorrhagic enteritis (Holroyd, 1991).
d. Very warm or fluctuating temperatures cause birds to bruise easily. When nights are cold and days are warm, there is an increase in bloody thigh and wing joints (Kranen *et al.*, 1996).
e. Proper stunning immobilizes the bird and stimulates the heartbeat to help bleed-out. Overstunning results in engorged blood vessels that the picker will burst, resulting in a red bruise-like appearance (Kirton *et al.*, 1981).
f. Pinkish red carcasses may result from incomplete or improper bleeding during

processing (Coelho, 1994).

g. Nitrates and nitrites in chicken feed increase the redness of cooked chicken meat. Chicken meat may also absorb enough nitrate or nitrite from the chill water or ice to produce pink flesh. Spices and vegetable ingredients used in processed products are also sources of nitrates (Holroyd, 1991).

h. Pinkness of the meat may also be caused by ammonia leakage from refrigeration or nitric oxide contamination of the gases used for freezing (Cornforth *et al.*, 1991).

i. Irradiation can cause a red color in irradiated meat that is stored at elevated temperatures in the absence of oxygen (Scheele, 1992).

j. A pinkish color may also result from the improper cooking of chicken meat. This is more prevalent in thin-skinned birds. One possible reason for pink discoloration in cooked turkey meat is reduced sensitivity of myoglobin to heat denaturation due to further processing before completion of the rigor process (Young *et al.*, 1996)

k. Salt and seasonings added to a tumbling solution may increase the pink color. Sodium chloride increases the heat stability of cytochrome c, which is one of the pigments responsible for unwanted pinkness (Kijowski and Niewiarowicz, 1978a; Acton *et al.*, 1983).

Poultry producers must follow good management practices such as feeding quality feed and water. They need to be careful when catching, crating, handling, hanging and processing birds, and the use of proper techniques for stunning, scalding and picking is important at the processing plant. The water used in the plant must be free of metals and nitrates. Chicken products must be formulated with high quality ingredients, followed with appropriate manufacturing processes aiming for mildly oxidizing conditions in some products during processing. People in the poultry industry must make sure that all equipment is clean and functioning properly, and then products are cooked to doneness.

5. Effect of feed and water withdrawal on meat quality

Withdrawal of feed and water prior to slaughter is important for maximizing yield, minimizing carcass contamination and improving line speeds, grower payments and product shelf-life. Proper programs for the withdrawal of feed and water require a team approach and good communication between live production and processing.

6. Carcass yield

For maximum yield, broilers should be processed within four hours of feed and water withdrawal (FWW) (Denton, 1985). This report suggested that the birds must be delivered plantside and processed as soon as possible after implementation of FWW. The time of FWW includes the time birds are off feed and water in the broiler house, during transportation to the plant and while in the plant's holding area before slaughter.

Live shrinkage of the birds increases with time and was significantly increased with each increased interval in hot and thermo-neutral weather. Intervals studied were withdrawal time, hauling and simultaneous withdrawal of both feed and water or feed only with an additional two hours of water. Hauling of the birds caused greater live shrinkage, as did simultaneous withdrawal of feed and water. Carcass yield has a negative correlation with live shrinkage. Greater shrink levels are reported in males and greater yield losses occur in old birds (Denton, 1985).

7. Contamination

The percent of fecal contamination of the meat declines after 6 hours through 8, 10 and 12 hours, and increases until the highest levels are obtained at 24 hours after FWW. If the physical condition of the fecal material is moist initially, it becomes firm between 8 and 10 hours following feed withdrawal, and then becomes loose and watery with withdrawal periods exceeding 12 hours (Farr, 1989).

8. Microbial quality

Salmonella is the major problem for microbial contamination, and the ceca is the primary site of the organism. Catching and cooping the birds results in stress which stops immediately the absorption of the remaining intestinal contents for several hours. The remaining intestinal contents are lost through defecation, dehydration then begins, and moisture is then reabsorbed from the body tissue into the large intestine. This process occurs generally 8 to 10 hours after withdrawal. As the withdrawal time increase, the large intestine becomes extended and the contents of the cecal pouches can be seen in the large intestine. This cecal material is higher in microbial counts, and has greater potential to contain pathogens. The gizzard also becomes more difficult to peel and the gall sack enlarges and increases the likelihood to rupture. These points are all negative for carcass yield and microbial quality (Nulder, 1993).

There are the two major sources of contamination which are the bacteria present in the gastrointestinal tract (internal) and those on feathers and skin (external). For instance, at the time of processing, Salmonella spp. occur internally (Bailey and Cox, 1991). Recently Musgrove et al. (1997) reported that cecal levels of gram-negative enterics were significantly higher for plugged birds, but there was not a significant differences between levels of cecal Campylobacter spp. between treatment groups. They concluded that intestinal carriage of both Campylobacters and gram-negative enteric bacteria appears to influence the microbial quality of the carcass during processing.

9. Feed withdrawal programs (FWP)

It is essential to adhere to the feed withdrawal program. Insure that feed withdrawal procedures are being carried out as planned by establishing a strong communication network among the processing plant, the live-haul, and the grow-out personnel. Also record and analyze the actual feed withdrawal time, arrival time of the catching crew, total live-haul and yard-time and actual plant containment-reprocessing to develop the FWW program appropriate for that operation (Denton, 1985; Bilgili, 1995).

10. The utilization of antioxidants for quality poultry meats

The British Nutrition Foundation (1992) has suggested that an increased and balanced intake of omega-6 and omega-3 polyunsaturated fatty acids (PUFA) may reduce blood triglycerides, reduce hypertension, coronary heart disease and cancer, and ameliorate inflammatory diseases such as psoriasis and rheumatoid arthritis. Increasing intakes of such PUFAa as linolenic acid (18:3 omega-3), eicosapentaenoic (20:5 omega-3 EPA), docosahexaenoic acid (22:6 omega-3, DHA) and docosapentaenoic acid (22:5 omega-3) involves increased intake of vegetables and fish oils (equivalent to 2 to 3 portions of salmon a week or three portions of cod a day). Intake of these fatty acids through other sources of foodstuffs such as poultry would be more desirable.

Increasing the PUFA content of meat makes it more susceptible to oxidation. Uncontrolled lipid peroxidation causes inflammation and oxidative damage, leading to free radical formation in tissues, is thought to contribute to life-threatening diseases in humans. Cardiovascular disease, stroke and certain types of cancers are considered to involve free radicals in their development (Ames, 1983, 1989). Free radicals attack DNA, proteins and PUFA found in the cell membrane. Attacks on the DNA are thought to result in mutagenesis and carcinogenesis. Although the body maintains enzyme systems and levels of natural antioxidants to terminate free radical formation, components of these enzymes and the antioxidants must be supplied from the diet. Feeding of supplemental levels of α-tocopherol to poultry with vegetable or fish oils increases the desirable PUFA content and stabilizes the meat against rancidity and fishy off-flavors.

Post mortem lipid oxidation (rancidity) is one of the causes of deterioration of the meat product quality, affecting the flavor, color, nutritive value and safety. Rancidity occurs mainly in the highly unsaturated, cell membrane phospholipids as an autocatalytic free-radical-mediated process. While it is recommended that more mono- and PUFA be consumed, these are more susceptible to oxidation than unsaturated fat (Dawson *et al.*, 1987; Birkhold and Sams, 1993).

Poultry meat contains more PUFA than red meat and is hence more susceptible to oxidation (Richardson, 1994). Vitamin E present in animal tissues in the form of α-tocopherol is associated with the membranes and can terminate peroxidation chain reactions by mopping-up free radicals. Use of vitamin E as a natural antioxidant administered through the feed has received considerable research interest.

Cooking and adding salt can serve as prooxidants. Addition of synthetic antioxidants can reduce oxidation, but it is more difficult to get them to the specific sites of oxidation and they are less acceptable to the consumer than addition of the natural antioxidants such as α-tocopherol to the diet. α-Tocopherol cannot fully protect against salt induced oxidation, but it reduces it well below that of non-supplemented meats.

Rancid oils, which may have been heat damaged (oxidized) during production, depress chick growth and reduce meat stability for long-term storage. They seem to reduce the availability of dietary α-tocopherol and therefore reduce tissue concentrations. Supplementation of oxidized oil diets with α-tocopherol acetate (200 mg/kg feed) significantly increases growth and the subsequent oxidative stability of the meat (Richardson, 1994). It has also been observed that oxidized sunflower oil causes a significant reduction in broiler body and carcass weights, whereas α-tocopherol and BHA or BHT dietary supplementation improved growth (Lin *et al.*, 1989). Although antioxidants control tissue lipid oxidation effectively (Lin *et al.*, 1989; Asghar *et al.*, 1990), information about their impact on broiler performance, carcass yield, and fatty acid composition of the lipid classes of white and dark edible broiler meat are limited, complicating, and confined primarily to total lipid fatty acid composition; particularly when the antioxidants are introduced into the muscle through the diet (Ajuyah *et al.*, 1993). Similarly, body weight gain and feed intake of turkeys increased with dietary beta-carotene supplementation (Stevens and Salmon, 1989). It has also been reported that the presence or absence of antioxidants (125 ug BHT/g fat) influenced the fatty acid composition and distribution in the phosphatidyl ethanolamine fraction of white meat (Ajuyah *et al.*, 1993). The white meat from birds fed diets containing antioxidants had elevated levels of C18:3n3, C20:5n3, C22:5n3 and C22:6n3 and reduced levels of total saturates and n-6 : n-3 as opposed to the 15% full-fat flax seed (FFS) and corn-soybean meal groups, which means it is more desirable to feed the birds the FFS diet with antioxidants.

Vitamin E levels in the meat make only very small contributions to the daily human intake, but its protective effect in meat is very important. Products of oxidative rancidity produce unpleasant flavors and some of the dietary lipid and cholesterol oxidation compounds have been shown to increase coronary heart disease, strokes and a number of other diseases (Sheehy *et al.*, 1993).

Tocopherol is fat soluble and it concentrates in cell membranes close to the phospholipids which it protects. Feed containing 15 to 20 mg tocopherol acetate/kg feed is sufficient to overcome problems such as low egg hatchability, encephalomalacia and exudative diathesis. In order to affect lipid stability higher levels (in the form of α-tocopherol acetate) should be fed. An effective dietary concentration of vitamin E is in the range of 100 to 200 mg α-tocopherol acetate/kg of feed (Sheehy *et al.*, 1993; Richardson, 1994). These values need to be redefined as new research results become available on how vitamin E affects growth, health and overall metabolism.

Vitamin E has a slow turnover rate in muscle and so it requires several weeks to accumulate. Maximum tissue contents of vitamin E can be obtained during the growth period with 200 to 250 mg tocopherol acetate/kg feed and these are obtained in a minimum of five weeks of feeding. Turkeys have a lower accumulating ability so they must be fed higher amounts for longer time. When chickens and turkeys were fed equivalent amounts of tocopherol acetate, the turkey liver and breast muscle had one-fifth and one-third, respectively, of the amount in chicken tissues (Sheehy *et al.*, 1991; Bartov and Kanner, 1996).

Interest has arisen in food derived from plants because of their concentrations of phytochemicals that may reduce lipid peroxidation and protect the body from free radical damage. Phytochemicals are abundant in many plants but research has concentrated on soybeans, garlic, cabbage, ginger, licorice, celery, carrots and flax. The plant phytochemicals include: carotenoids, tocopherols, phenolic and flavenoids. Studies directed to enrich poultry meat and eggs with antioxidant vitamins and phytochemicals could provide additional opportunities for developing designer foods (Caragay, 1992).

MANIPULATING THE CARCASS FAT OF BROILERS

The quanity of body fat deposited varies within wide limits, from as little as 9.5% of live weight to as much as 23% in broilers at processing age. The site of fat deposition depends on the amount of fat, with the abdominal cavity being the predominant storage area of excess fat. Broiler fat can be manipulated nutritionally by decreasing nutrient densities or increasing protein levels. Fat content can also be manipulated through genetic selection. Genetic methods are complicated and expensive, however, it has been shown that the nutritional program results in increased production costs.

1. Fat synthesis and lipid composition of chicken meat

In poultry, fat is synthesized in the liver primarily and it is transported to the adipose tissue in the form of very low density lipoproteins (VLDL). High deposition of adipose tissue is associated with high circulating levels of VLDL and high rates of hepatic lipogenesis. Significant correlations exist between body fat, hepatic activities of the lipogenic enzymes such as ATP-citrate lyase or malate dehydrogenase and plasma VLDL concentrations (Whitehead, 1985).

The total lipid content of white meat is approximately half of dark meat, and skin contains the highest proportion of lipid (Ratnayake et al., 1989). The total fat content of light muscle with skin has therefore been quoted as approximately 10 times higher (11.1 g/100 g muscle) than muscle without skin (Decker and Cantor, 1992). The triacylglycerol content of white meat was virtually half that of dark meat. In contrast, phospholipid and cholesterol were appreciably higher in white than in dark meat. In both muscle types, free fatty acids and diacyglycerols were present in only trace amounts. In contrast to the muscle tissues, the skin showed and almost total preponderance of triacylglycerol with traces of diacylglycerol, free fatty acid and phospholipid.

The principle fatty acid in all tissues has been found to be oleic acid, followed by palmitic and linoleic acids (Ratnayake et al., 1989). The levels of total saturates, total monosaturates and total polyunsaturates in the muscle tissues assumed an approximate 33% distribution of each. Monounsaturated fatty acids were higher in white meat. In contrast, total polyunsaturated fatty acids were higher in white meat. This difference is a reflection of the higher levels of both the total n-6 and total n-3 polyunsaturates in the white muscle. Among the long chain polyunsaturated fatty acids (both n-6 and n-3), arachidonic acid was the most prominent. In comparison with the muscle tissues, the skin contained much higher levels of oleic and palmitoleic aicds, which substituted for stearic acid and long chain polyunsaturated fatty acids.

2. Nutritional factors that influence fat content

Some well known non-nutritional factors that influence body fat are age, sex and ambient temperature. Since a report on the nutritional effects of varying dietary ingredients on broiler carcass fat was published (Fraps, 1943), numerous studies have reported that as the dietary calorie/protein (C/P) ratio is widened, carcass lipids increase. This effect appears to be independent of calorie source since fat substitution for carbohydrate, at constant CPR, has little effect on carcass fat.

3. Energy and protein requirements

Research studies have shown that increasing the levels of energy as well as protein results in improved growth rates and feed conversion. Increasing the levels of energy increases the carcass fat content, while increasing protein levels decreases carcass fat content.

A high energy density diet (H-H) throughout the growing period has been shown to result in a greater overall carcass meat yield, but the rate of gain was lower than when a low energy density phase was followed in the later stages of growth by a high energy density diet (Walker et al., 1995). The growth of fat was always greater with the H-H regime which contributes to the heavier carcass and greater return in a "whole bird market" irrespective of carcass composition. Furthermore, a narrow protein/energy ratio fed throughout the life of the bird compared with a widening ratio as the bird aged resulted in the greatest breast meat yield (665 g compared with 570 g) and also the greatest percentage breast meat yield (22.9% versus 21.7%). Results obtained from experiments to test the effects of different methionine plus cystine levels (0.60-0.95% of the diet) at two different levels of protein concentrations offered to Ross broiler males from 15 to 35 days indicated that increasing dietary protein by 3 to 4 percentage points had no effect on breast meat yield, and the breast meat proportion of the carcass was determined by the dietary content of sulfur amino acids (Degussa, 1995). These examples show that the distribution of protein as muscle in the carcass of the bird is sensitive to diet composition and therefore the nutrition of the bird must be adjusted to account for target meat production and not only for the growth rate or feed efficiency.

Energetic efficiency of ME use for tissue gain is dependent on many variables. The efficiency varies with the substrate source for lipogenesis at approximately 75, 84 and 61% for carbohydrates, fats and protein, respectively (Hoffman and Shiemann, 1971). Utilization of protein for tissue energy gain is dependent upon the biological value of the protein source and should not be constant (De Groote, 1973). The energetic efficiency of the bird for any substrate is the net result of partitioning the energy into maintenance needs as well as protein and fat accumulation.

4. Amino acid supplementation

Supplementation of poultry diets with amino acids such as methionine, lysine, glycine, tryptophan and amino acid mixtures can reduce body fat deposition (Takahashi et al., 1994). In one series of experiments, increasing the total sulphur amino acid content (TSAA) from 0.7% to 0.95% of the diet reduced the abdominal fat content of the carcass from 4.00% to 3.30%. In one review where different experiments were combined, the relative fattiness could be reduced by

28% and was minimum at a dietary TSAA content of 0.85% (Fisher, 1994). Reducing the crude protein content of the diet from 23% to 19.6% in young chicks reduced the level of response obtained from the TSAA supplementation (Takahashi et al., 1994).

The TSAA requirement has been found to be higher for maximum efficiency of feed utilization and breast meat yield than for obtaining maximum weight gain (Schutte and Pack, 1995). Based on feed conversion efficiency and breast meat yields, the requirements for TSAA were estimated to be at least 0.88% for the age period of 14 to 34 or 38 days. It was calculated that the estimated TSAA requirement was equivalent to approximately 0.75% apparent digestible SAA or 0.78% true digestible SAA.

These research results prove that level and balance of essential amino acids (EAA) can have a significant effect on feed intake, thereby influencing weight gain, carcass composition of fat and the protein content of the edible meat (Summers et al., 1992).

Carcass quality of broilers was adversely affected by inadequate dietary levels of lysine in the feeds. In one trial, broilers were provided feeds formulated to be submarginal in lysine (0.85%), marginal (0.95%) and adequate (1.05%) dietary levels (Moran, 1991). As the dietary lysine levels increased, the percent fat in the skin and thigh meat decreased. Fat in the breast meat was low, however, and remained part unchanged. The breast was most affected, with increasing meat as the lysine levels were increased.

5. Dietary fat

Carcass fattiness does not increase with an increasing content of dietary fat within normal nutritional limits at constant ME (Griffiths et al., 1977). A wide body of evidence suggests that adding fat to a diet, without changing the total dietary energy content, has little influence on the amount of body fat deposited (Deaton et al., 1981), because the higher fat content of a diet depresses lipogenesis in the bird. Although the dietary fat itself does not influence body fat content, the use of fat in diets is often associated with fatter birds. This is because diets that include higher fat levels are also diets of higher nutrient density.

The effects of dietary PUFA on the regulation of lipid metabolism and the level and composition of lipid metabolism and the level and composition of body fat appear to be diverse. Vegetable oils containing high levels of PUFA, such as soybean oil, are known to inhibit lipogenesis (Donaldson, 1985). It has been reported that soybean oil supplementation depressed body fat in broiler chickens selected divergently for high or low abdominal adipose tissue (AAT) content (Keren-Zvi et al., 1990). In terms of dietary fat supplementation, this work contradicts that of others who have reported that body fat increases with the amount of dietary tallow which is composed essentially of saturated fatty acids (Deaton *et al.*, 1981). The difficulties in interpreting such result are comprehensive.

The fatty acid (FA) composition is determined largely by the relative importance of hepatic lipogenesis and exogenous dietary fat as sources of FA deposits in the body. The supplementation of dietary fat influences both of these parameters such that they may act in the same or in opposite directions depending on the composition of the diet. Endogenous fat, measured in chickens fed a fat-free diet, is composed mainly of FA C16:0 and C18:1 with smaller amounts of C16:1 and C18:0 (Bottino *et al.*, 1970). FA C18:2 and C18:3 are essential and not synthesized but rather introduced into the tissues through dietary fat. The addition of soybean oil has been shown to significantly increase the concentrations of C18:2 and C18:3 in carcass fat (Nir *et al.*, 1988). The biochemical pathway of FA biosynthesis may be influenced by the availability of dietary FA.

It may be hypothesized that increased PUFA input plays a role in FA biosynthesis, reducing body fat deposition in the chicken. The FA composition of body or adipose tissue fat does not necessarily express the utilization rate of dietary FA, because unlike PUFA, saturated and monosaturated FA are synthesized in the body or incorporated from the diet. A mixture of vegetables oils (soybean to sunflower oil; 1:1, vol/vol) and beef tallow was used to supplement the broiler male chick diet to provided different PUFA (grams per 100 g dietary fat) (Pinchasov and Nir, 1992). This research showed that a significant linear effect was observed between PUFA and feed utilization. FA profiles in abdominal adipose tissue (AAT) and total body fat were correlated to dietary PUFA content, with the main effect of higher PUFA being a reduction in monoenoic FA (C16:1 and C18:1) and an increase in C18:2. The effect of dietary PUFA on the saturated FA (C16:0 and C18:0) was small and not statistically significant. Increased dietary PUFA modified FA composition such that C18:2, rather than C18:1 became the dominant FA in AAT, showing greater changes in FA composition of AAT rather than the whole carcass.

Selection of specific strains or lines of animals have proven valuable in evaluating the effects of nutrients on metabolism and physiology. Chickens from the low-weight (LW) line had greater in vivo lipogenic capacities compared with those from the high-weight (HW) line (Calabotta *et al.*, 1983). A difference in hepatic FA metabolism was found between the HW and LW lines than was unaffected by dietary n-6 or n-3 PUFA (Phetteplace and Watkins, 1992). They fed soybean oil, rich in n-6 or 50 g/kg of basal diet each to female chicks in two genetic lines (LW and HW), showing that concentrations of C18:1 FA isomers and total monosaturates were highest in liver and heart tissues of HW chickens. Feeding menhaden oil enriched the plasma, liver and heart with n-3 PUFA in both genetic lines.

6. Salt and water

The carcass fat content is inversely related to the water content. This correlation has led to suggestions that increasing the water consumption by broilers may inhibit fat deposition. Experiments have shown that adding salt in higher than normal amounts to the diet, or to the drinking water, is associated with decreased body fat contents (Lightscy *et al.*, 1983).

7. Feed restriction

One method of reducing body fattiness that has been studied is quantitative food restriction. A severe restriction (less than 75% of normal intake) was necessary to depress body fat content between two and four weeks of age but there was also depressed growth (Nitsan and Petihi, 1984). Other studies have examined the effect of food restriction during the final week and have shown similar responses, depressed body fat content but also a depression in non-fat body weight (Arafa *et al.*, 1983). Therefore, there needs to be a commercial advantage for lean carcasses in order for this technique to be economical.

8. Fatty acid composition in the diet

Ingested fatty acids (FA) are subjected to modification by chain elongation and desaturation. FA deposited in the body are a combination of synthesized and partially modified dietary FA. When the fat content of the diet is increased, its contribution to fat deposition increases and the overall composition of body fat more closely resembles that of the diet. The FA compositions of adipose tissue of various areas of the body are quite similar. Palmitic and oleic acids are the main long-chain FA synthesized during lipogenesis (Whitehead, 1985).

Scientists have observed that there was a considerable dietary effect on FA composition of genetically lean or fat broilers fed diets containing low (25 g/kg) or high (80 g/kg, provided partially by maize oil) total fat contents (Bartov and Bornstein, 1976). When diets contained high concentrations of linoleic acid, as with the diet containing 150 g maize oil/kg, the proportions of linoleic acid in adipose tissue can increase. In contrast, the addition of tallow to a maize/soybean diet decreased the proportion of linoleic acid and increased the proportion of oleic acid deposited in adipose tissue.

Tissue FA compositions can interact with the processing of carcasses. High proportions of unsaturated FA accelerate the liquification of subcutaneous and other fat depots during processing. This is disadvantageous, especially with "Oily Bird Syndrome". The tissue composition is not the only cause of this syndrome, since environmental temperature during rearing as well as other unknown factors appear to be involved (Hofman, 1994; Pesti, 1994).

9. Minerals, vitamins and drugs

Minerals such as sodium, potassium, chlorine, calcium, phosphorus and magnesium can affect carcass quality indirectly by influencing the occurrence of leg problems or water intake. These factors will influence carcass quality via the effects on hockburn, etc. and litter conditions. Deficiencies or imbalances of certain vitamins (e.g., vitamin A and D, nicotinic acid, panthothenic acid, pyridoxine, biotin, folic acid and choline) and trace elements (e.g. manganese and zinc) will also affect the incidence of leg problems (Combs, Jr., 1982; Wilson, 1987).

Certain anticoccidial drugs (the monovalent ionophores) and growth promoters may reduce water intake and hence improve litter conditions. The ionophores generally may help to control the incidence of Clostridia scours and the growth promoters also have a general antibacterial effect. The effects on litter condition and carcass quality may be particularly relevant on sites with a high bacterial challenge and if long withdrawal periods are used. One chemical coccidiostat (robenidine) may cause taint if fed without a withdrawal period. It has also been reported recently than feeding dietary garlic (1.4, 3.0 or 4.5% of a commercial garlic powder to the corn-soy control diet) and/or copper (63 or 180 mg/kg copper) for 21 days reduced dietary cholesterol levels of broiler meat without altering growth of the chickens or feed efficiency (Sosnicki and Wilson, 1991; Golden and Ramdath, 1993).

10. Environmental temperature

Bird maintenance energy needs are lower at higher temperatures and hence more of the feed consumed is available for fat deposition (Bray, 1982). The calculated relationship between temperature and fat deposition is 1.9 g fat/kg body weight per degree celsius.

Heat-exposed birds, like mammals, decrease feed intake in order to reduce metabolic heat production and maintain homeothermy, resulting in slower growth. Enhanced fatness has been observed in heat-exposed chickens (Geraert *et al.*, 1996). Decreased growth and an enhanced fatness in heat-exposed chicken could seem contradictory.

There has also been a report that unsaturated fatty acids as a percentage of total fatty acids were decreased, especially oleic (C18:1) and linoleic (C18:2) acids in fat tissues, although saturated fatty acids proportions, particularly palmitic acid (C16:0), were increased in heat-exposed birds (Baziz *et al.*, 1996). Under ad libitum feeding conditions, these scientists proved that heat exposure significantly decreased the unsaturated to saturated fatty acid ratio in the abdominal and subcutaneous fat tissues, but not in intermuscular and intramuscular fats.

11. Genetic manipulation

The faster growth seen in certain birds is influenced by an ability to increase nuclei in their muscle cells, which produce more RNA and more muscle protein (Marple et al., 1982). Faster growing birds are more physiologically mature at a younger age and contain higher proportions of body fat. In one study when chicks from both broiler and Leghorn groups were 42 g at the start of the study, the broiler chicks weighed twice as much as the Leghorns at eight weeks of age. After week two, the broiler chicks consistently had higher percentages of carcass fat than the Leghorns and consistently greater length, volume and weight of wing muscles (Marple et al., 1982). As a result of greater DNA and RNA concentrations, broiler chicks are able to synthesize more muscle protein per day, and this results in their faster growth. The dietary fat also had little effect on the total body lipid contents of the two lines. The proportion of abdominal fat was slightly higher in birds fed the low-fat diet, but the difference was not statistically significant (Whitehead and Griffin, 1984). Chickens from the lean line have much lower percentages of fatty tissue but their meat is just as flavorful because the amount of fat within the meaty tissue has not changed.

A genetic and breeding approach may be a more feasible long-term solution for reducing body fat. A selection program to reduce abdominal fat deposition and increase meat in broilers was undertaken (Lavis, 1989). This study showed that the response to the first cycle of selection was highly significant; percentage of abdominal fat of the high fat (HF) line exceeded that of the low fat (LF) line by about one-half (51 to 57%) and one third (33 to 38%) in the White Rock and Cornish stocks, respectively. Response of abdominal fat during the first cycle was similar in males and females, and there was practically no correlated response in body weight among lines. Also, the relative distributions of percentage abdominal fat within lines, as well as the differences between line means, were similar in both stocks. The proportion of the lean parts, however, was higher in the low fat line than in the high fat line. Differences between the lines in relative weight of the valuable lean part (thighs, drumsticks and breast) were 1.8 times higher than differences in abdominal fat. As can be seen from this study, a certain degree of genetic selection can provide a leaner product.

Broiler meat is composed of two major muscle types, i.e., light (breast) and dark (thigh and leg) muscles. The two types of muscle differ in biochemical properties, sensory characteristics (e. g., flavor and palatability), and economical value and marketability. These differences exist between light and dark muscles of broilers as related to genetic strains. There were also significant differences found among strains in chemical composition, pH and protein extractability for both breast and thigh muscles (Xiong et al., 1993). The correlation between percentage protein and fat was positive in the breast and negative in the thigh muscle. However, no significant correlations were observed between the chemical constituents of breast muscle with respective constituents of the thigh muscle.

IMPROVING MEAT QUALITY BY NUTRITIONAL CONTROL OF STRESS

Scientists have suggested that poultry breast muscle can exhibit the same pale soft exudative (PSE) characteristics as seen in pork (Van Hoof, 1979 and Barbut, 1993). Normal stress leads to muscular damage in these animals. They also may hyperventilate, develop tachycardia or cyanosis, or develop muscular paralysis (Wilson, 1990).

1. Effect of stress on the inside of muscle

Disruption of cell membranes due to various stressors from the environment, feed, management practices or other factors, leads to erythrolysis and increased levels of plasma pyruvate and creatinine kinase. Stressed birds also have increased endogenous mitochondrial camodulium and fatty acid concentrations, elevated phospholipase A_2 activity and higher mitochondrial and sarcoplasmic Ca^{2+} concentrations (Cheah et al., 1986). The phospholipase A_2 enzyme causes an increase of Ca^{2+} in the muscle. The sarcoplasmic reticulum releases additional Ca^{2+} in response to mitochondrial release of Ca^{2+} and oxidized phospholipids (Cheah and Cheah, 1985). The increased sarcoplasmic Ca^{2+} is responsible for increased glycolysis through the activation of myofibrillar ATPase and phosphorylase kinase (Scopes, 1974). At this time, glycolytic activity results in the depletion of adenosine triphosphate (ATP) and accumulation of lactate in the sarcoplasm reticulum loses its ability to control cytosolic calcium concentration, resulting in up to a 10-fold Ca^{2+} concentration increase (Goll et al., 1983). This increase activates myosin adenosine triphosphates, resulting in contraction of the muscle (rigor mortis).

Because rigor develops much faster in avian than in mammalian muscle (Sams and Janky, 1991), broiler carcasses are usually in the early stages of rigor when they emerge from the chiller and the muscles are rigid, firm and inextensible.

There are two main theories that explain the tenderization process. The first suggests that the increased ionic strength of the sarcoplasm due to the post-mortem influx of calcium ions solubilizes myofibrillar structural elements, resulting in their degradation (Ouali, 1990). The second theory supports the notion that endogenous calcium-activated proteinases (calpains) are activated by the reflux of calcium ions and that they subsequently proteolyze some of the structural elements, leading to degradation of the myofibrillar matrix (Koohmaraie, 1992). There is no preponderance of evidence to support either view, but results indicate that proteolysis is, at least in part, responsible for post-mortem tenderization (Whipple and Koohmaraie, 1991; Kendall *et al.*, 1993). Several attempts have been made to take advantage of the ability of the calpains to hasten tenderization of mammalian muscle tissue (Koohmaraie *et al.*, 1989, 1990). Recently, Young and Lyon(1997) reported that the treatments had no effect on meat pH either before or after cooking, but a calcium concentration increased, the normal post-mortem conversion of adenosine triphosphate (ATP) to inosine monophosphate (IMP) increased, according to the IMP: ATP ratios (R-values). They found that calcium treatment at all levels tested improved meat tenderness, but both marinade absorption and cooking losses increased as the calcium concentration in the marinades increased.

Malignant hyperthermia is the rapid rise in body temperature that occurs during periods of stress when glycolysis accelerates, blood pH decreases, lactate and pCO_2 concentrations rise and oxygen saturation decreases (Duthie *et al.*, 1987). One study (Judge *et al.*, 1972) concluded that the body temperature increases and acidosis results from heat and lactate produced by muscular anaerobic glycolysis.

2. Impact of stress on meat quality

Meat quality may be affected by preslaughter management practices such as catching, crating, loading and transportation. The increased production and utilization of epinephrine and glucocorticosteroid in animals exposed to antimortem stressors can affect post mortem metabolism and meat quality. Dark, firm and dry meat (DFD) in beef and PSE in pork are two commonly encountered problems in the meat industry. Preslaughter stress could be important factor in causing these conditions (Lawrie, 1966).

On the basis of post-mortem pH declines, PSE and DFD have been identified in chicken breast muscle (Kijowski and Niewiarowicz, 1978b). This condition causes problems with the texture, cohesiveness, color, and juiciness of processed turkey and broiler breast meat. This PSE like condition, which has been observed to affect as much as 40% of market tom flocks, is thought to be related to anaerobic muscle metabolism and growth alterations in the musculoskeletal system (Cherel *et al.*, 1992). Histopathological obervations have indicated that PSE-like breast meat of turkey have muscle fibrils rupturing out of the muscle fiber bundles, which is unlike PSE in pork meat (Sosnicki and Wilson, 1992). In turkeys, PSE seems to be related to poor cell membrane or collagen connective tissue integrity. Like pork PSE, this PSE-like problem in turkey breast meat is likely from stress susceptible turkeys.

3. The possible modulation of nutrients in PSE

Feed manufacturers may be able to use nutrient modulation to control PSE, even though it is genetically induced. Mineral and vitamin recommendations for controlling PSE are by Coelho (1994) for turkeys and broilers. The recommendation of each micronutrient for turkeys at 3 weeks preslaughter are: <75 mg Cu/kg, >50 mg Fe/kg, >1000 mg Mg/kg, >150 mg Mn/kg, 0.1 mg Se/kg, >175 mg Zn/kg, >50 mg ascorbic acid/kg, >50 mg riboflavin/kg and >100 IU vitamin E./kg. Suggested recommendations for young broiler at 2 weeks preslaughter were: <50 mg Cu/kg, >80 mg Fe/kg, >1000 mg Mg/kg, >110 mg Mn/kg, 0.1 mg Se/kg, >120 mg Zn/kg, >50 mg ascorbic acid/kg, >50 mg riboflavin/kg and >100 IU vitamin E/kg (Coelho, 1994).

Supplemental trace minerals such as manganese, copper, zinc and selenium, as well as riboflavin maximize the superoxide dismutase, glutathione peroxidase and glutathione reductase preventative systems. Poor membrane integrity (PSE-like meat) in stress-susceptible turkeys could be ameliorated by a surfeit of dietary vitamin E. A deficiency of the antioxidant enzyme, glutathione (GSH)-peroxidase has been observed in stress-susceptible pigs (Schnaus et al., 1981). In this study, it was postulate that PSE was consistent with an antioxidant disorder leading to oxidative damage of cell membranes. Both stress-susceptible pigs and vitamin E-deficient animals have elevated activities of pyruvate kinase and created creatinine kinase in the plasma and increased erythrocyte lysis due to free radical mediated damage to the cell membrane (Duthrie et al., 1987). Similar results were provided for turkey meat (Sheldon et al., 1997). These research reports showed that the 10X and 25X NRC (1994) diets produced the most typical and acceptable turkey meat flavors with the fewest oxidized off-flavor notes for both fresh and frozen samples (NRC 1994, recommendations). Mean color scores also increased, indicative of less pale meat, as the level and duration of feeding dietary vitamin E increased.

The antioxidants vitamin E and riboflavin should be added to feed at a rate of 100 IU and 50 mg, respectively, per kg of feed. Ascorbic acid should be supplemented at 50 mg per kg to regenerate vitamin E that may be oxidized. An inverse relationship was observed between the antioxidant vitamin/mineral model supplementation and PSE in turkeys. PSE was reduced from 30 to 2% when vitamin E supplementation was 100 to 200 IU /kg in turkey diets (Ferket, 1993, Personal communication).

FREE RANGE CHICKENS

1. What is a free range chicken?

All birds that are considered free range chickens are fed a natural diet containing no antibiotics or coccidiostats. When they were compared to conventionally raised chickens, the free-range chickens had similar growth rates and feed consumptions (Simopolos and Salem, 1989; Leskanich and Noble, 1997). Neither group was found to have effected in their intestine as determined by fecal flotation and inspection of the intestine for lesions. More research should be done about the production costs, growth rates and feed conversion.

2. Taste of free range chicken meat

A taste test was conducted to determine if a distinction in taste could be detected, but there was no difference in this test detected by the taste panel (Speake *et al.*, 1996; Leskanich and Noble, 1997), even though age, diet, strain or breed may originally have effected the taste tests. Farmers must experiment with creating a product unique to their own farm with the above ideas.

3. Disease susceptibility

Free range hens are basically susceptible to the same disease as intensively kept birds, and they are more prone to disease syndromes seldom seen in caged birds. While birds in cages seldom suffer from infestations of parasites, the conditions of the ground frequently found in free range houses is contaminated with high levels of excrement. This leads to the buildup of worms and coccidia to the detriment of the bird's health. Wild birds, vermin and insects also aid in the spread of diseases in free rage systems. Often soil type could also contribute as well. Producers should aim to provide 929 cm^2 (1 square foot) per bird in the housing, excluding space for feeders, water and nest boxes (Noble *et al.*, 1996; Leskanich and Noble, 1997).

COMPLETE QUALITY ASSURANCE (CQA) FOR POULTRY PRODUCTS

Poultry production must center on producing quality products under the most healthy and hygienic conditions, without adding harmful additives or using undesirable techniques. Public health concerns and consumer safety must be in the minds of producers at all times since public health relies on the quality and safety of the food available. The food supply must be safe, free from Salmonella or *E. coli* contamination, without chemical or drug residues and without any risk to our health (Nahm, 1996).

Raghavan (1993) and Mulder (1993) have suggested that the various steps to be supervised through a CQA program for poultry production for the market include: breeder farms and the production of day-old chicks; feed management; farm management; use of feed additives, residue problems and their control measures; and microbiological problems in poultry products.

Raghavan (1993) insisted that breeder farms must ensure the production of quality day-old chicks in order to compete in the marketplace. Breeder farms must not overproduce as this creates oversupplies which are harmful to the industry. Supply and demand will determine overproduction.

The performance of chickens in regards to weight gain, egg production and feed conversion ratios is determined by the feed quality. Consumers need to feel that what they buy is wholesome, satisfying and safe, with assurance that the poultry meat they buy was fed only quality feed.

No poultry producer will achieve quality poultry production if the farm management is substandard, no matter how good the feed is or how good the quality of the chicks are. Proper management programs must include vaccination programs for disease control and prevention.

Most feed additives such as anticoccidial drugs, chemotherapeutic agents, growth promoters and antibiotics follow a pattern of usage in manufactured feeds. Feed millers must advise farmers on the pattern of feeding these additives and the use of withdrawal feeds. The period of time needed for feeding withdrawal feeds must be based on the types of additives used and the withdrawal time needed for each additive.

And Muldar (1993) said that the numbers of microbial flora present on the processed chicken is an indication of the hygienic measures on the farm, during transport and at slaughter. Some microorganisms found on the farms and processing plants include those responsible for spoilage (i.e. Acinetobacter, Brochotrix, lactic acid bacteria and Pseudomonas) and potentially pathogenic microorganisms (Salmonella, Campylobacter, Listeria, Escherichia coli and Staphylococcus aureus). Rapid and safe marketing of poultry products is essential due to the presence of spoilage and pathogenic microorganisms. The whole production process utilizes good hygienic practices to ensure safety.

CONCLUSION

Carcass fat in broiler chickens is responsible for a considerable loss to the poultry industry as well as consumers. The trend in the 21st century toward increased consumer demand to leaner poultry products at nominal costs will necessitate producers to insure the quality and condition of market birds, control preslaughter events, and strive for leanness and uniformity by implementing nutritional and management programs that improve flock health.

The actual eating quality of poultry meat is the combination of texture, succulence and flavor. The eating quality is influenced by many factors such as reckless handling of live birds, improper house litter, feed and water withdrawal programs, improper electrical stimulation of the meat, and color problems.

Even though non-nutritional factors (age, sex and ambient temperature) influence the body fat deposition, broiler body fat deposition, broiler body fat is manipulated nutritionally by decreasing nutrient densities or increasing protein levels. Manipulating through genetic selection has possibilities, but it is also known to be very complicated and expensive.

Poultry breast muscle can exhibit the same pale soft exudative (PSE) characteristics as seen in pork. Feed manufacturers are able to use nutrient modulation with mineral (Cu, Fe, Mg, Mn, Se and Zn) and vitamins (ascorbic acid, riboflavin and vitamin E) recommendations to control PSE.

Some consumers have started to consider free range chickens that are fed a natural diet containing no antibiotics or coccidiostats, since they may be a healthier source of poultry meat. More research needs to be done, however, concerning the production costs, growth, rate, feed conversion and meat quality of these birds.

Finally, producing quality poultry products must be done under the most healthy and hygienic conditions, with no harmful additives fed or undesirable techniques for handling or processing the birds used. Poultry meat supplies, like other food supplies, must be safe and free from Salmonella and E. coli contamination.

ACKNOWLEDGMENTS

I would like to thank Dr. T. Savage (Dept. of Animal Science, Oregon State Univ.), Dr. R. Blair (Dept. of Animal Science, The University of British Columbia), and Dr. B. Winselman-Nahm (Lincolnway Animal Hospital, Matteson, IL) for their constructive criticism and corrections of this manuscript.

LITERATURE CITED

Acton JC, Ziegler GR, Burge DL 1983 Functionality of muscle constituents in the processing of comminuted meat products. CRC Crit Rev. Food Sci Nutr 18: 99-121.

Ajuyah AO, Hardin RT, Sim JS 1993 Effect of dietary full-fat flax seed with and without antioxidant on the fatty acid composition of major lipid classes of chicken meats. Poultry Sci 72:125-136.

Ames BN 1983 Dietary carcinogens and anticarcinogens. Science 221:1256-1260.

Ames BN 1989 Endogenous oxidative DNA damage, aging and cancer. Free Radical Res Comm 7:121-127.

Arafa AS, Boone MA, Janky DM, Wilson MR, Miles RD, Harms RM 1983 Energy restriction as a mean of reduction fat pads in broilers. Poultry Sci 62:314-320.

Asghar AC, Lin CF, Gray JI, Buckley DJ, Booren AM, Flegal CJ 1990 Effects of dietary oils and α-tocopherol supplementation on membranal lipid oxidation in broiler meat. J Food Sci. 55:46-50, 118.

Bailey JS, Cox NA 1991 Internal colonigation and external carriage of artificially inoculated Salmonella typhimurium from floor pens and cage reared chickens. Poultry Sci 70:(Suppl. 1) 142(ABSTR).

Barbut S 1993 Colour measurements for evaluating the pale soft exudative (PSE) occurrence in turkey meat. Food Res Int 26:39-43.

Bartov I, Bornstein S 1976 Effects degree of fatness in broilers on other carcass characteristics: relationship between fatness and the composition of carcass fat. Br Poult Sci 17:17-27.

Bartov I, Kanner J 1996 Effect of high levels of dietary iron, iron injection, and dietary vitamin E on the oxidative stability of turkey meat during storage. Poultry Sci 75:505-513.

Bilgili SF 1995 Feed withdrawal/fecal contamination. The National Turkey Federation's Annual Convention. Orlando, Fla.

Birkhold SG, Janky DM, Sams AR 1992 Tenderization of early-harvested broiler breast fillets by high-voltage post-mortem electrical stimulation and muscle tensioning. Poultry Sci 71:2106-2112.

Birkhold SG, Sams AR 1993 Fragmentation, tenderness and post-mortem metabolism of early-harvested broiler breast fillets from carcasses treated with electrical stimulation and muscle tensioning. Poultry Sci 72:557-582.

Bottino NR, Anderson RE, Reiser R 1970 Animal endogenous triglycerides: Rat and chicken adipose tissue. Lipids 5:165-170.

British Nutrition Foundation (BNF) 1992 Unsaturated fatty acids nutritional and physiological significance. The report of the British Nutrition Foundation's Task Force, Chapman and Hall, London, Page 211.

Bray T 1982 Gleadthrope Experimental Husbandry Farm, Poultry Booklet No. 9 Ministry of Agriculture Fisheries poultry meat growth. Poultry Int June Pages 20-21.

Broekhuyse CF 1994 Sturdy forecasts poultry meat growth. Poultry Int June Pages 20-21.

Calabotta DF, Cherry JA, Siegel PB, Gregory EM 1983 Lipogenesis and lipolysis in normal. 62:1830-1837.

Caragay AB 1992 Cancer preventative foods and ingredients. Food Technol 46(4): 65-68.

Cheah KS, Cheah AM, Waring JC 1986 Phospholipase A_2 activity calmodulin, Ca^{2+} and meat quality in young and adult Halothane-sensitive and Halothane-insensitive. Meat Sci 17:37-40.

Cherel Y, Wyers M, Dupas M 1992 Histopathological alterations of turkey muscles at the slaughterhouse. Proceedings of the 19th World's Poultry Congress. Vol. 3. Amsterdam, The Netherlands. Page 210.

Coelho MB 1994 Nutritional control of stress. Feed Management 45(2):24-26, Feb.

Combs GF, Fr 1982 Influence of diet on chick body composition. Feedstuffs 54 (18):20-23.

Cornforth D, Clkins CR, Faustman C 1991 Methods for identification and prevention of pink color in cooked meat. Reciprocal Meat Conf Proc 44:53-55.

Dawson PL, Janky DM, Dukes MG, Thomson LD, Woodward SA 1987 Effect of postmortem boning time during simulated commercial processing on the tenderness of broiler breast meat. Poultry Sci 66:1331-1333.

Decker EA, Cantor AH 1992 Fatty acids in poultry and egg products. In: Fatty acids in foods and their health implication (ed. Chow, K.K.), Marcel Dekker, New York, Pages 37-167.

De Groote G 1973 Een onderxo, over de volledige ver vanging van vismeel door sojaschroot in mestkuikensrantsoenen met varierend energiegehalte. Landbouwtijdschirft 26:826-843.

Degussa 1995 The impact of methionine and lysine on breast meat deposition in broilers. Feedback Special: p-2e, MP, 6.95.

Denton JH 1985 Four-hour maximum urged for feed-water withdrawal. Feedstuffs 59(52):8-9. Dec. 30.

Deaton, JW, McNaughton JV, Reece FN, Lott BD 1981 Abdominal fat of broilers as influenced by dietary level of animal fat. Poultry Sci 60:1250-1253.

Donaldson WE 1985 Lipogenesis and body fat in the chick: Effect of calorie-protein ratio and dietary fat. Poultry Sci 64:1199-1204.

Duthie GG, Arthur JR, Mills CF, Morrice PC, Nicol F 1987 Anomalous tissue vitamin E distribution in stress susceptible pigs after dietary vitamin E supplementation and effects on pyruvate kinase and creatinine kinase activities. Livestock Prod Sci 17:169-171.

Earnst M 1993 Egg processing. Poultry Int Jan, Pages 82-83.

Farr J 1989 Impact of feed withdrawal on meat quality. Poultry Int July Pages 32-36.

Ferket P 1993 Personal communication. North Carolina State University, Raleigh, North Carolina.

Fesher C 1994 Use of amino acids to improve carcass quality of broilers. Feed Mix 24:17-20.

Fraps GS 1943 Relation of the protein, fat and energy of the ration to the composition of chickens. Poultry Sci 22:421-424.

Geraert PA, Padihla JCR, Guillaumin S 1996 Metabolic and endocrine changes induced by chronic heat exposure in broiler chickens. 1. Growth performance, body composition and energy retention. Br J Nutr 75:(in press).

Golden MHM, Ramdath D 1993 Free radicals in the pathogenesis of kwashiorkor. Proc Nutr Soc 46:53-57.

Goll DE, Otsuk Y, Nagainis PA, Shannon JD, Sathe SK, Muguruma M 1983 Role of muscle proteinases in maintenance of muscle integrity. J Food Biochem 7: 137-177.

Griffiths L, Leeson S, Summers JD 1977 Fat deposition in broilers: Effect of dietary energy to protein balance, and early life caloric restriction of productive performance and abdominal fat pad size. Poultry Sci 56:639-646.

Gurer C 1991 Litter and transport effects on broiler meat quality. Poultry Int April Pages 30, 32, 34.

Hoffmann L, Schiemann R 1971 Verdaulichkeit und Energidknnzahlen Von futterstoffen veim Huhn. Archiv Tierrernahrung 21:65-81.

Hofman K 1994 Quality concepts for meat and meat products. Fleischwirtsh Int 2: 3-12.

Holroyd PH 1991 Factors which influence product eating quality. Poultry Int Pages 42-45.

Honikel KD, Fisher C. Hamid A, Hamm R 1981 Influence of post-mortem changes in bovine muscle on the water-holding capacity of beef: post-mortem storage of muscle at 25 C. J Food Sci 46:1-6.

Jones JM 1991 Eating quality of poultry meat. Poultry Int Mar Pages 26-30.

Judge MD, Kelenboom GE, Zuidam L, Sybesma W 1972 Blood acid-base status and oxygen binding during stress induced gypertherima in pigs. J Animal Sci 35:204-208.

Kendall TL, Koohmaraie M, Arbona JR, Williams SE, Young LL 1993 Effect of pH and ionic strength on bovine m-calpain and calpastain activity. J Animal Sci 71:96-104.

Keren-Zvi S, Nir I, Nitsan Z, Cahaner A 1990 Effect of dietary concentration of fat and energy on fat deposition in broilers divergently selected for high or low abdominal adipose tissue. Br Poultry Sci 31:507-516.

Kijowski J, Niewiarowicz A 1978a Emulsifying properties of proteins and meat from broiler breast muscles as affected by their initial pH values. J Food Tech 13: 451-459.

Kijowski J, Niewiarowicz A 1978b Effect of initial pH of broiler muscles on gel forming capacity of meat proteins and on rheological characteristics of frankfurter-type sausage. J Food Technol 13:461-468.

Kirton AH, Frazerhurst LF, Bushop WH, Winn GW 1981 A comparison of the effects of electrical captive bolt or percussion stunning on the incidence of blood splash in lambs. Meat Sci 5:407-411.

Koohmaraie M 1992 The role of Ca^{2+}-dependent proteases (calpains) in postmortem proteolysis and meat tenderness. Biochimie 74:239-245.

Koohmaraie M, Crouse JD, Mersmann 1989 Acceleration of postmortem tenderization in ovine carcasses through infusion of calcium chloride: effect of concentration and ionic strength. J Anim Sci 67:934-942.

Koohmaraie M, Whipple G, Crouse JD 1990. Acceleration of postmortem tenderization in lamb and Brahman-cross beef carcasses through infusion of calcium chloride. J Anim Sci 68:1278-1283.

Kranen RW, Veerkam CH, Sambooy E, Van Kuppevelt TH, Veerkamp JH 1996 Hemorrhages in muscles of broiler chickens: The relationships among blood variables at various rearing temperature regimens. Poultry Sci 75:570-576.

Lawrie RA 1966 Metabolic stresses which affect muscle. In: The Physiology and Biochemistry of Muscle as Food. Briskey EJ, Cassens RG and Trautman JC ed. The University of Wisconsin Press, Madison, WI Page 137.

Leskanich CO, Noble RC 1997 Manipulation of the n-3 polyunsaturated fatty acid composition of avian eggs and meat. World's Poultry Sci J 53:155-183.

Lightscy SF, Maurice DV, Jones EJ 1983 Dietary salt and abdominal fat in broiler. Poultry Sci 62:1352(Abstract).

Lin CF, Asghar J, Gray I, Buckley DJ, Booren AM, Carckel RL, Flegal CJ 1989 Effects of oxidized dietary oil and antioxidant supplementation on broiler growth and meat stability. Br Poultry Sci 30:855-864.

Lyon BG, Lyon CE, Papa CM, Reagan JP 1992 Texture profiles of canned boned chicken as affected by chilling-aging times. Poultry Sci 73:1475-1478.

Marple DN, Hentgas EJ, Roland DA, Pritchett JF 1982 The physical and physiological differences between fast and slow-growing animals. Highlights of Agricultural Research, Alabama Univ.

Maurer A 1988 Examining color and color problems in poultry carcasses and products. Hatch Univ of Wisconsin-Madison.

Moran ET 1991 Low dietary levels of lysine reduce broiler carcass quality. Feedstuffs 63(22):13-15. June 12.

Mulder RWAR 1993 Microbiology of poultry meat. Poultry Int. Nov. Pages 26-30.

Musgrove MT, Cason JA, Fletcher DL, Stern NJ, Cox NA, Bailey JS 1997 Effect of cloacal plugging on microbial recovery from partially processed broilers. Poultry Sci 76:530-533.

Nahm KH 1996 Korean research direction for animal science and technology in the 21st century. The Proceedings of the Korean Association of Animal Science. June 25-27. Pages 129-167.

Nahm KH, Chung SB 1995 A Textbook of Chicken Production (English version). Mun-Un Dang Pub Co, Seoul, Korea Pages 79-81.

National Research Council 1994 Nutrient Requirements of Poultry. 9th Revised Ed. National Academy Press, Washington, D.C.

Nir I, Nitsan Z, Keren-zvi S 1988 Fat deposition in birds. in: Leanness in Domestic Birds. B. Ieclcrcq and C.C. Whitehead, ed. Butterworths, London, England. Page 141.

Nitsan Z, Nir I, Petihi I 1984 The effect of meal-feeding and feed restriction of body composition, food utilization and intestinal adaptation in light-breed chicks. Bri J Nutr 51:101-109.

Noble RC, Speake BK, McCartney R, Foggin CM, Deeming DC 1966 Yolk lipids and their fatty acids in the wild and captive ostrich. Comp Bioch and Phys Series B 113B:753-756.

Ouali A 1990 Meat tenderization: possible causes and mechanisms. A review. J Muscle Foods 1:129-165.

Pesti GM 1994 Interpretation of nutrition research. Applying the law diminishing return. Feed Management 45(9):14-15,18.

Phetteplace HW, Watkins BA 1992 Influence of dietary n-6 and n-3 polyunsaturated on lipids in chicken divergently selected for body weight. Poultry Sci 71:1513-1519.

Pinchasov Y, Nir I 1992 Effect of dietary polyunsaturated fatty acid concentration on performance, fat deposition, and carcass fatty acid composition in broiler chicken. Poultry Sci 71:1504-1512.

Raghaven V 1993 Total quality assurance in broiler production. Poultry Int. June. Pages 14-16.

Ratnayake WMN, Ackman RG, Hulan HW 1989 Effect of redfish meal enriched diets on the taste and n-3 PUFA of 42-day-old broiler chickens. J Sci Food and Agr 49:59-74.

Richardson RJ 1994 Vitamin E in poultry meat. Poultry Int. Nov Pages 13-15.

Sams AR, Janky DM 1991 Characterization of rigor mortis development in four broiler muscles. Poultry Sci 70:1003-1009.

Sams AR, Janky DM, Woodward SA 1989 Tenderness and R-value changes in early harvested broiler breast tissue following postmortem electrical stimulation, Poultry Sci 68:1232-1235.

Savie D 1989 Low fat chicken by genetic selection. Poultry Int. May Pages 82-84.

Scheele CW 1992 Hormonal regulation for metabolism and the occurrence of ascites in broilers. Pages 549-553. In: Proceedings of the XLX World's Poultry Congress, Amsterdam, The Netherlands.

Schutte JB, Pack M 1995 Sulfur amino acid requirement of broiler chicks from fourteen to thirty-eight days of age. 1. Performance and carcass yield. Poultry Sci 74:480-487.

Scopes Rk, 1974 Studies with a reconstituted muscle glycelytic system. The rate and extent of glycolysis in simulated postmortem conditions. Biochem J 142: 79-83.

Sheehy PJA, Morrissey PA, Flynn A 1991 Influence of dietary alpha-tocopherol on tocopherol concentration in chick tissues. Br Poultry Sci 32:391-397.

Sheehy PJA, Morrissey PA, Flynn A 1993 Increased storage stability of chicken muscle by dietary alpha-tocopherol supplementation. Irish J Agr and Food Res

32:67-73.

Sheldon BW, Curtis PA, Dawson PL, Ferket PR 1997 Effect of dietary vitamin E on the oxidative stability, flavor, color and volatile profiles of refrigerated and frozen turkey breast meat. Poultry Sci 76:634-641.

Simopolos AP, Salem N 1989 n-3 fatty acids in eggs from range-fed Greek chickens. New Engl J Med 16:1412 (letter).

Sosnicki AA, Wilson BW 1991 Pathology of turkey skeletal muscle implications for the poultry industry. Food Struc 10:317-321.

Sosnicki AA, Wilson BW 1992 Relationship of focal myopathy of turkey skeletal muscle to meat quality. Pages 43-47. In: Proceedings of the 19th World's Poultry Congress. Vol. 3. Amsterdam, The Netherlands.

Speake BK, Cristofori C, McCartney RJ, Noble RC 1996 The relationship between the fatty acid composition of the lipids of the yolk and the brain of the duck embryo. Bioch Soc Tran 24:181S.

Summers TD, Spratt D, Atkinson JL 1992 Broiler weight gain and carcass composition when fed diets varying in amino acid balance, dietary energy and protein level. Poultry Sci 71:263-273.

Takahashi K, Konashi S, Akiba Y, Horiguchi M 1994. The effects of dietary methionine and dispensable amino acid supplementation on the abdominal fat deposition in male broilers. Animal Sci and Tech 65:244-250.

Trout G, 1989 Variation in myoglobin denaturation and color of cooked beef, pork and turkey as influenced by pH, sodium chloride, sodium tripolyphosphate and cooking temperatures. J Food Sci 54:536-544.

Van Hoof J 1979 Influence of anti-and perimortem factors on biochemical and physical characteristics of turkey breast muscle. Vet Q1:29-36.

Walker AW, Wiseman J, Lynn NJ, Charless DR 1995 Recent findings on the effects of nutrition on the growth of specific broiler carcass components. In: Recent Advances in Animal Nutrition(eds. Garnsworthy, P.C. and Cole, D.J.A.), Nottingham University Press Pages 169-184.

Whipple G, Koohmaraie M 1991 Degradation of myofibrillar proteins by extractable lysomal enzymes and m-calpain, and the expects of zinc chloride. J Anim Sci 69:4449-4460.

Whitehead CC 1985 Nutritional factors influence fat in poultry. Feedstuffs 57(7): 31-33, 36, 47. Fed. 25.

Whitehead CC, Griffin HD 1984 In: W. G. Hill, J. Manson & D. Hewitt(Ed): Poultry Genetics and Breeding. Br Poultry Sci Ltd Edinburgh (in press).

Wilson RL 1987 Vitamin E, selenium, zinc and copper interactions in free radical protection against ill placed iron. Proc Nutr Soc 46:27-31.

Wilson BW 1990 Developmental and maturational aspects of in herited avian myopathies. Proc Soc Exp Biol Med 194:87-90.

Xiong YL, Cantor AH, Pescatore AJ, Blanchard SP, Straw ML 1993 Variation in muscle chemical composition, pH and protein extractability among eight different broiler carcass. Poultry Sci 72:583-588.

Young LL, Lyon CE 1997 Effect of calcium marination on biochemical and textural properties of peri-rigor chicken breast meat. Poultry Sci 76:197-201.

Young LL, Lyon CE, Northcutt JK, Kickens JA 1996 Effect of time post-mortem on development of pink discoloration in crooked turkey breast meat. Poultry Sci 75:140-143.

Ziboh VA 1991 Designer food. World Rev Nutr Diet Basel Karger 66:425-431.

Manipulating the Fatty Acid Composition of Eggs and Poultry Meat for the Human Health

K. H. Nahm

Feed and Nutrition Laboratory, College of Natural Resources, Taegu University, Gyong San 712-714, South Korea

ABSTRACT

Among polyunsaturated fatty acids (PUFAs) targeted for manipulation in animal tissues (poultry eggs and meat), omega-3 PUFAs (n-3 PUFAs) are discussed in this review. 3 or 5% dietary menhaden oil (MO) supplemented layer diets were reported to increase docosahexaenoic acid (DHA) and eicosapentaenoic acid (EPA) contents in the egg. MO at 1.5% also increased the deposition of up to 180 mg total omega-3 fatty acids/yolk. Utilization of 5% ground flax seed (FS) resulted in similar total omega-3 fatty acid (FA) deposition as 1.5% MO. However, the basic feed formulations used in the Canadian feed industry usually include 10 to 20% FS in the egg laying diets. Recently several studies reported that addition of tocopherols in layer diets increased the tocopherol content more in the egg than any other tissue. One of reports said that 3.5% dietary oil with added tocopherols resulted in increasing tocopherol deposition and FA composition of the egg and other tissues.

In the poultry meat, redfish meal (RM; 4, 8, 12, 15 and 30% of diet) or redfish oil (RO; 2.1 or 4.2% of diet) added to the practical corn-wheat-soybean based diets resulted in an increase in omega-3 FA and docosapentaenoic acid (DPA) contents in broiler meat lipids. Linseed oil (LO; 1.0, 2.5, and 5.0% of broiler diet) supplemented in broiler diets also resulted in omega-3 FA and the ratio of omega-3:omega-6 being significantly higher in poultry meat lipid than MO. Concern about fish flavor resulted in research about fish oil (FO) supplementation in broiler diets. Without the use of antioxidants, no more than 1.5% FO should be fed to broilers due to unacceptable odors from the chicken carcasses. One recent research project found that over 50 mg/kg of vitamin E was required for maintaining the stability of unsaturated lipids in the meat. In regards to 'fishy' or 'crabby' taint in the eggs and poultry meat, poultry products remained acceptable when dietary fish oils were stabilized with antioxidants.

(Key words: Omega-3 PUFAs, flax seed, fish oil, antioxidant, EPA, DPA, DHA)

INTRODUCTION

It has been recognized that there is excess fat in the human diet and there is a definite need to produce leaner meats, especially chicken. The amount of fat we consume is not only too much, but the types of fat we consume is incorrectly balanced. For many years we have heard that the cholesterol in eggs is the major killer. Many national heart foundations have recognized their error in saying this and are now allowing four eggs to be consumed each week/person. We now know that dietary cholesterol for 98% of the population is not an important risk factor in heart disease. The normal human produces cholesterol for its own cellular requirements irrespective of dietary cholesterol (Van Elswyk, 1994).

Dutch scientists have found that people who consumed an average of 32 g of fish daily, compared to those who did not consume fish, had a 50% less chance of dying from coronary heart disease. But what is so special about fish? The important omega-3 fatty acids (FA) are found exclusively in fish in significant quantities. Fish is expensive and may often not be in regular supply; it can be contaminated with heavy metals, pesticide residues and contain pathogenic microorganisms. Some people do not like the taste of fish. This causes their supply of omega-3 polyunsaturated fatty acids (PUFA) to be small and they have large imbalance of omega-6:omega-3 PUFA (Farrell, 1993).

It is well known that the composition of fat in the egg yolk and poultry meat can be changed. Changing these fat compositions may provide an answer, which allows us to design foods to create designer eggs and designer poultry meat (Farrell, 1993).

Health-conscious consumers have raised a number of questions about the potential for altering the composition of poultry products through feed formulation-designing food, creating the so called "designer foods"(Barlow and Pike, 1991). Until now several research papers have explored the feasibility of using various oils such as fish oil, ground flaxseed, flax oil and other oils to produce eicosapentaenoic acid (EPA) and docosahexaenoic acid (DHA) enriched poultry products under laboratory as well as commercial conditions. Their research results have been strongly positive and will be discussed in this review.

THE CHEMICAL STRUCTURE OF OMEGA-3 AND 6 LIPIDS

Even though alpha-linolenic acid is required for nervous tissue and the retina, the primary FA for poultry is linoleic acid. Linoleic (18:2n6) and alpha linolenic (18:3n3) acids have two and three double bonds, respectively, and both are 18 carbons in length. Linoleic acid belongs to the omega-6 series of PUFA since the terminal double bond is located at the sixth carbon from the methyl end of the molecule. In the same manner, alpha-linolenic acid is a member of the omega-3 series of PUFA since the terminal double bond is at the third carbon from the methyl end. The principle PUFA are summarized in Figure 1 and Table 1 (Chung, 1991).

Linoleic acid, found in many seeds, is the parent member of the omega-6 family. The other essential fatty acid (EFA), linolenic acid, is present in leaves and green plants. It is the parent member of the omega-3 family. In animal studies, linoleic acid is converted to arachidonic acid. Alpha-linolenic acid is converted to EPA and DHA. The end products of desaturation and elongation serve as the eicosanoid precursors of the 2-series and 3-series lipid modulators of cell function. These lipid modulators include prostaglandins, thrombaoxanes, lipoxins and leukotrienes (Farrell, 1993).

FUNCTIONS OF POLYUNSATURATED FATTY ACIDS FOR EICOSANOID BIOSYNTHESIS

The PUFA are derived mainly from 18-carbon EFA of dietary origin. The most important of the long-chain PUFA are the 20 carbon fatty acids of the omega-6 and omega-3 series. The majority of eicosanoids (prostaglandins, leukotrienes and lipoxins) are biosynthesized from arachidonic acids that are maintained in membrane phospholipids. The long-chain PUFA are recognized as components of structural phospolipids in membranes of cells and subcellular organelles where they serve as precursors to prostaglandins. Arachidonic acid is the precursor for the 2-series of prostaglandins, but 20:3n6 and 20:5n3 are substrates of the 1-and 3-series prostaglandins, respectively. Prior to eicosanoid formation, phopholipase A2 cleaves arachidonic acid from the sn-2 position on the glycerol backbone of phospholipids (Watkins, 1991; Watkins et al., 1993). Once arachidonic acid is liberated, it can undergo controlled oxidative metabolism to form various eicosanoids that have different physiological effects. Prostaglandins have been described as "local" hormones synthesized in organs and cells in response to specific stimuli that exert their effect generally at the site of production.

Table 1. Types of unsaturated fatty acids

Types	Unsaturated Fatty Acid
Omega-3	Linolenic acid (C18:3), EPA (C20:5), DHA (C22:6), DPA (C22:5)
Omega-6	Linoleic acid (C18:2), Arachidonic acid (C20:4)
Omega-9	Oleic acid (C18:1)
Omega-7	Palmitoleic acid (C16:1)

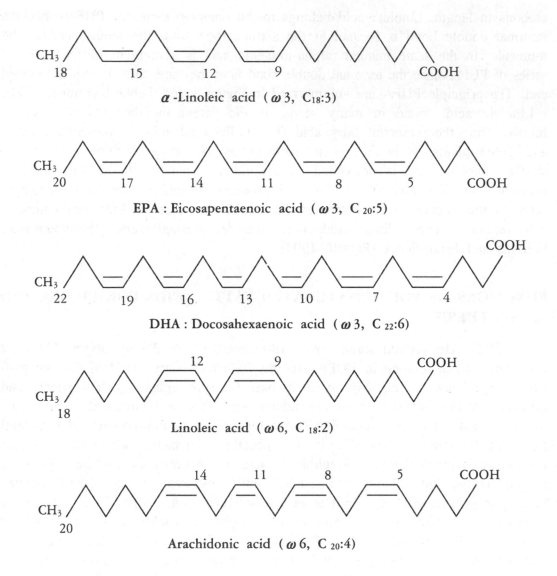

Figure 1. The chemical structures of omega-3 and omega-6 families

There are two primary requirements for PUFA in developing embryonic tissues. The first is to provide a supply of PUFA for glycerolipid synthesis during membrane formation. The second is for maintenance of adequate precursors for eicosanoid biosynthesis. The rapid tissue proliferation during mitosis requires that sufficient substrate be available to form cell membranes and organelles. It is vital that sufficient amounts of EFA and PUFA are supplied to the chick embryo. The immense metabolic conversion of yolk lipids provides PUFA for activities occurring in embryonic tissue growth, membrane formation in the brain and retina and eicosanoid synthesis during myoblast and chondrocyte cell differentiation (Van Elawyk *et al.*, 1991; Watkins, 1994).

Prostaglandins are mediators of cellular activity during oviposition in hens. Most of these compounds cause contractions of the uterine muscular wall. Prostaglandin F may also take part in ovulation by acting on the preovulatory follicle. Prostaglandins have also been known to have a role in long-bone development. At the cellular level, biologically produced cytokines, growth factors and prostaglandins orchestrate the events of bone formation and resorption (Watkins, 1992). There is considerable evidence for a role of eicosanoids in immune regulation. Although the relationship between eicosanoids and cellular and humoral immunity is complex, there appears to be opportunities to utilize dietary lipids to modulate immune responses.

THE ESSENTIALLITY OF OMEGA-3 FATTY ACIDS IN HUMANS

1. Proper amounts of omega fatty acids

The minimum requirements of omega-3 and omega-6 fatty acids are that these essential fatty acids (the sum of omega-3 and omega-6) should proved at least 3% of the energy intake of humans. In pregnant women, the fatty acids should provide 4.5% and for lactating women at least 6% of the energy. The omega-3 PUFAs should provide at least 0.5, 0.8 and 1.0% of the energy for these population groups, respectively (Nordic Council of Ministers, 1989; Bjerve, 1991).

In reality, the typical North American consumes about 17 g of omega-3 and omega-6 PUFA per day. The above requirements indicate the amount of omega-3 PUFA needed is about 3.0 g per day. In practice, the average U.S. citizen consumes 1.7 g of omega-3, with 90% of this being linolenic acid (C18:3 omega-3). This means that there is a deficiency in these diets of at least 1 g per day of omega-3 PUFA, principally of the long-chain type, namely EPA and DHA (Barlow *et al.*, 1990).

What is the optimum ratio of omega-6 PUFA to omega-3 PUFA in our diet? These fatty acids work together at the cellular level. The ratio in most of our diets of omega-6 to omega-3 is 25 or 30:1 ; the ideal ratio is less than 10:1 (Farrell, 1993). The proposed ratio of 5:1 between omega-6 and omega-3 fatty acids was based on the ratio found in fetal and neonatal structural lipids in the human, as well as the ratio found in some human milk (Nordic Council of Ministers, 1989).

What happens if there is an imbalance? In a variety of circumstances, if the smooth surface of the arterial wall is damaged, the repair mechanism may go wrong if there is a gross imbalance of omega-6:omega-3. This imbalance may also cause arteries to constrict, resulting in high blood pressure, which in turn damages the cells on the surface of the arterial wall (Farrell, 1993).

2. Healthy people

Animal experiments have shown that the brain, retina and nervous tissue have very high concentrations of DHA. A deficiency of omega-3 fatty acids decreases the animal's ability to learn and its ability to see properly (Crawford *et al.*, 1989). Limited observations have shown that there is a dramatic increases in DHA in the human brain during the last trimester of human fetus development, with the DHA level doubling during this period (Neuringer *et al.*, 1988; Campbell *et al.*, 1996). Babies fed infant formula milk with high ratios of linoleic to linolenic acid have poorer electroretinogram responses than those fed breast milk with lower ratios of linoleic acid to linolenic acid (9:1). The addition of fish oil to infant formulas improves some electroretinogram responses, even though fish oil is not recommended for infant milk formula. Visual activity also improved with fish oil supplementation during the first half of infancy, compared with formulas containing between 1.5 and 2.5% of the energy as linolenic acid. Thus, there seems to be a need for the preformed DHA (Carlson and Salem, 1991).

Adult diets deficient in omega-3 fatty acids resulted in scaliness and lesions of the skin of patients, which were cured when these fatty acids were added to the diet (Bjerve, 1991). He concluded that optimally 5.4% of the energy of the diet should be in form of total PUFA and 0.6% as linolenic acid with 0.2% as EPA and DHA.

Most of the effects of linoleic acid are directly related to eicosanoid biosynthesis. The type and amounts of eicosanoids produced vary between cells and tissues involved in regulating immune response, bone remodeling and oviposition. It must be recognized that linoleic acid will not substitute for alpha-linolenic acid in providing omega-3 PUFA to tissues. The long chain omega-3 PUFA derived from alpha-linolenic acid are present in the retina and nervous tissue (Rezanka, 1989). Recognized deficiency symptoms of omega-3 fatty acids in mammals include defective vision and impaired learning ability.

The long chain PUFA such as EPA and DHA are used to build structural lipids with varying degrees of fluidity to meet different structural and functional needs. These fatty acids may be found in areas of rapid biochemical reactions such as in signal transmitters and receptors in the brain and nervous, vascular and visual systems. In the photoreceptors, DHA represents 60% of the fatty acids (Watkins *et al.*, 1991).

Several studies have evaluated the effects on blood characteristics of consuming eggs containing an increased level of long chain omega-3 PUFA. In one study, eggs from hens fed a 10% menhaden oil diet were tested (Oh *et al.*, 1991). Healthy male volunteers consumed either four control eggs or four omega-3 fatty acid-enriched eggs per day for a four week period. The plasma levels of both cholesterol and triglycerol were increased in the volunteers who ate the control eggs and their blood pressure was unchanged. In contrast, the consumption of the omega-3 fatty acid-enriched eggs generated no change in blood cholesterol concentration, while the level of triglycerol was significantly reduced. Furthermore, both systolic and diastolic blood pressures were significantly reduced in subjects who consumed the fatty acid-modified eggs. Similar results were obtained in another study where marked increases in the omega-3 fatty acid levels in the blood were also noted (Jiang and Sim, 1994).

3. Patients with disease

Many human diseases have been associated at the biochemical level with a change in prostaglandins and leukotrienes. The metabolic half-life of the derivative of prostaglandin, prostacyclin, is less than one circulation time. Fish oils have been shown to change the balance of these powerful physiological agents (Lands, 1986). And prostacyclines and leukotrienes have been shown to play important roles in the development of coronary heart disease, strokes, inflammatory disease and tumors (Salem, 1989; Cane, 1991; Ferretti et al., 1991; Simopoulos et al., 1991).

ESSENTIAL FATTY ACIDS (EFA) IN POULTRY

1. Lipid composition of the egg yolk

All of the lipids of the egg are confined within the yolk. The yolk exists basically as an oil-water emulsion in the form of lipid spheres (25-150 μm diameter) held within an aqueous-protein phase (Noble et al., 1990). Almost all of the lipid is present as lipoprotein complexes, with the overall lipid: protein ratio being approximately 2:1. Two major yolk lipoprotein fractions have been identified based on their different physical properties and consequent separation during centrifugation. Thus "low" and "high" density fractions exist, with the most of the yolk lipid (over 90%) found within the low density fraction.

Yolk lipid is made up almost entirely of triacylglycerol (63% of total lipid) and phospholipid (30%). Free cholesterol (i.e. cholesterol not esterified to fatty acids) forms approximately 5% of the total weight of the yolk (Stadelman and Pratt, 1989).

The fatty acid composition of the triacylglycerol and phospholipid fractions of the yolk form a standard egg. In both fractions, oleic acid is the major fatty acid present. Together, palmitic and stearic acids account for more than one-third of the fatty acids, while substantial levels of linoleic acid are also present (Whitehead, 1984).

The fatty acids in the triacylglycerols of the yolk display a preferential distribution of the glycerol moiety. High levels of arachidonic and docosahexaenoic acids are present in the phospholipid fraction. In all of the lipid classes, palmitic and stearic acids together account for approximately 50% of the total fatty acids. The posphotidylcholine fraction contains the highest level of linoleic acid. The phophotidylethanolamine fraction contains high levels of arachidonic and docosahexaenoic acids (Brown, 1991).

The phospholipid contains higher levels of stearic, linoleic, arachidonic and docosahexaenoic acids than the triacylglycerol which contains a higher level of 2-linolenic acid. In both the triacylglycerol and phospholipid fractions, the chicken, turkey and quail were characterized by higher levels of linoleic acid than the duck, goose and pheasant. The level of DHA was highest in the yolk of eggs of the domestic fowl and goose (Whitehead, 1984; Stadelman and Pratt, 1989).

2. EFA deficiency symptoms and requirements

EFA deficiency symptoms in chicks include retarded growth, increased water consumption, reduced resistance to disease, enlarged liver with increased lipid content and an alteration of tissue fatty acid composition (Balnave, 1970). In males there may be a reduced testicle size and delayed development of the secondary sexual characteristics. In layers, linoleic acid deficiency results in decreased egg size, lowered egg weight and changes in egg yolk fatty acid composition. However, reproductive failure and increased susceptibility to disease might be more related to defective eicosanoid biosynthesis than to strictly EFA deficiency (Watkins, 1991).

For optimal growth in poultry, the linoleic acid requirement is suggested to be 1% of the diet (Oh et al., 1988), although other reports (Whitehead, 1984) concluded that 0.8% may satisfy the growth requirement in chickens. It is more difficult to determine the recommended levels for adult poultry since tissue reserves of the essential fatty acids are influenced by the composition of diets used for growth. Other investigators have suggested that the laying hen has two requirements for linoleic acid. Physiological maintenance may require 0.9% (Balnave, 1971), while an additional 2 to 4% may be needed for maximum egg size (Whitehead, 1984).

A number of workers have observed some adverse effects on the performance of feeding diets containing varying amounts of fish meal or fish oil. It has been observed that the feeding of isoenergetic and isonitrogenous redfish meal and redfish oil diets to broilers caused lowered feed consumption, body weights and poorer feed conversion efficiency than feeding the control diet (Hulan et al., 1989). These authors attributed the reduced performance of chickens given redfish meal to lower palatability and higher calcium levels.

Several studies have reported a lowering of egg or yolk weights or egg number when fish meal or fish oil diets were fed, although a number of other studies have observed no such effect. In one study, a linear decrease in egg weights with increasing amounts of dietary herring meal was observed (Nahm, 1996).

Effects on blood characteristics of chickens receiving fish oil or fish meal have been observed in line with changes which have been observed in mammals (Fritsche et al., 1993). Thus, as a result of omega-3 PUFA intake, the FA composition of the blood has shown dose response increases in the levels of omega-3 FA, while the levels of omega-6 FA have decreased (Huang et al., 1990; Hargis and Van Elswyk, 1993). Others have observed that as the level of dietary omega-3 FA increased, the amount of triacylglycerol decreased in the plasma and in the very low density plus low density lipoprotein fraction (VLDL+LDL) (Phetteplace and Watkins, 1990). The ratio of omega-6 to omega-3 FA in the plasma was reduced form 7.7 to 3.7 in chickens fed increasing amounts of herring meal and there was no effect of the modified diets on plasma total cholesterol (Nash et al., 1995).

3. The pattern of EFA absorption

Most poultry diets should provide adequate amounts of linoleic acid since plant oils in grains are usually rich sources of this EFA. Under certain conditions these diets may not contain adequate amounts of EFA. Certain nutrients and dietary factors may increase the EFA requirements. Biotin, antioxidants, fat soluble vitamins and trans-fatty acids effect the metabolism of EFA in poultry (Stadelman and Pratt, 1989).

Commercially blended feed-grade fats can be variable in their concentrations of linoleic and alpha-linolenic acid and they should be analyzed for fatty acid composition before use (Al-Athari and Watkins, 1988). Both linoleic and alpha-linolenic acids are readily absorbed through the intestinal wall where resynthesis of triacylglycerols and packaging of lipids into portomicrons occurs for transport to the liver (Krogdahl, 1985). Long-chain omega-3 PUFA present in marine oils and fish meals seem to be absorbed and metabolized to the same extent as the omega-6 PUFA (Phettplace and Watkins, 1990). Since varying the levels of EFA and PUFA in diets will modify the composition of long-chain PUFAs (omega-3 and omega-6 fatty acids) in poultry tissues, enriching poultry meat and eggs with specific PUFA may be done to meet consumer demands.

FATTY ACID MODIFICATION IN EGG PRODUCTION

For years we have been told that dietary cholesterol is a major killer and we should avoid foods high in cholesterol such as eggs. Today, we know that dietary cholesterol is not an important risk factor in heart disease. There are many other factors that are more important such as the amount and nature of the fat in the diet. A good example of this is the case of the Greenland Eskimo. They consume almost twice as much cholesterol in their diet than do their neighbors the Danes, but the incidence of deaths from heart disease is almost seven times higher in the

Danes. The answer lies, in part, in the source and nature of the fat consumed (Farrell, 1993).

Changing the quantity and or quality of the fat-rich components in the egg lipids has potential for manipulation of eggs to design the "modified" egg (Leeson, 1993). He stated that linolenic acid intake is important in its role as a precursor of docosahexaenoic acid, a metabolite found to reduce blood platelet aggregation and adhesiveness and plasma triglyceride levels. The current sources of linolenic acid are fish products and oil seeds, such as flax. When hens are fed flax, there is a considerable accumulation of linolenic acid in the egg, to the extent that the consumption of one or two "modified" eggs per day would provide most of the adult requirement for this nutrient.

One research paper has shown that inclusion of various fish oils, seeds, and seed oils in layer rations readily results in the incorporation of up to 220 mg of omega-3 FA per egg yolk (Hargis and Van Elswyk, 1993). This level of omega-3 FA is equivalent to that which would be consumed in a 100 g serving of lean fish; therefore consumption of one omega-3 fatty acid-enriched egg potentially could replace consumption of fish.

1. Feed-grade fats for poultry feeds

The addition of feed-grade fat (yellow grease or vegetable frying oil) to the poultry feed improves growth rate and feed conversion. Industry analysts predict that vegetable frying oil use will increase at the expense of animal tallow, resulting in an increase in the hydrogenated oil content in yellow grease. Since the primary component of blended fats is yellow grease, the concentration of trans-fatty acids (present in hydrogenated vegetable oils) will increase significantly in these products and in poultry feed. Trans-fatty acids form a side reaction isomerization during catalytic hydrogenation of vegetable and marine oils. Feeding experiments with hydrogenated soybean oil and native soybean oil indicated that hydrogenated oil had a lower ME value in broiler chicks (Brown, *et al.*, 1993). The lower ME value may be due to the trans-fatty acids in the hydrogenated soybean oil.

The nutritive value of rendered fats in animal feeds has been questioned due to the harsh treatment they undergo during processing. To prevent peroxidation, which decreases the feeding value of rendered fats, nutritionists recommend that antioxidants be added during processing. Antioxidants help prevent oxidative damage to unsaturated fatty acids and fat-soluble vitamins. They also insure that ingredient quality is maintained until the feed is consumed (Kim *et al.*, 1995).

2. Feeding to produce essential fatty acids in eggs

The findings that the consumption of omega-3 PUFA can have beneficial effects on important aspects of human health and disease have stimulated interest in the possible increase in the levels of these fatty acids in foods by the inclusion of dietary fish oil. Several investigations have been conducted with the aim of increasing the omega-3 PUFA composition of the egg yolk.

Since the chicken is a monogastric animal, much of the dietary fat is assimilated directly with minimal modification (Watkins, 1991).

Scientists (Reiser, 1951; Rhodes, 1958) reported the following.

- Egg pentaenoic and hexaenoic acids are increased by dietary cod liver oil.
- There is preferential insertion of marine fatty acids in egg phospholipids.
- The selective incorporation is at the expense of monounsaturated and diunsaturated fatty acids and yolk fatty acid can be modified by:
    a) dietary lipids in different systems of husbandry
    b) different strains of chickens, and
    c) different species of birds.

Several egg producers are marketing omega-3 PUFA enriched shell eggs and others are beginning to produce them. Canola oil, olive oil, flax seed oil and fish oils, such as menhaden oil, are available to the poultry industry for inclusion of omega-3 PUFA in the laying hen rations (Van Elswyk et al., 1991; Watkins and Elkin, 1992; Leeson, 1993).

Concentrations of omega-3 PUFA in poultry meat and eggs have been elevated to produce foods with new concepts by the commercial poultry industry through the feeding of flax seed and flax seed oil (Stadelman and Pratt, 1989). The overall nutrient content of feeds can be improved by adding flax seed due to its relatively high protein and energy levels. Flax seed oil is high in linolenic acid (omega-3 fatty acid), which has been shown to have positive health effects on people. Flax seed is included in animal feed mainly to increase the levels of omega-3 fatty acids in the animal products and increase the value of these products as sources of omega-3 fatty acids for human diets. The main difference from other oil seeds is its high levels of linolenic aicd, with approximately 55% of it oil being omega-3 fatty acid. This is four times the level found in canola and eight times the level in soybeans.

Flax seed in the laying hen diet significantly increases the linolenic acid content in the yolk. Dietary flax was shown to increase the proportion of linolenic acid and decrease the proportion of shorter chain saturated fatty acids in the yolk (Hickling, 1997). A typical western Canadian feed formula for layers containing flax seed increased the level of omega-3 fatty acids in the egg yolk from less than 1% to more than 5% of the total oil. The basic feed formulations used in the Canadian feed industry usually include 10 to 20% flax seed in the egg laying diets.

Most feeding programs use ground flax seed, but the chicken has a gizzard capable of grinding the seed so that whole flax seed can be used in the diet.

There does not seem to be an effect of egg production, but the level of omega-3 fatty acids may be reduced when whole seed is fed (Scheideler and Froning, 1996). Other reports, however, have shown that flax seed yielded no differences in total yolk omega-3 PUFA deposition as compared to equivalent amounts of ground flax seed. The advantage of using whole flax seed is that the feed will not go rancid and therefore will require less antioxidant stabilization. There may be problems with the mixing of the whole flax seed so it does not separate out in handling or the bird does not selectively consume more or less of the flax than is intended.

Ground flax seed has been promoted as being a more stable alternative to marine oils, but oxidative stability tests conducted with eggs from hens fed ground flax seed indicate an increase in the lipid peroxidation products in the egg yolk. Antioxidants are usually added to the feed in order to prevent rancidity from the oxidation of the dietary omega-3 fatty acids in the flax seed oil. Egg production and the sensory eating quality of the egg can both be affected by rancidity of the flaxseed oil. The ability to change the fatty acid composition through addition of flaxseed depends on the choice of antioxidant and the flaxseed processing methods (Hickling, 1997).

Dietary menhaden oil at 3% for 18 weeks increased egg EPA and DHA contents without altering egg output and total egg lipids (Hargis et al., 1991). 5% dietary menhaden oil also was reported to increase DHA content in the egg from 2.9 to 11.8% (Couch and Saloma, 1973). Inclusion of 1.5% menhaden oil in a laying hen ration has also been reported to result in the deposition of up to 180mg total omega-3 fatty acids/yolk. According to these results, it is possible to increase DHA contents of eggs. Another comparison of undeodorized and deodorized menhaden oil at 4% in layer diets showed that both sources were similar with respect to yolk content of EPA and DHA (Maurice, 1994).

Dietary fish oil has been indirectly implicated in "fishy" or "crabby" taint in eggs from hens fed different types of fish meal at different concentrations (Koehler and Bearse, 1975). In one study in which hens were fed a 3% menhaden oil diet, taste panelists were able to differentiate between omega-3 enriched and control scrambled eggs on the basis of flavor differences; some of the panelists reported that they noticed a "fish-like" flavor in the scrambled eggs (Van Elswyk et al., 1991). Hard boiled eggs were not distinguished on the basis of dietary treatment by panelists, but this was attributed to the fact that the scrambled eggs were presented to the panelists warm whereas the hard boiled eggs were presented at room temperature.

One alternative to feeding fish oil as a way of increasing the content of omega-3 PUFA without any off-flavors is to increase the levels of dietary alpha-linolenic acid. It has been observed that the feeding of high levels of alpha-linolenic acid does not entirely remove the threat of off-flavors (Hargis and Van Elswyk, 1993). In recent studies with fish oils, eggs remained acceptable with up to 3% (the maximum concentration studied) dietary fish oil stabilized with antioxidant (Huang et al., 1990). Feeding fish oil at or above 3% of the weight of the diet without adding antioxidants should be avoided (Van Elswyk et al., 1991).

Storage of feed containing 4% fish oil at 40℃ resulted in a significant decline in EPA and DHA after one week (Maurice, 1994). Therefore, egg producers should regularly turnover stored feed to prevent degradation of fish oil in the feed and to maximize egg enrichment of EPA and DHA. Eggs should be assayed during the egg production period to estimate variances in EPA and DHA to assure the desired concentrations of these in the eggs.

There has been some research done which has reported on the differences between feeding flax seed and fish oil. Hens fed flax seed laid eggs with 486 mg of omega-3 fatty acids per 60 g egg compared to 282 mg per egg from hens fed fish oil. However, eggs from hens fed menhaden oil contained 262 mg EPA and DHA per 60 g egg compared to 94 mg EPA and 23 mg DHA from hens fed flax seed (Maurice, 1994). It has also been reported that utilization of 5% ground flax seed resulted in similar total omega-3 fatty acid deposition as 1.5% menhaden oil. However, composition of the egg yolk profile is much different, which means the predominant omega-3 fatty acid deposited in response to dietary flax seed is linolenic acid, a shorter chain omega-3 fatty acid.

Recently, one study showed that feeding pearl millet which was substituted for corn produced eggs significantly enriched in omega-3 FA and dietary treatments (corn, equal amounts of corn and pearl millet) had no effect on feed intake, body weight, egg production, egg weight and yolk weight (Collings et al., 1997). These results reported that feeding millet to layers in place of corn significantly decreased yolk pigmentation and the ratio of omega-6 FA to omega-3 FA in eggs was 13.1, 10.1 and 8.3 for hens fed corn, corn + pearl millet and pearl millet, respectively. Pearl millet, the world's most drought resistant grain, has been studied for its possible use in the production of egg yolks high in omega-3 FA. Compared to common cereals, pearl millet is rich in oil, with a typical fat content above 5%. Linolenic acid (C18:3, n-3) comprises 4% of the total fatty acids in this oil, giving it a higher content to omega-3 FA than other cereal grains, which means further research is needed for this grain (Rooney, 1978).

There was a study utilizing four diets, including a control, cod liver oil, canola (rapeseed) oil or linseed oil at 7% of the diet. Forty-four human volunteers consumed 14 of the egg types weekly for nine weeks (Farrell, 1993). There were no significant changes in the blood parameters that could be attributed to the egg types. High density lipoprotein cholesterol (HDL) did show a small decline and there was a small increase in low density lipoprotein cholesterol (LDL), on the 7%

fish oil diet. A sensory panel in this trial was unable to distinguish between the four different egg types, but they were evaluated in only one way, as scrambled eggs microwave cooked. Further testing should be undertaken.

When adding dietary oils or seeds to the hen's diet in order to increase omega-3 PUFA in eggs, the use of antioxidants in the hens feed is still important. One report has indicated that incorporating antioxidants into poultry products, especially eggs, would increase oxidative stability and also provide a natural dietary source of antioxidants (Ajuyah et al., 1993). Recently, the effect of each 3.5% dietary oil (menhaden, flax, palm and sunflower oils) with added tocopherols was studied for their effect on the tocopherol deposition and fatty acid composition of the egg and other tissues (Cherian et al., 1996). Addition of tocopherols increased the tocopherol content more in the egg than any other tissue (liver, adipose tissue, dark meat and white meat).

3. Eggs from free range hens

There has been some debate as to the benefits or otherwise in terms of nutrition of consuming free range eggs. The observations of some scientists of an increased content of long chain omega-3 PUFA in eggs from free range hens in Greece are noteworthy (Simopoulos and Salem, 1991). These hens were said to consume large amounts of purslane (which is rich in alpha-linolenic acid) and other food sources such as grass, twigs, cereals and insects. The fatty acid composition of the eggs from the free range hens has been compared with that of a U. S. supermarket egg. The Greek eggs contained higher contents of saturated and monosaturated fatty acids than the supermarket eggs. In addition, the total content of omega-6 fatty acids was lower and that of the omega-3 fatty acids was markedly higher in the Greek eggs, with the result that the total omega-6 to total omega-3 fatty acid ratios were 1.3 to 19.4 for the Greek and supermarket eggs, respectively.

However, it is doubtful whether "free range" hens raised in large commercial numbers within a limited space on commercial diets would have access to sufficient quantity and variety of vegetation to give rise to omega-3 fatty acid enriched eggs. One review article noted the marked difference in fatty acid composition depending on the rearing conditions (Leskanich et al., 1997). In nearly all cases (chicken, duck, pheasant and ostrich), the contents of oleic and linoleic acids were higher in the commercial than in the free living animals.

4. The amount of omega fatty acids supplied by one designed egg

The optimal human dietary requirement of 18:3 omega-3 fatty acid, in the absence of EPA and DHA, has been estimated at 860 to 1220 mg per day or 1.0 to 1.2% of the total energy intake. The optimal requirement of EPA and DHA has been estimated at 350 to 400 mg per day or 0.4% of energy intake (Bjerve,

1991). Based to these estimates, one designer egg, enriched with EPA and DHA from feeding 3 to 4% menhaden oil, would provide about 50 to 65% of the estimated requirement.

Such designer eggs could be promoted in all markets or to specifically targeted groups. Eggs enriched in EPA and DHA will provide consumers with the opportunity to exercise personal choice. The three top motivators in purchasing food-taste, price and healthfulness-will determine the demand for designer eggs (Nahm and Chung, 1995).

Anticipated success of omega-3 PUFA shell eggs in the marketplace was demonstrated recently in a survey (Marshall *et al.*, 1994). 73% out of five hundred consumers indicated they would be interested in purchasing omega-3 PUFA eggs. They would be willing to pay more for the eggs: 60% would pay an additional $0.50/dozen, 40% would pay $1.00/dozen more (Elswyk, 1994).

FATTY ACID MODIFICATION IN POULTRY MEAT PRODUCTION

Consumers are striving to reduce fat consumption in their diet. As a result, there has been a great deal of interest in investigating methods that are effective in reducing abdominal fat in broilers. Most research has shown that increasing energy levels tends to increase the carcass fat content, while increasing levels of protein tends to decrease carcass fat content. Health conscious consumers are going one step further. Their behaviors regarding food choices are changing and they are continuing to be interested in the composition of food and the diet as a whole. A good example of this is the interest in omega-3 fatty acids which have been recognized for their benefits to human health, as the dietary lipids exert a marked effect on the composition of poultry meat lipids. This provides broiler producers with a technological option to manipulate broiler meat fatty acids and create "modified" meats for specific markets.

1. Feed manipulation for fatty acid modification in poultry meat

Scientists have insisted that dietary manipulation has the potential for modifying the fatty acid content and protein content of poultry meat. When the dietary protein level was increased from 24 to 36%, the absolute quantity of carcass protein increased only one gram (from 233 to 234 g), while the absolute quantity of carcass fat decreased 31 g (from 210 to 179 g) (Barlow *et al.*, 1990; Leeson, 1993). Dietary energy levels have the same basic effect, except in the opposite manner. Increasing the dietary energy levels significantly increases the percentage of carcass fat. Increasing the levels of dietary energy significantly reduces the percentage of carcass protein (because of the increase in fat content) while the absolute quantity of carcass protein changes very little (Leeson, 1993).

The poultry carcass is primarily composed of protein, fat, moisture and ash. The absolute values of protein and ash do not appear to change much. The absolute values for fat and moisture can change markedly due to dietary composition, feeding programs and other management programs. Fat and moisture basically interchange.

Scientists observed that chickens could chain elongate and desaturate dietary sources of alpha-linolenic acid (18:3n3) to form eicosapentaenoic acid (20:5n3) (Phetteplace and Watkins, 1990) These scientists reported that the omega-3 PUFA contained in these products are readily incorporated into tissue lipids of the broiler, when fish meal and menhaden oil are fed to broilers. Chickens fed linseed oil, which is also a rich source of long-chain omega-3 PUFA (18:3n3), accumulate these fatty acids in their tissues. The chicken can modulate its concentrations of PUFA by the types and amounts of fatty acids it consumes (Watkins, 1991).

The liver of the chicken contains desaturation and elongation enzymes to facilitate the formation of omega-3 PUFA. When the dietary concentration of 18:3n3 increases relative to the 18:2n6, there is an elevation in the omega-3 PUFA. Feeding sources of omega-3 PUFA to poultry increases the carcass concentration to 20:5n3 but lowers that for 20:4n6. When both 18:2n6, 18:3n3 are deficient, mead acid (20:3n9) is formed from oleic acid. In most practical poultry diets, the EFA linoleic acid (18:2n6) is at a higher concentration than alpha-linolenic acid (18:3n3). When this happens greater amounts of omega-6 PUFA are formed compared to the amounts of omega-3 PUFA (Watkins, 1991; Watkins *et al.*, 1993).

Feeding incrementally higher levels of redfish meal or oil results in an increased accumulation of beneficial fatty acids in edible chicken meat lipid. The 5000 broiler chickens were fed practical corn-wheat-soybean based diets containing 0, 4, 8, 12, 15 and 30% redfish meal (RM) or 2.1 or 4.2% redfish oil (RO) (Hulan, 1988). The addition of RM and RO resulted in a substantial increase in omega-3 fatty acids and in the accumulation of significant amounts of docosapentaenoic acid in the edible meat lipids of the broilers. The breast meat was found to be lower in lipid and triglyceride but higher in free cholesterol and phospholipids than thigh meat. The carcass lipid content or composition was not affected by the dietary treatment. Breast meat contained more of the docosapentaenoic acid and total omega-3 PUFA.

The addition of plant seed or oil (flax seed or linseed oil) to the broiler diet also increased the level of omega-3 fatty acids in the poultry meat. Studies have shown that levels of omega-3 PUFA as well as linoleic acid increased the lipid content of both dark and white meats. The proportion of oleic acid decreased to compensate. It appears that flax seed changes the pattern of fatty acid composition in broiler meat in a very similar manner that the fatty acid composition of egg yolks are altered by feeding flax seeds to layers (Ajuyah, *et al.*, 1991). Many practical questions about the meat stability and sensory properties need to be studied before there will be commercial feeding of flax to broilers.

There has also been a report that birds supplemented with linseed oil (1.0, 2.5 or 5.0%), rich in linolenic acid (18:3n3), had significantly higher levels of omega-3 FA and higher omega-3 : omega-6 ratios than those supplemented with the same level of menhaden oil, primarily due to an accumulation of 18:3n3 (Chanmugam *et al.*, 1992). Levels of EPA were increased with the controls fed the same level of corn oil, in groups fed the two higher levels of linseed oil, and in all the groups fed menhaden oil. Linolenic acid is less susceptible to antioxidation, and is less likely to impart an off-flavor to the muscle.

Another recent research report showed that adding tocopherols to the 3% plant oils (menhaden, flax, palm and sunflower) increased the content of tissue tocopherols in the liver, adipose tissue, dark meat and white meat of the chicken (Cherian *et al.*, 1996). Dietary tocopherols in this study resulted in a significant increase in the content of C20:5n3 and C22:6n3 in adipose tissue and white meat from birds fed menhaden plus tocopherol diets.

On the other hand, another researcher has calculated the amount of long chain omega-3 PUFA which could be supplied to human as a result of consuming the fatty acid modified meat (Hulan *et al.*, 1988). In this study, it was stated that a 100 g portion of fat-modified chicken meat equally divided between 50 g breast meat and 50 g thigh meat would provide approximately 142 mg of EPA + DPA (C22:5n3, docosapentaenoic acid) + DHA (61 mg from the breast + 81 mg from the thigh). This provided slightly more than the 138 mg of these fatty acids found in 100g of cod flesh. In their subsequent study, they also observed that feeding a 12% redfish meal diet would provide about 197 mg of EPA + DPA + DHA per 100 g of chicken (Hulan *et al.*, 1989).

2. Conversion of omega-3 PUFA

Humans can convert omega-3 short-chain fatty acid (linolenic acid-C18:3) to long chain omega-3 fatty acids by desaturation and chain elongation steps (Brenner, 1989). This transformation is very slow, the delta 6-desaturation being the rate limiting step (Crawford *et al.*, 1989). Therefore, the C18:3 omega-3 fatty acid (linolenic acid), through a precursor of EPA and DHA in humans, has not been considered a significant source. Enriching the diet with a linolenic acid does not appear to produce the clinical effects that EPA and DHA produce (Barlow *et al.*, 1990).

Livestock animals are also believed to convert linolenic acid to EPA and DHA, but at a slow rate. This conversion is also influenced by the ratio of omega-6 : omega-3 fatty acids; the higher the ratio the slower the conversion. In chickens, increasing the omega-3 long chain (LC) PUFA content of the diet increases the EPA and DHA content of chicken meat. A review of literature shows that there appears to be a linear relationship between the EPA plus DHA content of the diet and that in chicken meat (De Thomas and Mercuri, 1971). Consequently the amount of EPA and DHA in the tissues of land animals fed diets lacking in EPA and DHA are small (Huang et al., 1990).

3. Use of antioxidants for poultry meat flavor

Fish oil and the oil in fish meal are a rich source of EPA and DHA (Young, 1986). However, they can cause off-flavors in the meat if included at high levels. These off-flavors and fishy taints occur through the oxidation of omega-3 LCPUFA. Some of the aldehydes produced like 2-trans, 4-cis, 7-cis-decatrienal and 4-cis-heptenal, have been isolated and are claimed to have a fishy flavor. Use of antioxidants to avoid the production of these compounds is necessary if the omega-3 LCPUFA in animal products are to be increased.

Without the use of antioxidants, unacceptable odors have been observed in the carcasses of chickens fed fish oil at level of 4% (Dansky, 1962), 2.5% (Holdas and May, 1966), 2% (Edwards and May, 1965) and 1.8% (Hardin et al., 1964). It has therefore been recommended that no more than 1.5% fish oil should be fed, and that this level should be reduced in proportion to the amount of fish meal in the diet (Fry et al., 1965). In broilers, no effect on off-flavor has been observed with respect to the sex or genotype. Recent reports showed that the levels of fish meal and fish oil in broiler diets should be no more than about 12% and 1% by weight of the diet, respectively (Klaus et al., 1995).

Antioxidant treatment is standard practice for livestock animals and farmed fish. There is evidence that increasing the vitamin E content of the animal's diet helps to stabilize the tissue lipids. It has been recommended that diets for broilers should be supplemented with 50 mg/kg of vitamin E above that required for normal nutritional maintenance to improve the stability of unsaturated lipids in the meat (Klaus et al., 1995; Leskanich et al., 1997).

CONCLUSION

Growing interest in the role of dietary fat in development of chronic disease has promoted debate concerning the potential benefits of modifying polyunsaturated fatty acid (PUFA) composition of animal products. Among PUFA targeted for manipulation in animal tissues, omega-3 PUFA (n-3 PUFA) have received considerable attention. Omega-3 PUFA are long chain fatty acids proposed to reduce the incidence of coronary heart disease in humans. Recent findings indicate that omega-3 PUFA play an essential role in growth and development of brain and retinal tissue in the newborn infant.

Desires to design such egg and meat products has resulted in more research in the area of modifying fatty acid composition of eggs and poultry meat through feed manipulation, particularly of the omega-3 PUFA. Plant seeds or oils (flax seed, flax seed oil, canola oil, linseed oil, sunflower oil, and palm oil), and fish oils (such as menaden oil) have been focused on for this research as sources of omega-3 PUFA for feed rations. Scientists reported that 10 to 20% flax seed in the egg laying diets, less than 3% fish oil by weight in the diet without additional antioxidant, or substituting entirely corn with pearl millet in the layer diet increased the egg EPA and DHA content without altering egg output and total egg lipids, Studies have proven that these seeds and oils also have the potential for modifying the fatty acid content of poultry meat. 4, 8, 12, 15 and 30% redfish meal or 2.1 to 4.2% redfish oil in the broiler diet, up to 5% linseed oil, 3% palm oil or 3% sunflower oil in the broiler diet resulted in a substantial increase in omega-3 fatty acids and in the accumulation of significant amounts of docosapentaenoic acid in the edible meat lipids of broilers.

It is a common practice to add antioxidants to the feed in order to prevent rancidity from the oxidation of the dietary omega-3 fatty acids in the plant and fish oils. In recent studies with fish oils, poultry products remained acceptable (in regards to "fishy" or "crabby" taint in the eggs and poultry meat) when dietary fish oils were stabilized with antioxidants.

ACKNOWLEDGMENTS

I would like to thank Dr. T. Savage (Dept. of Animal Science, Oregon State Univ.), Dr. R. Blair (Dept. of Animal Science, The University of British Columbia), and Dr. B. Winselman-Nahm (Lincolnway Animal Hospital, Matteson, IL) for their constructive criticism and corrections of this manuscript.

REFERENCES

Ajuyah AO, Lee KH, Hardin RT and Sim JS 1991 Changes in the yield and in the fatty acid composition of whole carcass and selected meat productions of broiler chickens fed full-fat oil seeds. Poultry Sci. 70:2304-2314.

Al-Athari AK and Wakins BA 1988 Chromatographic analysis of 18:1 isomers in blended feed-grade fats used in poultry diets. Poultry Sci. 67:307-312.

Balnave D 1970 Essential fatty acids in poultry nutrition. World's Poultry Sci. J 26:442-460.

Balnave D 1971 The contribution of absorbed linoleic acid to the metabolism of the mature laying hen. Comp Biochem Physiol 40A:1097-1105.

Barlow S and Pike IH 1991 Humans, animals benefits from omega-3 polyunsaturated fatty acids. Feedstuffs May 13. pp. 18-26.

Barlow SM, Young FVF and Duthie IF 1990 Nutritional recommendation for omega-3 polyunsaturated fatty acids and the challenge to the food industry. Proc. Nutr. Soc. 40:13-21.

Bjerve KS 1991 Omega-3 fatty acid deficiency in man: Implications for the requirement of alpha linoleic acid and long-chain omega-3 fatty acids. World Rev. Nutr. Diet. Basel, Karger, 66:133-142.

Brenner RR 1989 The Role of Fats in Human Nutrition by Vergroesen, A. J. and M. Crawford, 2nd edition. Academic Press, London.

Brown PK 1991 Saturation and isomerization of dietary fatty acids influence nutrient absorption and metabolism in the chicken. Ph. D. dissertation, VPI & SU, Blacksburg, Va..

Brown PK, Potter LM and Watkins BA 1993 Metabolizable energy values of soybean oil and hydrogenated soybean oil for broilers. Poultry Sci. 72:794-797.

Campbell FM, Gordon MJ and Dutta-Roy AK, 1996 Preferential uptake of long chain polyunsaturated fatty acids by isolated human placental membranes. Molecular and Cellular Biochemistry 155:77-83.

Carlson SE and Salem N Jr 1991 World Rev. Nutr. Diet., Karger 66:74-86.

Cave VT 1991 Dietary n-3 polyunsaturated fatty acid effects on animal tumorigenesis. FASEB J 5:2160-2168.

Chanmugan R, Boudreau M, Boutte T, Park RS, Hebhrt J, Berrio L and Hwang DH 1992 Incorporation of different types of n-3 fatty acids into tissue lipids of poultry. Poultry Sci. 71:516-521.

Cherian G, Wolfe FW and Sim JS 1996 Dietary oils with added tocopherols: Effects on egg or tissue tocopherols, fatty acids, and oxidative stability. Poultry Sci. 75:423-431.

Chung DH 1991 Textbook of Biochemistry (Korean edition). SunJin Pub. Co., pp. 217-232.

Collings VP, Cantor AH, Pescatore AJ, Straw ML and Ford MJ 1997 Pearl millet in layer diets enhances egg milk yolk n-3 fatty acids. Poultry Sci. 76:326-330.

Couch JR and Saloma AE 1973 Effect of diet on triglyceride structure and composition of egg yolk lipids. Lipids 8:385-388.

Crawford MA, Edoyle, WG. Williams and Drury PJ 1989 Fats and EFA's in early development. In: The Role of Fats in Human Nutrition by Vergroesen, AJ and Crawford M 2nd ed., Academic Press, London.

Dansky LM 1962 The growth promoting properties of menhaden fish oil as influenced by various fats. Poultry Sci. 41:1352-1354.

Edwards HM, Jr and May KN 1965 Studies with menhaden oil in practical-type broiler rations. Poultry Sci. 44:685-689.

Earnst M 1993 Egg processing. Poultry Int., Jan. pp. 82-84.

Farrell DJ 1993 UNE's designer egg. Poultry Int., May. pp. 62-66.

Ferretti A Juddi JT, Ballard-Barbash R, Nair PP, Taylor PR and Clevidence BA 1991 Effect of fish oil supplementation on the excretion of the major metabolite of prostaglandin E in healthy male subjects. Lipids 26:500-504.

Fritsche KL, Huang SC and Cassity NA 1993 Enrichment of omega-3 fatty acids in suckling pigs by nutritional dietary fish oil supplementation. J Animal Sci. 71:1841-1847.

Fry JJ, P Van Walleghem, Waldroup PW and Harms RH 1965 Fish meal studies. 2. Effects of levels and sources on "fishy flavor" in broiler meat. Poultry Sci. 44:1016-1019.

Hardin JD, Milligan JL and Sidwell VD 1964 The influence of solvent extracted fish meal and stabilized fish oil in broiler rations on performance and on the flavor of broiler meat. Poultry Sci. 43:858-860.

Hargis PS and Van Elswyk ME 1993 Manipulating the fatty acid composition of poultry meat and eggs for the health conscious consumer. World's Poultry Sci. J 49:251-264.

Hargis PS and Van Elswyk ME and Hargis BM 1991 Dietary modification of yolk lipid with menhaden oil. Poultry Sci. 70:874-879.

Hickling D 1997 Flax has potential in livestock, poultry and pet diets. Feedstuffs, Jan. 20. P. 16-17.

Holdas A and May KN 1966 Fish oil and fishy flavor of eggs and carcasses of hens. Poultry Sci. 45:1405-1407.

Huang ZB, Leibovitz J, Lee CM and Millar R 1990 Effect of dietary fish oil on omega-3 fatty acid levels in chicken eggs and thigh flesh. J Agric Food Chem. 38:743-748.

Hulan HW 1988 Redfish meal oil raises fatty acid level of poultry meat. Feedstuffs, April 11. P. 13-15.

Hulan HW, Ackman RG, Ratnayake WMN and Proudfood FG 1989 Omega-3 fatty acid levels and general performance of commercial broilers fed practical levels of redfish meal. Poultry Sci. 68:153-162.

Jiang Z and Sim JS 1994 Fatty acid modification of yolk lipids and cholesterol-lowing eggs. In: Sim JS, Nakai S, eds. Egg uses and processing technologies: new development. Oxon, UK: CAB International, 1994:349-361.

Kim DJ, Myang WJ, Nahm KH, Ko YD and Chang MB 1995 A Textbook of Feed Resources (Korean edition). Hyang Mun Pub. Co., Seoul, Korea. pp. 324-354.

Klaus AM, Fuhrmann H and Sallmann HP 1995 Peroxidative and antioxidative metabolism of the broiler chicken as influenced by dietary linoleic acid and vitamin E. Archiv. Fur Geflugelkunde 59:135-144.

Koehler HH and Bearse GE 1975 Egg flavor quality as affected by fish meals or fish oils in laying rations. Poultry Sci. 54:881-885.

Lands WEM 1986 Fish and Human Health, Pub: Academic Press.

Leeson S 1993 Potential of modifying poultry products. J Appl. Poultry Res. 2: 380-384.

Leskanich CO, Matthews KR, Warkup CC, Noble RC and Hazzledine M 1997 The effect of dietary oil containing (n-3) fatty acids on the fatty acid, physicochemical and organoleptic characteristics of pig meat and fat. J of Animal Sci. 75:673-683.

Marshall AC, Kuben KS, Hinton KR, Hargis PS and Van Elswyk ME 1994 Omega-3 fatty acid-enriched table eggs- A survey of consumer acceptability. Poultry Sci. 73:1334-1340.

Maurice DV 1994 Dietary fish oil: Feeding to produce designer eggs. Feed Management 45(2):29-30, 31.

Nahm KH 1996 Korean research direction for animal science and technology in the 21st century. The Proceedings of the Korean Association of Animal Science. June 25-27. pp. 129-167.

Nahm KH and Chung SB 1995 A Textbook of Chicken Production (English version). MunUn Dang Pub. Co., Seoul, Korea.

Nash DM, Hamilton RMG and Hulan HW 1995 The effect of dietary herring meal on the omega-3 fatty acid content of plasma and egg yolk lipids of laying hens. Canadian J Animal Sci. 75:247-253

Neuringer M, Anderson GJ and Conner WE 1988 Ann. Rev. Nutr. 8:517-541.

Noble RC, Cocchi M and Turchetto E 1990 Egg fat A case for concern? World's Poultry Sci. J 46:109-118.

Nordic Council of Ministers: Nordic Nutrition Recommendations. 2nd ed 1989 Report 1989:2 (English version), Copenhagen.

Oh SY, Hsieh T, Ryue J and Bell DE 1988 Effects of dietary eggs enriched in omega-3 fatty acids on plasma cholesterol, lipoprotein composition and blood pressure in human. Lipoprotein and Cholesterol Metabolism I:751-756.

Oh S, Ryuc J, Hsieh CH and Bell DE 1991 Eggs enriched in omega-3 fatty acids and alterations in lipid concentrations in plasma and lipoprteins. Am. J Clin. Nutr. 54:689-695.

Phetteplace HW and Watkins BA 1990 Effects of various omega-3 lipid sources on fatty acid composition in chicken tissues. J Food Comp. Anal. 2(2):104-117.

Reiser R 1951 The synthesis and interconversions of polyunsturated fatty acids by the laying hen. J Nutr. 44:159-162.

Rezanka T 1989 Very-long-chain fatty acids from the animal and plant kingdoms. Prog. Lipid Res. 28:147-187.

Rhodes DN 1958 The effect of cod-liver oil in the diet on the composition of hen's egg phospholipids. Biochem J 68:380-387.

Rooney LW 1978 Sorghum and pearl millet lipids. Cereal chem. 55:584-590.

Salem N Jr 1989 Omega-3 fatty acids: molecular and biochemical aspects. In: New Protective Roles for Selected Nutrients. G. A. Spiller and J. Scala, ed. Allan R. Liss, Inc., New York. p. 109.

Scheideler SE and Froning GW 1996 The combined influence of dietary flax seed variety, level, form, and storage condition on egg production and composition among vitamin E supplemented hens. Poultry Sci. 75:1221-1226.

Simonpoulos AP, Kifer RR and Wykes AA 1991 World Rev. Nutr. Diet., Basel, Karger, 66:51-57.

Simopoulos AP and Salem N Jr 1992 Egg yolk as a source of long-chain polyunsaturated fatty acids in infant feeding. Am. J of Clinical Nut. 55:411-414.

Stadelman WJ and Pratt DE 1989 Factors influencing composition of the hen's egg. World's Poul. Sci. J 45:247-266.

Van Elswyk MV 1994 Looking ahead: Will eggs become dietary alternative to fish? Poultry Int. pp. 82-88. Dec.

Van Elswyk ME, Sams ER and Hargis PS 1991 Composition, functionality and sensory evaluation of eggs from hens fed dietary menhaden oil. J Food Sci. 57:342-349.

Watkins BA 1991 Importance of essential fatty acids and their dervatives in poultry. J Nutrition 121:1475-1485.

Watkins BA 1994 Polyunsaturated, labeling to give rise to designer foods. Feedstuffs, Jan. 17. pp. 40-42.

Watkins BA and Elkin RG 1992 Dietary modulation of oleic and stearic acids in egg yolk. J Food Compos.Anal. 5:209-215.

Watkins BA, Whitehead CC and Duff SRI 1991 Hydrogenated oil decreases tissue concentration of n-6 polyunsaturated fatty acids and may contribute to dyschondroplasia in broilers. Br. Poultry Sci. 32:1109-1119.

Watkins BA, Xu H, Elkin RG and Vimini RJ 1993 Rapid changes in n-3 polyunsaturated fatty acids (PUFA) in turkey meat. XII. International Congress of Nutrition 1:206.

Whitehead CC 1984 Essential fatty acids in poultry nutrition. In: Fats in Animal Nutrition. Wiseman, J editor. Butterworths, London, England.

Young FVK 1986 The chemical and physical properties of crude fish oils for refiners and hydrogenators. IAFMM Fish Oil Bulletin. No. 18.

A Strategy for Quality Poultry Egg Production
I. Eggshell strength and pigmentation

K. H. Nahm

Feed and Nutrition Laboratory, College of Natural Resources, Taegu University, Gyong San 712-714, South Korea

ABSTRACT: Eggshell strength and eggshell pigmentation are described in this paper since these are needed for quality egg production. A strong eggshell is determined by the components of the shell (cuticle, true shell and membranes) as well as the proper function of the gastrointestinal tract the shell gland, the kidneys and the endocrine system. When the pullet reaches sexual maturity, the medullary bone must be ready for the laying hen at the peak eggshell formation. The amount of calcium in the layer ration, sources of calcium feed, the ration of calcium and phosphorus in the layer diet, adequate levels of Vitamin D and the dietary mineral (electrolyte) balance in the body fluid are important factors along with the levels of other nutrients. Biological, environmental and managerial factors such as the age of laying flock, temperature and humidity of the hen house, bird strain, disease, egg collection through transportation and others can influence the shell breakage at various stages of movement of the eggs from the producer to the consumer. The pigments present in eggshells are protoporphyrin-IX, biliverdin-IX and its zinc chelate and occasional traces of coproporphyrin-III. However, there are several causes of changes in eggshell pigmentation such as the age of hen, disease, drugs and surface defects due to abnormal post-cuticular deposits.
(Key words: Eggshell strength; Shell gland; Endocrine system; Calcium; Eggshell pigments)

INTRODUCTION

There is no question that the world's population will increase in the 21st century, which means increased demand for products and increased competition as well. For agriculture then, the 21st century will mean people demanding higher quality diets. Future poultry farming also demands the production of high quality products which can be differentiated from poultry products of neighboring farms and neighboring countries. Quality egg production is one of the methods to survive in serious competition. There is likely to be an increased recognition of niche markets and the development of products such as omega eggs with altered fatty acid content to meet specific consumer demand (Blair, 1996).

Generally speaking, quality egg production involves strong eggshells, eggshell pigmentation attractive to the consumer, perfect egg quality, reduced cholesterol content, yolk pigmentation favorable for consumers and marketing, controlled egg weight and introduction of 'organic eggs'.

This paper is the first part of a series entitled "Factors to be considered for quality egg production". It will describe eggshell strength and eggshell pigmentation, which are necessary for quality egg formation.

EGGSHELL FORMATION AND STRENGTH

Cracked and broken eggshells are a major source economic loss for producers. Between the hen and the consumer's carton, about 6 to 8 % of the eggs annually produced are broken or cracked. A strong eggshell allows the egg to resist dynamic and static forces encountered during production, packaging, transport and handling. The integrity or soundness of the eggshell is determined by the components of the shell (cuticle, true shell and membranes) as well as the proper function of the gastrointestinal tract, the shell gland, the kidneys and the endocrine system.

Cracked and broken eggs may result in a reduction in the value of output and may pose a human health hazard via Salmonella contamination (St. Louis, 1988).

1. Measurement of eggshell strength

Eggshell strength has been measured using numerous techniques. Eggshell thickness has been measured directly (destructive), specific gravity (SG) has been used to indirectly estimate thickness (non-destructive), and expensive, complicated and sophisticated measures such as quasi-static compression using an Instron Testing Instrument or Holographic Interferometry which uses a laser beam have been used.

Specific gravity is a very useful measurement to differentiate in a nondestructive manner between thick and thin shells. This method is based on the assumptions that all thick egg shells are strong shells and there is a simple linear relationship between SG and shell breakage. Both of these assumptions are incorrect. Thin shells are not necessarily weak shells (Potts and Washburn, 1974). Eggshell strength is dependent on many factors, including the nature of the organic matrix and crystal structure (Simons, 1971; Roland 1980b). The relationship between SG and shell breakage is curvilinear (Maurice, 1982), and not linear as assumed. Further there are numerous sources of error associated with the measurement of

SG and errors up to 0.006 could occur (Voisey and Hamilton, 1976).

The latest results from scanning electron microscope technology have revealed more details on the shell strata and their individual contributions to fracture resistance (Bain, 1992). This study has lead us away from such parameters as shell thickness and into more qualitative, descriptive traits to reveal how the stresses associated with insults such as quasi-static compression lead to fractures of the shell.

The incidence of structural aberrations is also thought to vary in response to external stressors such as population density, housing systems, etc. Genetic variation may also be anticipated. The contribution of the protein matrix within the shell proper, in contrast to that in the membranes, has come under scrutiny. Although comprising less than 1% of the total weight of the shell, these proteins are now believed to contribute in an important way to its structure and strength (Hincke *et al.*, 1992; Krampits, 1993). A number of protein components have also been identified and a model for their contribution to calcification of the shell has been proposed (Arias and Fernandez, 1993). The main steps in this proposal are: 1) fabrication of the first organic matrix; 2) Nucleation of the calcium carbonate crystals in the mammillary layer; and 3) shell matrix deposition during subsequent crystal development.

The shape of the shell is another important contributor to the resistance to cracking. It has been shown that shell thickness accounted for about 56% of the variation in crushing strength, and that egg shape index explained 15 to 35% of the remaining variation (Richards and Swanson, 1965). The unique shape of the egg shell, coupled with the accepted fact that the material it contains is not homogenous, precluded the use of conventional stress analysis in describing egg shell strength (Voisey and Hunt, 1974). In another report, it was concluded that a small rounded shape was more desirable in terms of improving the strength of the egg shell (Bain, 1991).

For formation of the eggshell, the ovum passes through the various parts of the oviduct including the infundibulum, magnum, isthmus and uterus. When the egg passes into the uterus (The egg spends most of its time here, from 20 to 21 hours), a spongy or palisade layer is laid down and this layer contributes to the main strength and thickness of the shell. This palisade layer begins at the lower portion of the mammillary layer and extends within a short distance of the surface of the shell. This palisade layer is composed of crystal columns running parallel to the surface of the egg. It is of uniform consistency and appears to serve as the cement between the mammillary crystals. The thickness of the palisade layer seems to the most significant factor in determining eggshell strength. Formation of this layer demands much calcium since the eggshell is made-up of 93 to 98% calcium carbonate.

The final step of formation of the egg prior to oviposition is the deposit of the cuticle, or the thin, smooth, porous, outer covering of the shell. The cuticle also has a role in maintaining the strength of the shell (El Boushy and Raterink, 1989). In the vagina, the egg is laid large end first, revolving end on. An air cell forms after the egg is first laid, formed by cooling of the contents of the egg. These processes occur when everything is going according to plan.

2. Medullary bone function in shell formation

When the pullet reaches sexual maturity, estrogen is released from the maturing ovary, which acts in synergism with the androgens and induces the formation of medullary bone in the marrow cavity, especially in the long bones of the skeleton. The medullary bone is formed 10 days before the first egg is laid under the influence of hormones. Skeletal weight of hens increases about 20% during this period. During the prelaying period, body weight increases by 400 to 500 g and total skeletal weight of the pullet increases by 15 to 20 g. This represents storage of an additional 4 to 5 g of calcium (Scott *et al.*, 1982; Scott, 1991).

The laying hen at peak eggshell formation cannot absorb adequate amounts of calcium from her diet. At these times she draws calcium from the specialized medullary bone. The laying hen contains approximately 20 g of calcium, most of which can be found in the skeleton. The average egg shell contains about 2.3 g of calcium. The medullary bone of the hen breaks down to provide calcium during eggshell formation and is built up for storage at other times. Different bones have the ability to provide calcium for eggshell formation to different degrees. The bones of the ribs, sternum, pelvis and spine are considered labile bones, while the skull, shank, and toe are considered nonlabile bones, and the femur, tibia and fibula are considered intermediate bones. Labile bones provide the most calcium for eggshell formation. Medullary bone formation appears to be influenced by dietary calcium levels, since pullets that receive diets containing 3.3% calcium from 18 to 22 weeks of age produce better medullary bone compared to pullets that received only 0.6% calcium during this period (Hurwitz and Bar, 1971; El Boushy and Raterink, 1985). Dietary calcium levels also had a significant effect on total medullary Ca reserves of laying hens. Previous dietary Ca levels had no significant effect upon medullary bone Ca reserves after subsequently feeding the low-Ca diet (Clunies *et al.*, 1992a).

Formation of the egg shell takes place for the 20 hours prior to the egg being laid. This 20 hour period is usually at night. The amount of calcium available for absorption from the intestine at night is affected by the amount and type of calcium ingested by the laying hen during the day. Laying hens usually choose to ingest more calcium near the end of the day. Large particle calcium sources persist longer in the intestinal tract than finely ground calcium sources (El Boushy and Raterink, 1985, 1989).

The laying hen must consume large amounts of calcium on a daily basis. When the hen is receiving insufficient amounts of calcium in the diet an overall negative calcium balance occurs and the rate of secretion of parathyroid hormone (PTH) is greatly increased. This causes the release of calcium from medullary bone which helps to maintain blood calcium levels. In acute calcium deficiencies, egg production ceases and the medullary bone is resorbed to maintain the vital functions requiring calcium (Wideman *et al.*, 1985).

Poor bone structure of laying hens may be due to inadequate skeletal development prior to egg production, a lack of exercise and deficient nutrition during egg production. Outbreaks of poor bone structure have been associated with birds starting to lay at an early age when skeletons have been immature. Special rations for the prelaying period are desirable to provide adequate mineral formation of medullary bone (El Boushy and Raterink, 1985, 1989).

Experiments were carried out to investigate the Ca and P metabolism of hens laying thick- (THK) or thin-shelled (THN) eggs on shell-forming days (SF) and days on which shell formation does not occur (NSF) (Clunies *et al.*, 1992b). Feed, Ca and P intake did not differ significantly between the two groups of hens, however, feed intake and Ca retention increased significantly on SF compared with NSF days. The THN hens retained significantly more Ca compared with the THK hens. No differences were recorded for egg production, although there were differences in egg weight and shell deformation between the two groups of hens. Increased egg weight did not account for differences in eggshell formation. Although percentage shell Ca was not significantly different, total shell Ca was different between the two groups.

In the series of research projects (Clunies *et al.*, 1992b), they reported that feed, Ca and P intake of hens increased significantly on SF days compared with NSF dietary Ca levels had a significant effect on feed and Ca intake of hens. On SF days, hens retained more dietary Ca, both as a percentage and per gram Ca basis, compared with NSF days. As dietary Ca increased the percentage Ca retained decreased and per gram Ca retained increased. Dietary Ca had no effect on egg weight or egg production. Increasing dietary Ca significantly decreased shell deformation and increased shell Ca. Ca retention increased linearly as Ca intake increased, and shell weight increased quadratically. There was a diminishing response of shell weight to Ca intake at higher levels.

3. Effect of calcium and phosphorus on eggshell formation

1) Calcium utilization by layers

When hens receive 3.5 to 4% calcium in all mash laying rations, they only retain about 50% of the ingested calcium. This means that a hen ingesting 3.6 g of calcium per day retains about 1.8 g, or 1800 mg, of calcium during the approximately 18 hours that the feed is available. The hen, therefore, retains about 100 mg of calcium per hour. This absorption rate of 100 mg per hour is exceeded when the egg is in the uterus and is much lower when no eggshell is being deposited (Scott *et al.*, 1982; El Boushy and Raterink, 1985).

Eggshell represents about 10% of the weight of the egg. Egg weight continues to increase and reaches an average of 62 g after 30 weeks of production (50 weeks of age) and these eggs should have a shell weighing 6.2 g (Scott *et al.*, 1982; Scott, 1991).

Recent genetic improvements in egg production and egg size have it necessary to review the nutritional requirements of hens, not only during early laying stages, but also during the late stages. Most present-day laying strains peak at more than 90% production and produce large eggs in less than eight weeks after the onset of egg production (El Boushy and Raterink, 1985, 1989).

Because the eggshell is almost totally calcium carbonate, and calcium represents 40% of the calcium carbonate molecule, the hen requires 2.48 g of calcium per day to lay a large egg (62 g) with a good shell. Work at Rutgers University and Israel has indicated that hens are only able to absorb 1.88 g of calcium from a diet containing 3.75% or more calcium as pulverized limestone. This is because hens can retain only 50% of the ingested calcium in 3.5 to 4.0% containing mash diets. According to these calculations a hen would need to remove 0.6 g (2.48-1.88 = 0.6) of calcium from her bones to make a good eggshell (Scott *et al.*, 1982; Scott, 1991).

2) Sources and solubility of calcium feed

Except for dried green meals, feedstuffs of plant origin are low in calcium. Fish meal, meat and bone scraps, bone meal, calcium phosphate supplements, limestone and oyster shells are the major feedstuffs that supply the calcium needs of layers. If the levels of calcium carbonate (limestone) and calcium phosphate are high, the diet may become unpalatable and other dietary component may be diluted. If a calcium source contains high levels of magnesium (as does dolomitic limestone), it should probably not be used in poultry diets. It was reported that crushed coral can serve as a satisfactory calcium source for for laying hens (NRC, 1994).

The eggshell is composed almost entirely of calcium carbonate, and calcium represents 40% of the calcium carbonate molecule as it was indicated before. Calcium carbonate is insoluble in water and is not absorbed from the digestive tract. Calcium absorption depends upon the degree to which calcium carbonate is dissolved by the hydrochloric acid (HCl) of the proventriculis and gizzard of the hen. This occurs according to the following reaction:

$$CaCO_3 + 2HCl = Ca^{++} + H_2CO_3 + 2Cl^-$$

Because the acidity of the chicken's gizzard is approximately the same as 0.1 N HCl, this was used to determine relative solubility of calcium carbonate, with 100 cc of 0.1 N HCl dissolving exactly 500 mg of $CaCO_3$ (Scott et al., 1982).

Experiments with oyster shell show that when oyster shell contributed 50-66% of the supplemental calcium, breaking strength was significantly improved in eggs of hens fed this diet when compared to hens receiving only pulverized limestone. Thus, 4% oyster shell combined with 3.5% pulverized limestone (a total dietary calcium of about 3.5%) would insure maximum calcium absorption throughout 24 hours each day. Particle size of the calcium carbonate needs to be large and hard enough to remain in the gizzard throughout the night. The particles should be sufficiently hard and of sufficient surface to allow the gastric activity to dissolve them at a rate that releases approximately 75 mg of calcium ion per hour into the blood (Scott et al., 1971; Summers and Leeson, 1984).

Laying hen research has shown that there was no significant differences in eggshell quality or layer performance due to switching limestone with oyster shell, lower soluble limestone to higher soluble limestone and higher soluble limestone to lower soluble limestone (Coon and Cheng, 1986). This study concluded that hens can adapt to different sources of limestone and oyster shell if a large portion of the calcium is in a larger particle size and the calcium intake is adequate. Their data suggested that there is a larger difference in limestone solubility between particle sizes of the same limestone source than between limestone sources.

Specific gravity is in terms of "floating". The specific gravities are used to compare various samples. Water has a specific gravity of 1.0. Anything with a specific gravity less than 1.0 will float in water and those with a higher specific gravity will sink. Imagine that feed in a trough resembles flowing water, then one would expect those materials that have specific gravity values nearest to that of feed to sink more slowly through the feed than those materials with a much higher specific gravity. In one solubility study, the specific gravities of the sample feeds were carefully compared by determining the weight of 30 cc of each material (Scott, 1991). These results revealed the fallacy of supposing that the larger particles are more apt to "float" in the feeds. The results indicated that: (a) The large, hard limestone particles, which showed acid solubilities ranging from 22.5 to 42%, had specific gravities ranging from 1.37 to 1.45 g/cc. These samples not only showed poor acid-solubilities, but also were so much heavier than the feed that they could be expected to sink through the feed as it traveled along the line. (b) The results with the granular limestone samples showed that these had specific gravities that were higher than the particular pulverized limestone used. (c)

The oyster shell had the lowest specific gravity, being only slightly higher than that of the corn-soybean diet, thereby presenting a possible reason for the observation that oyster shell does not settle out during its transport along the chain feeder. Granular oyster shell also showed good solubility.

The most useful calcium supplement, to be used together with oyster shell particles, would be granular oyster shell. The only other material to come close to oyster shell in usefulness appeared to be the pulverized limestone sample designated as 80-mesh. This sample had the highest acid solubility of all and also had a low specific gravity (Scott *et al.*, 1982; Nahm and Chung, 1995).

High producing hens may retain the egg in the uterus for a much shorter time than do hens laying at lower rates. These high producing hens need oyster shell much more than hens that retain the egg in the shell gland over a longer period of time (Scott *et al.*, 1982; Nahm and Chung, 1995).

3) Calcium requirements

(1) Calcium content of the grower diet

The incidence of osteoporosis (cage layer fatigue) is a problem faced by the industry during the early stages of egg production. Current commercial egg strains reach sexual maturity as early as 17 to 18 weeks. Some producers traditionally, or due to scheduling conflicts, hold the birds that are already producing eggs in growing houses and on a low calcium diet up to 20 to 21 weeks of age. As a result, much of the medullary calcium storage has already been utilized for shell formation by the time of housing. During the early stages of egg production laying hens are in a negative calcium balance which cannot be alleviated by increasing the dietary levels of calcium, so the presence of adequate medullary bone is crucial for maintaining eggshell quality and bone integrity. An extra demand for calcium from the bones for shell formation during the early stages of egg production causes the bones to weaken to the extent that these birds show signs of osteoporesis (Summers and Leeson, 1984; Nahm *et al.*, 1997).

An experiment was conducted to determine the effect of feeding a high calcium diet for various durations in the latter part of the growing period on growth and subsequent performance (Keshavarz, 1987a). Pullets were fed a 3.5% calcium diet with adequate levels of available phosphorus (0.42%) for 2 to 6 weeks prior to housing at 20 weeks of age. The bone ash and bone calcium contents were increased due to consumption of the high calcium diet for two or more weeks. Shell quality was not influenced by the calcium level fed in the growing period of this experiment. Other investigators, however, have reported favorable effects on the shell quality during the early part of the production cycle due to feeding high calcium diets in the pre-laying period (Hurwitz and Bar, 1971). These researchers recommended that growing diets should be changed to laying diets either when the secondary signs of sexual maturity (development of the comb and wattle) appear in the flock or when egg production reaches 2 to 5%, regardless of the chronological age.

Increasing the calcium level 2 to 3 weeks prior to housing does not cause nephritis in the growing or laying periods (Keshavarz, 1987b). The incidence of nephritis (urolithiasis) in the growing or laying periods may be seen when pullets are fed a high calcium diet, particularly with low dietary phosphorus content, for long durations (10 to 14 weeks) during the growing period (Wideman et al., 1985).

(2) Calcium content in the layer diet

− Calculation of calcium (Ca) requirement

The eggshell represents about 10% of the weight of the egg. The eggshell is almost totally calcium carbonate and the carbonate molecule contains about 40% calcium (Scott et al., 1982; Scott, 1991).

Step 1: The calculation of calcium (Ca) content in the eggshell

For example, an egg weighing 62 g would require 2.8 g of calcium to form a form a good shell

> Feed Ca content: 4%
> Egg weight: 62 g
> Eggshell weight: 62 g × 0.1 = 6.2 g
> Ca content in shell: 6.2 g × 0.4 = 2.8 g

Step 2: The calculation of the solubility of calcium diet.

In order that a dietary intake of 4.0 g of calcium provides the needed 2.8 g of calcium for eggshell formation, the solubility of the limestone and oyster shell would need to be

$$2.8 \div 4 = 70\%.$$

Step 3: The calculation of calcium content in the ration

If pulverized limestone (88% solubility) and oyster shell (45% solubility) were used in a 50:50 mixture, the solubility of the calcium source would be 88 + 45 = 133 ÷ 2 = 66.5%. The solubility at step 2 (70%) can be used with the different ratio of limestone and oyster shell instead of 50:50. Thus the 2.8 g of calcium needed from the diet could be achieved from 4.21 g of total calcium intake (2.8

÷ 0.665 = 4.21 g).

In the above two examples, the 2.8 g of calcium needed did not include the calcium which can be supplied by other ingredients in the diet other than the limestone and oyster shell. In practical ration formulation, all sources of calcium must be included in the calculation.

A trial was conducted to determine the relationship of in vitro solubility of Ca sources (77.8% pulverized oyster shell and 46.0% pulverized oyster shell) with their in vivo utilization for bone and shell formation (Keshavarz *et al.*, 1993). This research did not show the important relationship between solubility of the Ca sources and eggshell quality and bone formation. This trial suggested that Ca sources with a solubility of less than 46.6% were needed to detect the Ca solubility effects on shell quality and bone formation. The results also indicated that a daily Ca intake of about 3.75 to 4 g/hen/day is required for optimum shell and bone formation. This is consistent with the 1984 NRC calcium recommendation of 3.75 g/hen/day, and suggests that the newly updated 1994 NRC recommendation of 3.25 g/hen/day may be inadequate for optimum eggshell and bone formation.

– Calcium separation and its reduction in the commercial layer diet

Extensive Ca separation takes place in various phases of the feed handing system (Keshavarz and Ackerman, 1984). This practical study showed that extensive calcium separation took place during a period of 4 to 6 days when feed was stored under normal bulk bin conditions. Calcium levels as low as 1.7 to 1.9% were determined in feed samples during their storage in bulk bins.

Extensive calcium separation was also found to take place along the feeding line. When the Ca level in a chain type feeding system was about 4 to 5% in the beginning of the feeding line, the Ca level was as high as 11 to 13% at the end of the feeding lines due to separation (Keshavarz, 1995). The pattern of separation was not similar in different farms and varied depending on the type of feeding system and the speed of movement along the feeding lines. With increases in the calcium separation, the phosphorus content remained the same and the protein content was reduced as the feed moved along the feeding lines. Calcium separation occurring on commercial farms can be a significant factor in reducing shell quality, performance, and liveability.

Laying hens can safely tolerate a diet with 6.5% Ca when the dietary available phosphorus was adequate (0.5%) (Keshavarz, 1987b), Although production was reduced, mortality increased mainly due to visceral gout when hens were fed diets containing 6.5% Ca and a marginal level of available phosphorus (0.2%). This calcium: available phosphorus (AP) ratio of 32.5:1 is detrimental to performance and liveability. This ratio is similar to a diet containing 13% Ca and a normal level of AP (0.4%) which has been observed under field conditions due to Ca separation. An excess of dietary Ca interferes with the availability of other minerals such as phosphorus, magnesium, manganese and zinc. A ratio of 2 Ca to 1 nonphytate phosporus (wt/wt) is appropriate for most poultry except for those that are laying. In laying hens, a much higher Ca level is needed to form eggshells, and ratios as high as 12 Ca to 1 nonphytate phosphorus (wt/wt) may be appropriate.

An interesting study was conducted to investigate in more detail the Ca and AP requirement to laying hens for optimum performance and eggshell quality (Keshavarz and Nakajima, 1993). The dietary treatments consisted of Ca levels from 3.5 to 5.5% in increments of 0.5% with constant levels of dietary AP of 0.4% (T1-T5); a step-up Ca phase feeding regimen of 3.5, 4.5 and 5.5% with a constant level of AP (O.4%) (T6); a step-down AP phase feeding regimen on 0.4, 0.3 and 0.2% with a constant level of Ca (3.5%) (T7); a concurrent step-up Ca phase feeding and step-down AP feeding regimen with or without substitution of 50% oyster shell for pulverized limestone (T8 and T9); and a regimen similar to T9 with a step-up cholecalciferol phase feeding of 2200, 4400 and 8800IU/kg (T10). These results also indicated that the tolerance for Ca in laying hens is relatively high when the AP content of the diet is adequate. The AP level can be reduced in diets with no adverse effects on hen performance. Production performance and shell quality were not influenced by these dietary treatments, except when oyster shell was added to the diet. Beneficial effects of oyster shell on eggshell quality were obtained even when the Ca content of the diet was plentiful. This suggests that the residence time of the calcium sources in the digestive system is an important factor for the improvement of eggshell quality. About 50% of the supplemental Ca in the laying ration should be provided in particle form with a high solubility. Another field study indicated that with the chain-type feeding system, both oyster shell and Ca chips were uniformly distributed along the feeding lines (Keshavarz et al., 1991). Oyster shell has also been shown to have a beneficial effect on shell quality under both cold and warm environmental temperatures and with a normal level of dietary Ca (Keshavarz and McCormick, 1991).

The study also proved that the reduction in shell quality with aging was not due to the hen's reduced ability to absorb and mobilize Ca. Plasma levels of Ca and P, bone Ca and absolute retention of Ca were not influenced by dietary treatments in each phase of this experiment (Keshavarz and Nakajima, 1993). Regardless of the dietary treatments, the absolute retention of Ca did not reduce with aging, and in fact it tended to increase. It is more logical to assume that reduced eggshell quality with aging is due to increased egg weight without a concomitant increase in the hen's ability to increase the absorption and retention of Ca needed for larger eggs. A step-down phosphorus regimen with aging can also be used during the laying period to reduce the feed cost and environmental pollution attributed to phosphorus.

Every effort should be made to reduce Ca separation in different phases of the feed handling systems. The extent that calcium separation is usually occurring in different phases of the feed handling systems on commercial farms can be an important factor for problems associated with performance and eggshell quality. Since different patterns of calcium separation occur with different feeding systems, every producer needs to evaluate his situation independently and appropriate measures must be taken to overcome the problems.

The following are a few tips for reducing calcium separation at different phases in the feed handling system (Keshavarz, 1995).

- Auger systems for feed delivery result in less calcium separation than air systems for feed delivery.

- Bulk bins should have a feed distribution system at the top and a device at the bottom to remix ingredients to prevent separation.

- Running the feeding systems at their maximum speed reduces preferential selection of ingredients by hens which may contribute to nutrient separations.

- Augers in good working condition vibrate less and may cause less separation.

- Allow the birds to clean up the feed in the trough once daily to prevent accumulation of fines in the trough which may result in excessive calcium intake by the hens.

— Time of calcium intake by layers

The time of calcium intake of layers is also important for shell formation. It has been found that the most important time for the hen to receive calcium is during the afternoon. Intake of high calcium containing feed was higher from 6 to 8 a.m., and then decreased progressively until 2 p.m.. From 2 to 4 p.m., consumption of the high calcium feed increased. Eggshell calcification continues in may hens until 8 p.m.. Most eggs are laid between 8 a.m. and 2 p.m.. After 2 p.m. another eggshell begins to form. Hens prefer a higher percentage of calcium in the feed when the eggshell is being calcified than when the calcium is being deposited in the bone (Roland and Farmer, 1984).

The beneficial effect of evening feeding of calcium on eggshell quality may be due to the following mechanism. The route calcium takes to the eggshell in morning fed bird is via the small intestine to blood to bone to egg gland and then to the eggshell. Hens fed calcium in the afternoon at the beginning of eggshell calcification can directly deposit the calcium on the egg via the blood and bypass the bone. If this mechanism is correct, an eggshell from hens fed in the morning will contain more skeletal calcium than that from hens fed in the afternoon.

– Particle size of the calcium sources

Feeding larger particles of $CaCO_3$ to laying hens in the summer improves eggshell strength, however, it was of no benefit during the winter months. When hen-sized limestone, oyster shell or pullet-sized limestone composed two-thirds of the calcium content of the diet, egg shell quality, measured by specific gravity, increased during the summer months only. There also was no difference in shell strength found between oyster shell and limestone (Roland et al., 1953).

Eggshell quality was improved by the use of large particles when the diet contained 3% or less of calcium. However, when a higher level was used, the large particles gave no response (Roland and Harms, 1972). When the diet contained 4 or 4.5% Ca, no improvement was obtained from the use of large particles. This data indicates that the biological availability of calcium is higher from the larger particles. Producers can use a slightly lower level of calcium when larger particles are fed. Larger particles of limestone or oyster shell will not produce better eggshells if the feed contains adequate calcium.

4) The influence of phosphorus on eggshell quality

– Levels proposed for commercial practice

The paper frequently cited to support the proposition that high dietary phosphorus depresses shell strength (Taylor, 1965) does not provide sufficient evidence of the detrimental effect of 1.0% dietary phosphorus. Shell strength does decrease by 2% at 1.0% phosphorus as compared to 0.46% phosphorus. This difference was significant but of questionable value in the delineation of a nutrient window for commercial formulation. Within the range of 0.4 to 1.4% P, changes in shell strength are on the order of 0.3 to 1% and such changes are unlikely to result in a measurable reduction in shell breakage (Miles and Harms, 1982). The high cost of phosphorus supplements is an incentive to lower dietary phosphorus. Hence in commercial practice, there is a greater change for a phosphorus deficiency. Egg shell strength is much more sensitive to P deficiency than to an excess (Maurice, 1988).

– Physiology of phosphorus for eggshell formation

Approximately 2100 mg or 2.1 g of calcium in the medium weight egg are found in an eggshell. In contrast to this, the eggshell contains only 20 mg of phosphorus while there are approximately 130 to 140 mg of phosphorus in the egg's yolk. There is only a total of approximately 160 mg in the entire egg (El Boushy and Raterink, 1985).

The amount of phosphorus consumption of hen varies during the daily feeding period. A study (Harms et al., 1965; Roland and Harms, 1976a) reported that hens consumed a fairly high level of phosphorus from 6 to 8 a.m.. At 8 a.m., the consumption from the cup containing the high level of phosphorus increased. It started to decrease by 2. p.m. and continued to decrease until 8 p.m. (Harms, *et al.*, 1965; Roland and Harms, 1976b). This data indicated that the hen requires a higher level of phosphorus when minerals were being deposited in the bone from 8 a.m. to 2 p.m.. After eggshell calcification began, a lower phosphorus intake is required. If the levels of phosphorus were then changed in the feed in the morning and afternoon, its effect upon change eggshell quality could be determined. These hens had been receiving a diet containing 0.75% phosphorus. One group in this study continued to receive this diet and served as a control. All hens received this feed during the morning until 11 a.m.. From 11 a.m. to 3 p.m., the feed was removed from the troughs which allowed feed to clear from the bird's digestive tracts. At 3 p.m., one group of hens received a diet with all of the supplemental phosphorus removed: one group continued to receive the feed containing 0.75% phosphorus and the phosphorus was increased in the third group. Result indicated that decreasing the phosphorus level in the afternoon resulted in improved eggshell quality, while increasing the phosphorus levels in the afternoon resulted in decreased eggshell quality.

Levels of phosphorus in the blood also vary. Blood phosphorus exhibits a cyclic pattern which is closely related to the egg formation cycle (Miller *et al.*, 1979). The serum phosphorus peaked at 6 mg% approximately 30 minutes before the hen laid an egg, then dropped to 4.5 mg% within 30 minutes following oviposition. This level of 4.5 mg% was maintained for the next five hours. Then the phosphorus level began to rise gradually until the next morning 30 minutes before the next egg was laid, If the hen is placed on a phosphorus deficient diet, the serum phosphorus level will be 4.5 mg% 30 minutes before the egg is laid, and then it falls to 2.5 mg% and remains at this level for the next five hours. It then repeats in the same manner.

Calcium and phosphorus are supplied in the feed during eggshell calcification, but calcium is also withdrawn from bone. When calcium is released from the bone, phosphorus must accompany it. Bone calcium is deposited in the eggshell, along with the calcium from the feed, and increases the level of blood phosphorus. Some of this phosphorus is deposited into the developing yolk of the egg, as previously mentioned. The hen's demand for phosphorus for yolk formation is not nearly as high as the amount made available from bone and that supplied by feed. This explains the continued increase in blood phosphorus during eggshell formation. It has been suggested that if a high build-up of phosphorus in the blood can be avoided, the hen would be able to withdraw more of the calcium from the bone and improve eggshell quality, This would explain the increase in feed phosphorus levels causing decreased eggshell quality. It also may explain why eggshells are better when phosphorus is removed from the feed in the afternoon, and why eggshell quality is reduced when additional phosphorus is added to the feed in the afternoon (Maurice, 1982; Maurice, 1988; Kim *et al.*, 1995).

A marginal level of phosphorus in the diet may lead to "cage layer fatigue" (osteoporosis). This phosphorus deficiency results in high mortality, with the major portion of this mortality due to "cage fatigue" (Singsen *et al.*, 1962). In their study, diets containing various levels of phosphorus were fed to commercial layers maintained in cages and floor pens. As the level of phosphorus in the diet increased, mortality decreased in the birds maintained in cages. Phosphorus levels in the diet did not influence mortality of hens maintained on the floor.

Minimizing phosphorus levels in also advantageous for maintaining eggshell quality, especially under heat stress conditions. Since phosphorus is very costly nutrient, high levels in the feed are usually not encountered, but limiting this nutrient in the range of 0.3 to 0.4%, depending on flock conditions, seems ideal for maintaining egg quality (Owings *et al.*, 1977; Leeson and Summers, 1983). Unaccountable losses in shell quality may occur occasionally, and some of these may be related to nutrition. For example, vanadium contaminated phosphates cause unusual shell structures, and certain weed seeds, such as those of the lathyrus species, can cause disruption of the shell gland (Holder and Huntley, 1978).

5) Vitamin D and absorption of calcium and phosphorus

Vitamin D has been reported not to be involved in the deposition of calcium, but it has a major role in the absorption of calcium. Phosphate absorption has also been shown to be stimulated by vitamin D. 1-alpha $25(OH)_2D_3$ is transferred to the nucleus of the intestinal cell where it interacts with chromatin. In response, specific RNAs are elaborated by the nucleus. When these are translated into specific proteins by ribosomes, this enhances calcium and phosphorus absorption. The presence of a calcium binding protein is correlated with calcium absorption. This protein does not appear to be a simple transport protein, since calcium absorption is complex and probably requires other factors besides this protein. Calcium seems to be absorbed from the intestine into the mucosal cell by an active transport system and by facilitated diffusion. These mechanisms are both vitamin D dependent (Maurice, 1988; Leeson and Summers, 1992).

When inadequate levels of vitamin D_3 or deficiencies of D_3 are present, induced calcium deficiency results quickly. In addition to the uncomplicated deficiencies of vitamin D_3, certain mycotoxins can create problems. Zearalenones, produced by Fusarium molds, can effectively bind vitamin D_3 and result in poor egg shell quality. Under these circumstances dosing birds with 2000 to 25000 IU of water soluble vitamin D_3 for three consecutive days may be advantageous (Bar and Hurwitz, 1987; Hargis, 1990).

The effect of dietary supplements of vitamin D metabolites on shell strength has been variable. In some experiments, a positive response was obtained with metabolites of vitamin D (McLoughlin and Soares, 1976), while others failed to detect a beneficial response (Roland and Harms, 1976b). This discrepancy may be attributed to age differences since old hens lose their adaptive potential (Bar and Hurwitz, 1987). Exogenous 1, 25-dihydroxy vitamin D was ineffective in altering shell strength in young and old hens (Castaldo and Maurice, 1988).

4. Effects of other nutrients on eggshell formation

1) Dietary electrolyte balance and calcium metabolism

Recently, the impact of dietary mineral (electrolyte) balance on body fluid acid-base and calcium metabolism has been researched. High dietary levels of acidogenic salt (calcium salts of chloride, phosphorus and sulfate) have detrimental effects on shell quality and resulted in acidemia and increased Ca excretion (Austic, 1984). While high dietary levels of phosphorus in dibasic form is a mild acidogenic anion, high dietary levels of phosphorus in monobasic form is a strong acidogenic anion and caused serious adverse effects on performance of the hens.

2) Sodium bicarbonate

The inclusion of sodium bicarbonate in layer feeds at levels of between 1 to 5 kg per metric ton reduced the proportion of downgrade eggs by 1 to 2% (Imperial Chemical Industries, 1987). They concluded that refined sodium bicarbonate had three beneficial effects when added to layer feeds. It:

a. Increased shell strength and cut downgrades
b. Optimized egg production, and
c. Improved utilization of dietary protein.

Their research maintained the balance of sodium (0.14 to 0.28%) and chloride (0.20 to 0.24%) ions by using a non-chloride containing sodium source such as sodium bicarbonate, At a phosphorus level of 0.75%, sodium at 0.55% derived from sodium bicarbonate increased egg output. At a lower phosphorus content of 0.30%, the same addition of sodium from either bicarbonate or chloride decreased egg production (Imperial Chemical Industries, 1987). Studies have also indicated that at high ambient temperatures, carbon dioxide is expired from hens and their bicarbonate levels fell, resulting in poor quality shells unless sodium bicarbonate was added.

— Salt

Sodium chloride is predominantly a feed additive and the contribution from drinking water varies with the area. Egg production was reduced by more than 10% when NaCl in the feed exceeded 2%, and shell strength was maintained even at 6% NaCl in the diet for 3 weeks (Damron and Kelly, 1987). In contrast, chickens provided 1 to 2% NaCl in the drinking water ceased laying (Heller, 1931). Layers are extremely sensitive to the NaCl level in the drinking water.

A study involving a dose-response examination of NaCl concentrations between 0 and 600 ml/l identified a significant linear increase in eggshell defects and corresponding linear decreases in various eggshell quality measurements with increasing NaCl concentrations (Balnave and Yoselewitz, 1987). However, the increased incidence of eggshell damage was not related to decreased feed intake or increased egg production or egg weight. It has also been found that administering a commercial electrolyte replacer containing 2.2 g NaCl and 4 g potassium citrate/l of drinking water for 7 days significantly increased the incidence of eggshell defects in 48-and 72-week-old laying hens (Yoselewitz and Balnave, 1989a).

Classification of the types of eggshell damage showed that, irrespective of the NaCl content of the drinking water, the major types of shell damage consisted of fine cracks, hole and star cracks. The incidence of broken and shell-less eggs increased markedly with the presence of NaCl in the drinking water (Yoselewitz and Balnave, 1989b). The poorer eggshell quality from hens receiving saline drinking water is reflected in increased damage during transport to, and during handling at, the packing station.

The impact of saline drinking water on eggshell quality is likely to be most severely felt with breeder flocks and day-old chick production. Artificially inseminated hens receiving drinking water containing 2 g/l NaCl produced significantly fewer day-old chicks than hens receiving unsupplemented water (Zhang et al., 1991). This reduction in day-old chick production was associated with reduced numbers of settable eggs and with lower hatchability of fertile eggs.

Attempts to offset the effects of saline drinking water had no, or only limited, value. In recent studies with ascorbic acid (Balnave and Zhang, 1992) and with zinc-methionine (Moreng et al., 1989) have identified two nutritional procedures for off-setting the adverse effects of saline drinking water on eggshell quality. However, these treatments are preventative rather than remedial in nature. Depending on the economics of production, the best remedy may be desalination of the drinking water (Balnave, 1993).

3) Manganese

The only trace element of concern in commercial layer diet formulation is manganese. Manganese is involved in the synthesis of components of the organic matrix (Leach, 1982), and its deficiency causes changes in the mammillary cores

(Leach and Gross, 1983). Disorganized or impaired mammillary core formation causes low shell strength. Adequate manganese levels are not provided by corn-soybean meal diets and various supplements provide variable bioavailability. High levels of calcium and phosphorus reduce the availability of dietary manganese by preventing its absorption. Manganese availability can also be reduced by vitamin-mineral imbalances. Most of the B vitamins can act as metal chelators. Excess amounts of vitamins used in feed could influence manganese availability.

The manganese requirement under practical conditions to reduce eggshell breakage is considerably higher than the current NRC (1994) recommendation of 20 mg/kg. At 200 mg/kg, shell breakage was reduced 27% in one experiment and switching hens from a low (25 mg/kg) to a high manganese diet reduced shell breakage (Whisenhunt and Maurice, 1985). Laying hens fed 0 to 6400 mg/kg supplementary manganese showed no adverse effects. Shell breakage exhibited a significant quadratic response with minimum shell damage at 400 mg/kg (Maurice, 1982).

4) Protein and amino acids

Excess dietary protein levels in feed may result in increased endogenous acid production. Complete oxidation of one mole of methionine and cystine produces 2 moles of hydrogen ions. These ions are excreted as ammonia ions and acid phosphates resulting in decreased renal resorption of calcium. However, decreasing dietary protein from 18 to 15% at 12 week intervals had no significant effect on shell surface density in four strains of hens fed a practical diet (Ousterhout, 1981). It is also questionable whether reducing methionine intake increases shell quality. Lysine inhibited calcium absorption in one study, yet in another study, neither lysine nor arginine affected the absorption of calcium in the ligated loop preparations of chick intestine. It is unlikely that economically feasible variations in dietary protein and amino acids influence eggshell strength (Wasserman *et al.*, 1957; Sallis and Holdsworth, 1962; Roland, 1980a).

5. Biological, environmental and managerial factors

Several factors can influence shell breakage at various stages of movement of the eggs from the producer to the consumer.

1) Late-day feed deprivation

Deprivation of feed in the latter part of the birds light day may result in broken or cracked eggs. If hens accidentally go off their feed for even four hours, they will produce poorer eggshells the following day, but if they are not fed for 24 hours they will produce poorer shells for the next three days. Full-fed hens consume about 65% of their feed needs in the latter part of the day, but when restricted to a 4 a.m. to noon feeding period, feed consumption quickly rose from 44% of normal the first day to more than 70% the second day (Arrington, 1986). This study showed that eggshell quality fell on the day following feed restriction, but began improving by the sixth day of restriction. Hens normally consume most of their daily feed intake during the second half of the day. Feed deprivation later in the day is therefore more serious since the hen cannot make up for the loss from deprivation.

2) Age of the laying flock

Eggshell quality is influenced by the hen's age. There have been reports of 2.7% breakage during the first month of lay and 13.5% in the 15th month of lay. There was no apparent effect of age on the proportion of breakage that occurred between the hen and the processing plant and the in-plant breakage. Egg size is also affected by age and this may partially explain decreases in eggshell quality after the first laying period. Egg size increases more rapidly than shell weight so there is a concomitant decrease in shell thickness and percent shell. Eggshell quality in older hens may therefore be improved by controlling egg size (Hamilton et al., 1979).

In one study, the average percentage of broken or cracked eggs was not significantly different among three young flock groups (Bell et al., 1983). They noted egg breakage did increase substantially in the youngest group while decreasing substantially in the 60 to 79 week-old group. They also noted that the pattern in the older group of decreasing egg breakage with increasing egg weight paralleled the pattern of increasing eggshell thickness in those eggs. Apparently, they said, increasing egg weight had a positive effect on shell thickness as the birds aged. They also reported that egg weight and shell thickness were significantly different by strain but that overall egg breakage was similar.

By shell thickness, the workers said that the average broken or cracked egg had an average thickness of 0.0330 cm, which was 5.4% thinner than the average sound egg with a thickness of 0.0373 cm, The thinnest shelled eggs (less than 0.0305 cm) had a mean breakage rate 12.3 times that of the thickest shelled eggs (greater than 0.0406 cm). The probability of the thinnest shelled egg breaking before reaching the processing plant was more than 25% (Bell et al., 1983). There was also a significant change in the type of breakage reported as the birds aged. Collision cracks decreased and line cracks increased as the birds aged and the shells thickened. Shell thickness can be controlled through strain selection, proper nutrient formulation and sound housing and other management programs (Bell et al., 1983).

3) Time of day when eggs are laid

Shell quality and breakage are also affected by the time of day that the eggs are laid. Eggs laid in the afternoon have higher specific gravities so their shells are stronger. This factor is related to the shell formation period in hours, since an eggs that stays longer in the uterus will put down a stronger shell (Huges *et al.*, 1986).

4) Temperature

It is known that high environmental temperatures are associated with a decrease in shell quality. The relationship between environmental temperature and shell thickness is curvilinear when the temperature ranges from 26.5 to 35℃. The domestic hen responds to high environmental temperatures by panting to resist rises in body temperature. This panting results in chemical changes in the blood characterized by an increase in pH. There are also decreases in the concentration of blood carbon dioxide (CO_2) and a loss of blood bicarbonate (HCO_3). The physiological state of alkaline blood (increased pH) produced during thermal panting would become life threatening to the hen if allowed to persist. Poultry have evolved compensating processes which help to reduce this rise in blood pH during panting. To prevent alkalosis the bird increases the excretion of blood HCO_3 into the urine. This action by the kidneys is an attempt to maintain the balance of the basic HCO_3 in the blood relative to the blood acid components. The maximum rate of HCO_3 loss from the kidneys occurs approximately two hours after the beginning of heat stress (Summers and Leeson, 1984; Leeson, 1986).

Time of day when eggs are laid, humidity, evaporative coolers, strain of bird, disease, egg collection, processing and packing, and transport also should be considered for strong eggshell formation (Nahm and Chung, 1995).

EGGSHELL PIGMENTATION

1. The major pigment for eggshell color

The pigments present in eggshells are protoporphyrin-IX, biliverdin-IX and its zinc chelate, and occasional traces of coproporphyrin-III (Kennedy and Vevers, 1975). No pigments were found in the white eggshells of the fulmar, imperial pigeon, dipper, roseate, cockatoo and ring-necked parakeet. Other apparently white eggshells contained only protoporphyrin such as with the white stork, Barbary dove, Scops owl and roller. Other shells contained both protoporphyrin and biliverdin such as those from the black-footed penguin, Humbolt's pigeon, mandarin duck and wood pigeon.

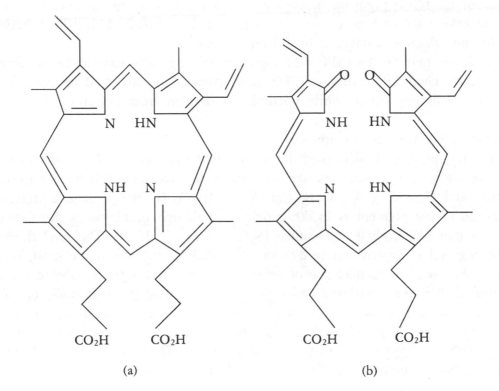

Figure 1. Structures of protoporphyrin-IX (a) and biliverdin-IX (b)

2. Eggshell pigment formation

Porphyrin derivatives play an important role in the biochemistry of all living systems, indeed, they have been called the pigments of life (Battersby, 1985). The porphyrin structure is found in pigments such as chlorophylls and haem. Porphyrins and their derivatives are also present in a wide variety of other biocatalysts, e.g., cytochromes, vitamin B_{12} and prosthetic groups of enzymes whose biosynthesis was likely to be contemporary with the appearance of life on earth (Simioneseu *et al.*, 1978). Porphyrins comprise cyclic tetrapyrrole structures and are related to the parent compound porphine. The most common form of the fifteen possible isomers among four different possible combinations of the side chains on the porphyrin nucleus is protoporphyrin-IX (Fig. 1). In porphine, the methyl, vinyl and propionic acid side chains are replaced by hydrogen atoms. All carbon and nitrogen atoms of the porphyrin ring are derived from glycine and succinic acid.

In contrast, the bile pigments are open chain tetrapyrroles. They are derived in nature by oxidative degradation and ring opening of the prosthetic groups of haemoproteins (Hudson and Smith, 1975). Biliverdin-IX (Fig. 1) is formed by the rupture of the blood pigment, hemoglobin, with the loss of the meso-carbon of the methine bridge (as carbon monoxide). In man and mammals, biliverdin is reduced to bilirubin which is catalyzed by biliverdin reductase.

This shows that the two different pigments of eggshells have different origins, despite their chemical similarities. The porphyrins are synthesized de novo in the cells in which they occur, while biliverdin is derived from erythrocytes.

3. Eggshell pigment distribution

In poultry, pigment is deposited during the entire process of shell formation, but the deposition rate accelerates the last three to five hours before oviposition (Warren and Conrad, 1942; Lang and Wells, 1989). In brown eggs a significant proportion of the pigment is in the cuticle even though porphyrin is distributed in the shell membrane, shell and cuticle (Schwartz et al., 1975). The total thickness of the eggshell is approximately 375 μm. The shell membrane is the most internal layer of the shell and is made up of an inner (15 μm) and outer membrane (50 μm). The true shell is the next layer and is the thickest at 300 μm. It is made up of the cone, palisade and surface crystal layers. The cuticle is the outermost layer with a thickness of only 10 μm (Tullett, 1984). The cuticle acts as the carrier of pigment and the color of eggs is due to this colored coating. The role of the cuticle in this manner is not recognized by the poultry industry.

4. Factors for eggshell pigment formation

1) Blood

The porphyrins found in eggshells are derived from erythrocytes, which are known to synthesize these pigments (Kennedy and Vevers, 1975). There are arguments that the erythrocytes disintegrate in the mucous layer of the shell gland.

2) Shell gland

Examination of the inner surface of the shell gland under ultra-violet light reveals a bright red fluorescence, confined to its epithelial cells (Tamura et al., 1965). The shell gland mucous epithelium secretes pigment granules at different rates depending on the area of the reproductive tract. The secretion begins at a slow rate in the magnum where the albumen is formed. The rate continues to increase in the isthmus and proximal uterus where the shell membrane formation takes place. The rate is the highest in the uterus during shell formation and peaks in the area where the cuticle is formed. The granule formation in the uterine epithelium sharply drops distal to the area of cuticle formation (Tamura and Fujii, 1966). These authors concluded that the large granules contribute to the organic matrix, while the cuticular prophyrin was derived from small pigment granules.

And prophyrin concentration increases during shell formation (Baird *et al.*, 1975). The avian shell gland is the site of biosynthesis of the egg shell porphyrins, but further research is needed (Stevens *et al.*, 1974).

3) Causes of shell pigmentation change

There are several causes of change in eggshell pigmentation.

- Age: The intensity of shell color changes as the hen ages.

- Disease: Disease, such as that caused by infectious bronchitis virus, is known to cause a marked increase in the incidence of pale-shell eggs (Cooke, 1986).

- Drugs: Sharp declines in the shell pigment can occur through ingestion of drugs, such as the coccidiostat Nicarbazin (Schwartz *et al.*, 1975).

- Surface defects due to abnormal post-cuticular deposits (Hulan, 1988).

- The genetic effects on eggshell color

The inheritance of eggshell color in chickens has been of interest to scientist for many years. In their experiments, genetic effects, including single gene or polygene, sex-linkage, dominance, epistasis and heritability and some environmental effects such as season and egg production were investigated.

One study indicated that the inheritance of eggshell pigmentation depended on a large number of genes, each contributing a small amount of the trait (Hunton, 1962; Gowe *et al.*, 1965). And age, hatch group and crosses each contributed significantly to the variation seen in the eggshell color (Wei *et al.*, 1992). Distribution comparisons indicated that two major autosomal loci affected the trait in these lines: one gene having incomplete dominance controls the amount of pigment deposition; the second completely inhibits pigment deposition when homozygous recessive. No sex-linked effects were noted. Another study also suggested that some major genes causing the segregation of shell color seen in brown egg flocks probably had dominance effects based on the higher variance associated with dams as compared with sires (Gowe *et al.*, 1965).

CONCLUSION

Eggs have to compete with other foods since a wide variety of products are becoming available to consumers. The disadvantages of egg consumption are becoming more relevant because the consumer is demanding guarantees for quality. The quality of an egg is a complex relationship between the eggshell strength, shell color, internal quality, cholesterol content, yolk color and egg size.

Between 6 to 8% of the eggs annually produced are broken or cracked, which causes economic losses for the producer, but may also pose a human health hazard via Salmonella contamination. Eggshells break due to the relationship between eggshell quality and many biological, environmental, managerial, and nutritional factors.

In many countries, the color of the eggshell is an important aspect of egg quality so importance should be placed on the biochemical and physiological processes involved in pigment formation and deposition in and on the shell.

Other factors involved in quality egg production will be discussed in the other paper.

ACKNOWLEDGMENTS

I would like to thank Dr. T. Savage (Dept. of Animal Science, Oregon State Univ.), Dr. R. Blair (Dept. of Animal Science, The University of British Columbia), and Dr. B. Winselman-Nahm (Lincolnway Animal Hospital, Matteson, IL) for their criticism and corrections of this manuscript.

REFERENCES

Arias JJ, Fernandez MS 1993 Molecular control of avian eggshell biomineralisation. Proceedings 5th European Symposium on the Quality of Eggs, Tours, France, pp. 116-126.

Arrington L, 1986 Eggshells weakened most by late-day feed deprivation. Feedstuffs, July 14. pp. 15-17, 23.

Austic RE 1984 Excess dietary chloride depress eggshell quality. Poultry Sci 63: 1773-1780.

Austic RE 1996 Dietary Protein levels and the response to dietary amino acids. Cornell Nutr Conf Report pp. 168-181.

Bain ME 1991 Future considerations. In: Eggshell Quality, Wolfe Publication Ltd., London. Chapter 8.

Bain ME 1992 Eggshell strength: a relationship between the mechanism and the ultrastructural organisation of the mammillary layer. Br Poultry Sci 33:303- 319.

Baird T, Solomon SE, Tedstone DR 1975 Localisation and charaterisation of eggshell porphyrin in several avian species. Br Poultry Sci 16:201-208.

Balnave D, Yoselewitz I 1987 The relation between sodium chloride concentration in drinking water and eggshell damage. Br J of Nutrition 58:503-509.

Balnave D 1993 Influence of saline drinking water on eggshell quality and formation. World's Poultry Sci J 49(2):109-119.

Balnave D, Zhang D 1992 Responses in eggshell quality from dietary ascorbic acid supplementation of hens receiving saline drinking water. Aust. J. of Agric. Res. 43:1259-1264.

Bar A, Hurwitz S 1987 Vitamin D metabolism and calbincin (calcium-binding protein) in aged laying hens. J Nutr 117:1775-1779.

Battersby AR 1985 Biosynthesis of the pigments of life. Proc. of the Royal Soc. B225:1.

Bell D, Ernst R, Adams C, Johnson G 1983 Management programs which emphasize strong eggshells and careful handling can keep this breakage at a minimum. Progress in Poultry pp. 23-36.

Blair R 1996 Future of feeding poultry to vary by region, Feedstuffs, Dec. 16. pp. 17-20, 31.

Castaldo DJ, Maurice DV 1988 The role of calcitriol in eggshell strength. Poultry Sci 67:65-71.

Clunies M, Emslie J, Leeson S 1992a Effect of dietary calcium level on medullary bone calcium reserves and shell weight of leghorn hens. Poultry Sci 71: 1348-1356.

Clunies M, Parks D, Leeson S 1992b Calcium and phosphorus metabolism and eggshell thickness in laying hens producing thick or thin shells. Poultry Sci 71:490-498.

Cooke JKA 1986 Pale shelled eggs can be caused by IB virus. Misset International Poultry 2:38-48.

Coon C, Cheng TK 1986 Effect of limestone solubility on layer performance and shell quality. Feedstuffs, Oct. 3. pp. 12-14, 16.

Damron BL, Kelly LS 1987 Short-term exposure of laying hens to high dietary sodium chloride levels. Poultry Sci 66:825-831.

El Boushy AR, Raterink R 1985 Eggshell strength: The causes of egg breakage in relation to nutrition, management and environment. Feedstuffs, Aug. 12. pp. 7-9, 32.

El Boushy AR, Raterink R 1989 Various aspects of egg yolk pigmentation explored. Feedstuffs, Jan. 30. pp. 41-48. Cited in Romanoff and Romanoff (1949), Cited in Williams et al. (1963), Cited in Nakaue et al. (1966), Cited in Netke(1976).

Gowe RS, Budde HW, McGann PJ 1965 On measuring eggshell color in poultry breeding and selection programs. Poultry Sci 44:264-270.

Hamilton RMG, Hollands KG, Viosey PW, Grunder AA 1979 Relationship between eggshell quality and shell breakage and factor that affect shell breakage in the field. World's Poultry Sci J 35(3):177-185.

Hargis PS 1990 Dietary modification of fatty acid composition of shell eggs. Proceedings of fat and cholesterol reduced foods. Mar. 22-24. New Orleans, LA, IBC USA. Inc., 8 Pleasant St., Bldg. D. South Natick, Mass. 01760.

Harms RH, Darmron BL, Waldroup PW 1965 Influence of high phosphorus in caged layer diets. Poultry Sci 44:1249-1254.

Heller VG 1931 Oklahoma's water supply. Report of Oklahoma A & M College Agric. Expt. Sta. pp. 181-183.

Hincke MT, Bernard AM, Lee ER, Tsang CPW, Narbaitz R 1992 Soluble protein constituents of the domestic fowl's eggshell. Br Poultry Sci 33:505-516.

Holder DP, Huntley DM 1978 Influence of added manganese, magnesium, zinc and calcium level on eggshell quality. Poultry Sci 57:1629-1639.

Hudson MF, Smith KM 1975 Bile pigments. Chem. Soc Rev 4:363-399.

Huges BO, Gilbert AB, Brown MF 1986 Categorization and causes of abnormal eggshells: relationship with stress. Br Poultry Sci 27:325-337.

Hulan HW 1988 Redfish meal oil raises fatty acid level of poultry meat. Feedstuffs, April 11. pp. 13, 15, 17.

Hurwitz S, Bar A 1971 The effect of pre-laying mineral nutrition on the development performance and mineral metabolism of pullets. Poultry Sci 50:1044-1050.

Hunton P 1962 Genetics of eggshell color in a light Sussex flock. Br Poultry Sci 3:189-193.

Imperical Chemical Industries(ICI) 1987 Sodium bicarbonate boosts egg production shell strength. Feedstuffs, Aug. 10. pp. 16-18, 27. Cited in Choi and Han, 1987.

Kennedy GY, Vevers HG 1975 A survey of avian eggshell pigments. Compar Biochem and Phys 558:117-123.

Keshavarz K 1987a Interaction between calcium and phosphorus in laying hens. Nutr Rep Int 36:9-16.

Keshavarz K 1987b Influence of feeding a high calcium diet for various durations in prelaying period on growth and subsequent performance of white Leghorn pullets. Poultry Sci 66:1576-1583.

Keshavarz K 1995 An overview of calcium and phosphorus nutrition of growing pullets and laying hens. Proceedings 1995 Cornell Nut. Conf., Oct. 24-26. pp. 161-170.

Keshavarz K, Ackerman SE 1984 On farm survey finds calcium formation problems. Feedstuffs 56(24):18-20, 25.

Keshavarz K, Ackerman SE, Park KS 1991 How uniformly are the particulated sources of calcium distributed along the feeding line? Feedstuffs, Oct. 6. pp. 12-14, 25.

Keshavarz K, McCormick CC 1991 Effect of sodium aluminosilicate, oyster shell and their combinations on acid-base balance and eggshell quality. Poultry Sci 70:313-319.

Keshavarz K, Nakajima S 1993 Re-evaluation of calcium and phosphorus requirement of laying hens for optimum performance and eggshell quality. Poultry Sci 72: 144-149.

Keshavarz K, Scott ML, Blanchard J 1993 The effect of solubility and particle size of calcium sources on shell quality and bone mineralization. J Appl Poult Res 2:259-264.

Kim DJ, Myang WJ, Nahm KH, Ko YD, Chang MB 1995 A Textbook of Feed Resources (Korean edition). Hyang Mun Pub. Co., Seoul, Korea. pp. 324-354.

Krampits G 1993 Molecular mechanisms of eggshell formation. Proceedings of 5th

European Symposium on the Quality of Eggs. Tours, France. pp. 99-109.

Kuit AR 1984 Egg's interior quality. Feedstuffs, Sept. 24. pp. 14-16.

Lang MR, Wells JW 1989 A review of eggshell pigmentation. World's Poultry Sci J 43:238-246.

Leach RM 1982 Biochemistry of the organic matrix of the eggshell. Poultry Sci. 61:2040-2049.

Leach RM, Gross JR 1983 The effect of manganese deficiency upon the ultrastructure of the eggshell. Poultry Sci 62:499-517.

Leeson S 1986 Nutritional considerations of poultry during heat stress. World's Poultry Sci J 42:69-76.

Leeson S, Summers JD 1983 Performance of laying hens allowed self-selection of various nutrients. Nutr. Rep. Int. 27:837-844.

Lesson S, Summers JD 1992 Commercial Poultry Production. Guelf University Press, ON. Canada. (1st Ed.).

Maurice DV 1982 Dietary manganese and eggshell quality. Proc. Maryland Nutrition Conference, U. of Maryland. pp. 90-96.

Maurice DV 1988 Diet and eggshell strength. 49th Minnesota Nutri. Conf., Sept. 19. pp. 212-223.

McLoughlin CP, Soares JP Jr 1976 A study of the effects of 25-hydroxycholecalciferol and calcium source on eggshell quality. Poultry Sci 55:1400-1409.

Miles RD, Harms RH 1982 Relationship between egg specific gravity and plasma phosphorus from hens fed different dietary calcium, phosphorus and sodium levels. Poultry Sci 61:175-181.

Miller ER, Harms RH, Wilson HR 1979 Cyclic changes in serum phosphorus of laying hen. Poultry Sci 56:586-593.

Moreng RE, Balnave D, Zhang D 1992 Dietary zinc methionine effect on eggshell quality of hens drinking saline water. Poultry Sci 71:1163-1167.

Nahm KH, Chung KK, Go YD, Kim DH, Kim YK 1997 Animal Nutrition (Korean edition). Yu Han Pub. Co..

Nahm KH, Chung SB 1995 A Textbook of Chicken Production (English edition). MunDang Pub. Co., Seoul, Korea.

National Research Council 1994 Nutrient Requirements of Poultry. 9th Revised Ed. National Academy Press, Washington, D. C..

Ousterhout LE 1981 The effects of phased feeding protein and calcium on egg weight and shell quality with four strains of white Leghorn hens. Poultry Sci 60:1036-1042.

Owings WJ, Sell JJ, Balloun SL 1977 Dietary phosphorus needs of laying hens. Poultry Sci 50:2056-2062.

Potts PL, Washburn KW 1974 Shell evaluation of white and brown egg strains by deformation, breaking strength, shell thickness and specific gravity. Poultry Sci

53:1123-1129.

Richards JF, Swanson MH 1965 The relationship of egg shape to shell strength. Poultry Sci 44:1555-1558.

Roland DA Sr 1980a Eggshell quality. I. Effect of dietary manipulations of protein, amino acids, energy and calcium in aged hens on egg weight, shell weight, shell quality and egg production. Poultry Sci 59 (in press).

Roland DA Sr 1980b Eggshell quality. II. Effect of dietary manipulations of protein, amino acids, energy and calcium in young hens on egg weight, shell weight, shell quality and egg production. Poultry Sci 59:2047-2052.

Roland DA Sr, Farmer M 1984 Importance of time of calcium intake with emphasis on broilers breeders. World's Poultry Sci J 40(3):255-260.

Roland DA Sr, Harms RH 1972 Calcium metabolism in the laying hen. Poultry Sci 52:369-378.

Roland DA Sr, Harms RH 1976a The influence of feeding diets containing different levels of phosphorus. Poultry Sci 55:637-642.

Roland DA Sr, Harms RH 1976b The lack of response of 25-hydroxy vitamin D_3 on eggshell quality or other criteria on laying hens. Poultry Sci 55:1983-1989.

Roland DA Sr, Sloan DR, Harms RH 1953 Effects of various levels of calcium with and without pellet-size limestone on shell quality. Poultry Sci 53:662-670.

Sallis JD, Holdsworth ES 1962 Influence of vitamin D_3 on calcium absorption in the chick. Am J Physiol 203:497-503.

Schwartz S, Stephenson BD, Sarkar DH, Bracho MA 1975 Red, white and blue eggs as models of porphyrin and heme metabolism, Annals of New York Academy of Sciences 244:570-588.

Scott M 1991 How can calcium be supplied to high-producing hens? Feedstuffs, Sept. 3. pp. 16-17.

Scott ML, Hull SJ, Mullenhoff PA 1971 The calcium requirement of laying hens and effects of dietary oyster shell upon eggshell quality. Poultry Sci 50: 1055-1063.

Scott ML, Nesheim MC, Young RJ 1982 Nutrition of the Chicken. 3rd ed. Ithaca, N. Y., M. L. Scott.

Simioneseu CI, Mora R, Simionescu BC 1978 Porphyrins and the evolution of biosystems. Bioelectrochemistry and Bioenergetics 5:1-17.

Simons PCM 1971 Ultrastructure of the hen egg shell and it physiological interpretation. Agriculture Center, Publication and Documentation, Wageningen, The Netherlands.

Singsen EP, Spandorf AH, Matterson LD, Sorafin JA, Tlustohwicz JJ, 1962. Phosphorus in the nutrition of adult hens. Poultry Sci 41:1401-1410.

St. Louis ME, Morse DL, Potter ME, Guzewich JJ, Blake PA 1988 The emergence of grade A eggs as a major source of Salmonella enteritidis infections. J Am Med Ass 259:2103.

Stevens EV, Miller LK, Weinsteins S, Kappas A 1974 Biosynthesis of 5- aminolevulinic acid and porphbilinogen in the domestic fowl. Comp Biochem and Phys 478: 779-789.

Summers JD, Leeson S 1984 Poultry Nutrition Handbook. The University of Guelph, ON. Canada.

Tamura T, Fujii S 1966 Histological observations on the quail oviduct, on the secretions in the mucous epithelium of the uterus. J. of Faculty of Fisheries and Animal Husbandry. Hiroshima Univ 6:357-371.

Tamura T, Fujii S, Kunisake H, Yamane M 1965 Histological observations on the quail oviduct; with reference to pigment in the uterus. J. of Faculty of Fisheries and Animal Husbandry, Hiroshima Univ 6:37-57.

Taylor TG 1965 Dietary phosphorus and eggshell thickness in the domestic fowl. Br Poultry Sci 6:70-79.

Tullett SG 1984 The porosity of avian eggshells. Comp. Biochem. And Phys. 78A:5-13.

Voisey, P. W. and R. M. G. Hamilton, 1976 Notes on the measurement of egg specific gravity to estimate egg shell quality. Report 7322-598. Engineering Research Service, Agriculture, Ottawa, Canada.

Voisey PW, Hunt JR 1974 Measurement of eggshell strength. J. of Texture Studies 5:135-182.

Warren DC, Conrad RM 1942 Time of pigment deposition in brown shelled hen eggs and in turkey eggs. Poultry Sci 21:515-520.

Wasserman RH, Comar CL, Schooley JC, Lengemann FW 1957 Interrelated effects of L-lysine and other dietary factors on the gastrointestinal absorption of calcium 45 in the rat and chick. J Nutr 62:367-370.

Wei R, Bitgood JJ, Dentine MR 1992 Inheritance of tinted eggshell colors in white shell stocks. Poultry Sci 71:406-418.

Whisenhunt JE, Maurice DV 1985 Effect of dietary manganese and phosphorus on the strength of avian eggshell. Nutr Rep Int 31:757-762.

Wideman RF Jr, Closser JA, Roush WB, Cowen BS 1985 Urolithiasis in pullets and laying hens: Role of dietary calcium and phosphorus. Poultry Sci 64: 2300-2311.

Yoselewitz I, Balnave D 1989a Electrolyte replacer and eggshell quality. In: Recent Advances in Animal Nutrition in Australia 1989. (Ed. Farrell, D. J.). U. of New England, NSW, Australia. P. 1A.

Yoselewitz I, Balnave D 1989b Classification of eggshell damage resulting from the use of normal and saline drinking water. Proceedings of Australian Poultry Science Symposium. p. 90.

Zhang D, Moreng RE, Balnave D 1991 Reproductive performance of artificially inseminated hens receiving saline drinking water. Poultry Sci 70:776-779.

A Strategy for Quality Poultry Egg Production

II. Egg Interior Quality, Cholesterol Content, Egg Yolk Pigmentation, Controlling Egg Weight and Organic Eggs

K. H. Nahm

Feed and Nutrition Laboratory, College of Natural Resources, Taegu University, Gyong San 712-714, South Korea

ABSTRACT: The egg's interior quality is the most important criteria for commercial producers and consumers. Internal quality is complex, including aesthetic factors such as taste, freshness, nutritional and processing values, and the genetic influences upon these factors ranges from none to considerable. The rate of cholesterol synthesis in the hen is very high compared to other animals and humans. Genetic selection, diet, drugs and other chemicals can alter cholesterol concentration in the plasma of laying hen, but attempts to manipulate the cholesterol concentration in the egg yolk are generally unsuccessful since the cholesterol can only be changed to a small extent. Factors which may affect the degree of pigmentation of the yolk include the type of xanthophyll and its concentration in the feed, the feed composition, and the health of the hen. Several feed ingredients interact with carotenoid pigment to improve or reduce their deposition rates in yolks. Egg weight is determined by genetics, body size prior to first egg housing density, environmental temperature, lighting program, total feed consumption, calcium, phosphorus, niacin, water, methionine, total sulfur amino acids, energy, linoleic acid, fat and protein levels. Eggs need to be promoted as a versatile commodity and new processed egg items need to be developed. Organic eggs are laid by hens that are raised in chemical and drug free environments. There are still difficulties in producing these eggs due to the availability of organic poultry feeds and the cost of organic grains.

(Key words: Egg quality; Cholesterol; Egg pigmentation; Egg weight; Organic eggs)

INTRODUCTION

The 21st century will mean more people demanding higher-quality diets. One of the major difference that will be apparent between the egg products industry of today and that of the year 2000 will be the emphasis on the product safety and quality. This change will be brought about by more stringent consumer requirements and sophisticated in-house quality control (Nahm, 1996). In the developed nations like North America, UK, European countries and Australia where heart disease is responsible for half of annual mortality, quality egg products which contain low cholesterol, low fat or are fat free and high in omega-fatty acids would be in demand. As a result of this, Blair (1996) said that there is likely to be an increased recognition of niche markets and the development of products such as omega eggs with altered fatty acid content to meet specific consumer demands.

Generally, quality egg production involves strong eggshells, eggshell pigmentation, reducing cholesterol content, yolk pigmentation favorable for consumers and marketing, controlling egg weight and developing the concept of 'organic eggs.'

This review paper is the second of a series entitled "Factors to be considered for quality egg production", and it describes methods to reduce the cholesterol content of eggs, yolk pigmentation favorable for consumers and marketing, controlling egg weight and developing the concept of 'organic eggs.'

EGG QUALITY

1. Interior quality of eggs

The egg's interior quality is what is the most important for commercial producers, processors, traders and consumers. Interior quality is complex, including aesthetic factors such as taste, freshness, nutrition and processing values, and the genetic influences upon these factors ranges from none to considerable.

1) The visible characteristics and flavor

Aesthetic factors of the egg's interior quality are divided into visible characteristics, odor and taste. Albumin and yolk color, inclusions such as blood and meat spots, and the yolk's position are the most obvious visible concerns. Blood and meat spots have been shown to he heritable characteristics, with significant differences existing between breeds. Blood spots are more common in white-egg layers and meat spots are found more commonly in brown-egg layers. There has been no connection found between albumin firmness or genetics and the yolk's position, but storage conditions do affect the position (Kuit, 1984).

As for the flavor or taste, the concept of positive flavor is disputed. Studies

(Sim and Bragg, 1977; Hargis, 1990) have shown that hens vary by strain and within strain in the ability to break down trimethylamine from feed ingredients into a neutral product. Failure to neutralize this compound results in an odor or taste in the egg.

2) Freshness

Freshness means that the egg does not contain a visible embryo. More specifically, freshness involves albumin quality, degree of moisture loss, degree of oxidation and microbiological status. The latter three factors are affected most by eggshell quality and storage conditions and time. Egg freshness has been traditionally associated with the albumin height. Research dating back twenty years demonstrated that strain, laying stage and storage conditions affect albumin height. The genetic influence on albumin height is moderate while the genetic role in interior quality is minor (Nahm and Chung 1995).

3) Nutrition

The egg is considered an excellent food for most people, since it is an excellent source of iron, phosphorus, trace minerals, unsaturated fatty acid and vitamin A, B, D, E and K, especially vitamins B_{12} and D. The egg is the standard or perfect protein, yet it is the least expensive protein food (Nahm et al, 1997).

The effects of methionine intake on liquid egg component yield and composition were examined (Shafer et al., 1996). They reported that the 512 mg methionine/hen -day (HD) intake significantly increased the egg weight, component mass and total solids in both albumin and yolk compared to 326 mg methionine/HD. And methionine intakes of 392 and 423 mg/HD did result in significantly increased crude protein contents of albumin and yolk compared to 328 and 354 mg/HD methionine.

2. Food safety and egg quality

The emergence of *Salmonella enteritidis* as a public health concern in the past decade has important consequences for the egg industry. Salmonella has historically been linked to poultry consumption and may cause flu-like symptoms, and worse, it may be fatal.

A variety of techniques may be implemented in egg production programs which can result in low incidences of Salmonella. Of the 2500 types of salmonella bacteria, only one- *Salmonella enteritidis* is associated with eggs.

The American Egg Board (AEB) recommended the following safety tips to protect against Salmonella poisoning.
- Avoid eating raw eggs. Cook to destroy the bacteria.
- When separating eggs, do not pass from shell to shell. Use an egg separator to

ensure safety.
- When coloring hard-boiled eggs, always wash your hands.

1) Eggshell quality

Eggshell breakage is a continuous source of frustration for producers and irritation for consumers. The eggs are much more likely to be contaminated due to bacterial invasion from the shell contamination. The two factors that determine if an egg will crack are the strength of the insult and the strength of the shell. The insults to the egg are random and unpredictable, and each event leading to the cracking of an egg is unique and difficult to study or analyze.

On the other hand, shell quality and the factors that affect it have been extensively studied. The role of calcium in eggshell formation has provided and several researchers have reported that oyster shell was superior as a source of calcium than calcium carbonate of mineral origin (Scott *et al.*, 1982). Genetics, mycotoxins, molting and other environmental stresses on the shell structure and quality are important in eggshell formation. The structure of each shell results from a unique combination of these and other factors. Fertile eggs have no documented nutritional benefit other than revenue to the producer. The type of egg, such as brown, organic or fertile, has no effect on shelf life. Eggs should be stored in a refrigerated enclosure. They can pick up odors from the food stored next to them (Nahm and Chung, 1995).

2) Washing shell eggs to increase quality

Washing shell eggs was in the past widely condemned due to increased spoilage during storage. At the same time, it is clearly necessary to wash soiled eggs, both because of their appearance and the shell surface contamination that exists when the egg contents when they were broken out. It was then determined that spoilage occurred when eggs were washed in water colder than the egg contents. This caused the egg contents to contract and draw bacteria through the pores into the interior. When eggs were washed in water warmer than the egg contents, this effect did not occur and washing of eggs was not detrimental to quality (Moats, 1978). Presently, washing eggs in universally practiced and even required by regulatory agencies.

Alkaline egg cleaning formulations are used in commercial egg washers and these give a pH of almost 11 in the wash water. During operations, the wash water is recirculated and becomes contaminated with the contents of broken eggs. manure and other soils washed from the egg. The wash water must be continuously diluted by rinse water and allowed to overflow during the course of the operation. Some operators add additional cleaning formula at intervals to compensate for dilution. The wash water is completely replaced at certain intervals, usually at the end of each shift (Moats, 1981a).

It used to be thought that Salmonella bacteria on the shell surface contaminated the contents of the egg. Now it appears that some eggs contain Salmonella when they are laid. The number of bacteria on the shell have been counted by removing the egg contents and grinding the shells in a blender to release bacteria imbedded in the pores. Moats (1978, 1979, 1981b) and Kinner and Moats (1981b) reported that: bacteria on the shell surface were effectively removed by ordinary washing; bacteria embedded in the shell pores were not removed by washing and were also unaffected by rinsing the shells with chlorinated sanitizers; bacterial numbers on the shells after washing were not correlated with numbers in the wash water; and bacterial numbers on the shells after washing were correlated with numbers on the equipment surfaces. They also reported that thorough cleaning of equipment surfaces is necessary. The alkaline egg cleaners were found by these researchers to be effective in killing Salmonella and *Escherichia coli* bacteria at normal egg washer temperatures. It is important to maintain levels of the cleaning formulation in the wash water to keep the pH at 10 or higher. The chlorine in chlorinated egg cleaning formulations is rapidly inactivated in wash water, indicating that the use of chlorinated egg cleaning formulations would be of no benefit under commercial conditions. Use of a chlorinated rinse following washing was no more effective than a water rinse in removing bacteria. Bacteria not removed by washing were not susceptible to a chlorinated rinse.

Some washing procedures have also been found to damage the protective cuticle layer on the surface of the egg shell. which resists bacterial penetration. This is not a problem unless the eggs become wet during storage. Since eggs are dried and packed after washing they are not likely to be exposed to water containing bacteria.

3) Problems with eggshell types and within eggs

Good laying hens when properly cared for can lay up to 300 eggs in a year. With such a large number of eggs being produced, it should not be surprising that some abnormalities in the egg producing mechanism may occur which results in problems with eggshell types (flat sided eggs, body-check eggs, pimples or calcium spots, stained or discolored eggs, soft shelled and shell-less eggs, misshapen eggs) and problems within eggs (blood and meat spots, mottled egg yolks, milky white eggs, double and triple yolked eggs, eggs within an egg, roundworms in eggs) (Nahm and Chung, 1995).

CHOLESTEROL CONTENT OF EGGS

For many years the general public has been told that cholesterol is a major killer and that food high in cholesterol such as eggs should be avoided. This has been extremely damaging to the egg industry. Many national heart foundations have recognized their serious error and now recommend four eggs be consumed by each person per week. It is now known that dietary cholesterol is not an important risk factor for 98% of the population. There are many other important factors such as the amount and nature of the fat in the diet.

Greenland Eskimos consume almost twice as much cholesterol in their diet than their neighbor the Dane, but the incidence of heart disease related deaths is almost seven times higher in the Dane. The answer to this fact lies in the source and nature of the fat consumed by each group. Dutch scientists have found that people who consume 32g of fish daily are 50% less likely of dying from coronary heart disease than those who did not consume fish (Band and Dyerburg, 1972).

1. Egg lipid synthesis and composition

The average egg of 60 g contains approximately 6 g of lipid, which is almost wholly confined to the yolk. Consistent patterns of egg laying involve the sequential maturation of the ova or yolk at approximately 24 h intervals. With the approach of the onset of egg laying, both the weight and lipid content of the liver undergo dramatic increases (Band and Dyerburg, 1972).

The changes in the liver lipid levels are in response to the lipid requirements for egg production and are manifested through extensive and interrelated hormone changes (Miettinen, 1971). The gross lipid changes are accompanied also by changes in fatty acid composition (Balnave, 1970). The accumulation of lipid in the liver largely occurs through a stimulation of fatty acid and lipid synthesis which, in contrast to mammals, is predominantly associated with the liver rather than the adipose tissue (Hargis and Van Elswyk, 1993). The liver lipid changes are accompanied by marked increases in the concentrations of plasma lipids, in particular triglycerides.

Almost all the lipid of the yolk exists in the lipoprotein form. The overall lipid protein ratio of the yolk is about 2:1. Extractable lipid accounts for about 33% of the total weight of the yolk and 60 to 65% of its dry matter content. The major yolk lipid fraction is triglyceride (63.1%), which is accompanied by a substantial quantity of phospholipid (29.8%); the only other major component is free cholesterol (4.9%) and cholesteryl esters (1.3%)(Moore, 1989; Hargis, 1990).

The fatty acid compositions of the major lipid factions (triglyceride) are oleic acid (40.1%), palmitic acid (29.1%) and linoleic acid (18.0%). The phospholipid fraction contains a high level of other PUFA (Beitz, 1990).

About 5% of the yolk fat is free cholesterol and it is accompanied by approximately 1% of the cholesterol in an esterified form. By comparison, the free cholesterol level in liver fat is approximately 8% which, with the addition of that present in the esterified form, gives a proportion of total cholesterol in liver fat of nearly twice that of the egg yolk. Comparisons of the individual and total PUFA levels in the yolk and liver are also interesting. The level of linoleic acid in the yolk is approximately 16% of the total fatty acids, which, with the addition of C_{18}, C_{20}, and C_{22} PUFA give a total PUFA content of some 20%. By comparison, the levels of linoleic and total PUFA in the fat of the liver, 7 and 13% respectively, are only about one-half that for egg yolk fat. Of the remainder of the fatty acids in the yolk, mono-unsaturates account for approximately 46% and saturates 34%. Thus, yolk fat can be considered as predominantly unsaturated (Griffin, 1990; Richardson and Jimenez-Flores, 1990).

A recent parameter of PUFA adequacy in the diet is the ratio of total polyunsaturated to saturated fatty acids (the P/S ratio). As an objective to healthy eating is was suggested that a higher P/S ratio 0.32 be consumed (Hargis and Vans Elswyk, 1993; Farrell, 1997).

2. Regulation of cholesterol production in the human body

Human beings, as well as other higher animals, make their own body supply of cholesterol from acetate, a simple two-carbon molecule produced from energy yielding nutrients and metabolites.

When the energy inputs from nutrients such as protein, carbohydrate and fat are in excess, acetate is also generated in excess. As a result, there is a larger acetate supply that is used for making fatty acids and cholesterol. Body fat is produced from the fatty acids and this results in body weight gain. Interestingly, obese subjects make 20% more cholesterol per unit of body weight than normal subjects (Miettinen, 1971). Obesity is related to increased cholesterol production in humans. Excessive cholesterol production in humans may be avoided by maintaining proper body weight.

Acetate has a more specific role in the regulation of cholesterol in the body. A complex chemical mechanism in the body converts acetate molecules into cholesterol, but a control point exists at which the enzyme HMG-Co A reductase is essential in controlling cholesterol production. Hormones such as insulin and glucagon influence this mechanism, but it is also affected by intermediate products leading to cholesterol production. Cholesterol itself has a very important role in limiting the activity of this enzyme and therefore exerts feedback control on body cholesterol production (Hargis, 1990).

Normally the body regulates cholesterol production by making more cholesterol in response to lowered body levels of cholesterol. When dietary cholesterol is reduced, the body would respond by increasing cholesterol production. Limiting dietary cholesterol would not result in limited body and blood cholesterols when cholesterol regulation is normal. Abnormalities in cholesterol metabolism in humans are related to cholesterol carriers or receptors and inadequate regulation of HMG-CoA reductase resulting in elevated blood and tissue cholesterol levels. Limiting dietary cholesterol under these abnormal conditions may help to reduce blood cholesterol levels.

Liver and intestinal synthesis in the body contributes about twice as much cholesterol as does the normal human diet, 800 versus 400 mg per day. This means that changes in dietary cholesterol intake would be expected to be compensated for by changes in synthesis of cholesterol by the body (Hargis, 1990; Moore, 1989).

Cholesterol balance is also controlled by outputs. This involves the conversion of cholesterol in the liver to neutral sterols and bile acids that are released into the intestine and recycled or excreted from the body. Loss in the feces is compensated for by inputs from diet and synthesis. Drugs that reduce blood cholesterol reduce liver synthesis of cholesterol or increase conversion to and excretion of bile acids and neutral sterols (Griffin, 1990).

An egg yolk contains an average of 5 g of fat. Cholesterol contents depend on the egg with a small egg containing 160 mg and a jumbo egg containing 270 mg. The National Cholesterol Education Program in the U. S. recommends less than 300 mg of cholesterol be consumed each day, so three or four egg yolks should he eaten weekly (ANON, 1989; Froning, 1991).

3. Egg cholesterol resists change

The normal diet of the laying hen contains little or no cholesterol since most of the ingredients are products of plant origin. Despite some notable exceptions, most published studies indicate that the amount of cholesterol in the egg yolk is relatively resistant to change. The rate of cholesterol synthesis in the hen is very high compared to other animals and humans. This is a point in that cholesterol balance in laying hens is very different from humans. This cholesterol input side of the balance is driven almost entirely by a high rate of liver synthesis in normal laying hens. The major output of cholesterol by the hen is transport of cholesterol and ovarian transport to the egg. Smaller amounts of output occur in bile acids and sterols in the feces (Vargas *et al.*, 1986).

The cholesterol content of the egg is regulated mainly by the rate of cholesterol synthesis in the hen, so factors that might regulate synthesis in the hen may be expected to influence the cholesterol in the egg. The manner in which the cholesterol output into the eggs takes place also influences cholesterol content to a minor degree. Larger eggs that have large yolks have higher cholesterol contents than small eggs with small yolks. Hens producing more eggs will lay eggs containing less cholesterol than hens with lower rates of production. The number and size of ova undergoing rapid development in the ovary affects the cholesterol output of individual yolks (Weiss *et al.*, 1967).

Most of the cholesterol in the yolk (> 90%) is present as free (non-esterified) cholesterol in the lipoprotein of the yolk. Almost all of the cholesterol in the body of the hen and in the egg is synthesized in the liver of the hen as a response to estrogen and is transported by the blood to the ovary. The lipoproteins and other yolk precursors pass into the capillaries of the developing follicles. They pass through the various tissues (the capillaries in the thecal layer, the basal lamina layer and between the granulosa cells before binding to the oocyte plasma membrane) that form the follicle wall and are taken up into the oocyte (yolk) through receptor-mediated endocytosis (Fig. 1) (Griffin, 1990).

The lipid composition of the yolk is determined by the lipid composition of the individual lipoproteins since the plasma lipoproteins are taken up into the yolk intact. The affinity of the lipoprotein receptors on the oocyte plasma membrane is high. Plasma lipoprotein concentration does not affect the rate of uptake of yolk precursors from the plasma and their concentration in the yolk. Cholesterol, phospholipid and protein combine to stabilize the surface of the lipoprotein (Fig. 2) (Froning *et al.*, 1990; Griffin, 1990).

The resistance of yolk cholesterol to change may be due to the specific needs of the embryo. Studies on the lipid metabolism, however, suggest that the amount of cholesterol in the yolk is greater than the need for chick growth. There is also no reason why the embryo cannot synthesize its own cholesterol (Hargis, 1990; Froning, 1991).

Lipoproteins synthesized in the liver of the layer are unusually small and regular in size. This is important in allowing them to pass through the basal lining of the follicle wall. The connective tissue of this layer acts like a selective filter that allows the small yolk precursors to pass through but excludes from the yolk the larger lipoproteins synthesized in the intestine. Variation in the lipoprotein surface area: volume ratios (and cholesterol contents, since cholesterol is a surface component) is limited by the synthesis of small lipoproteins by the liver (Griffin, 1990).

4. Changing egg cholesterol by dietary alterations

Genetic selection and diet can alter cholesterol concentration in the plasma of laying hens but these effects seem to be due to changes in lipoprotein concentrations rather than lipoprotein composition. Eggs from hens fed diets containing 30% vegetable oil contained significantly more cholesterol than did those from hens on a low fat control diet. It was later established that high levels of dietary unsaturated fat stimulate the hen to synthesize more cholesterol in the liver and to deposit increased amounts in the egg (Naber, 1983).

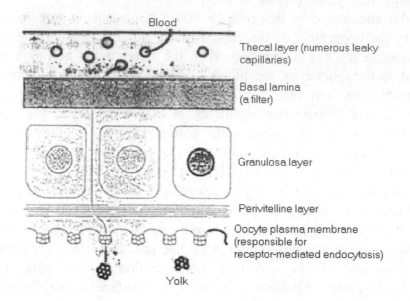

Figure 1. Cross-section through the wall of the ovarian follicle (a copy reproduced by kind permission of H. D. Griffin, Roslin Institute, UK).

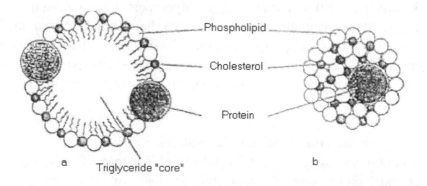

Figure 2. Structure of triglyceride-rich lipoproteins, with non-esterified cholesterol, phospholipid and apoptoteins combining to stabilize the lipoprotein surface and triglyceride and cholesterlol esters forming the "core". a. section; b. surface view (a copy reproduced by kind permission of H. D. Griffin, Roslin Institute, Roslin, UK).

While dietary cholesterol increases egg cholesterol, dietary plant sterols may reduce egg cholesterol. The plant sterols contribute to the inhibition of cholesterol absorption in the gut because the fecal excretion of sterol metabolites is enhanced when soysterols and cholesterol are fed (Sim et al., 1980). Two to four percent sitosterol emulsifed in carboxymethylcellulose to make this sterol absorbable had to be used (Clarenburg et al., 1971). And 2% soybean sterols added to laying diets containing 8% coconut oil or safflower oil reduced blood and egg yolk cholesterol concentration (Sim and Bragg, 1977). These scientists found a significant reduction in cholesterol levels in both serum and egg yolk (ranging from 16 to 33% depending upon the lipid in the diet) when 2% soysterols were added to diets containing saturated or unsaturated oil with or without cholesterol. These reductions in yolk cholesterol levels are encouraging but, again, probably not significant in practical terms to the industry. A minimum decrease of 50% in yolk cholesterol to levels ranging from 100 mg to 150 mg cholesterol per egg (one-half the recommended maximum daily intake level of cholesterol) would potentially be of benefit commercially. Still, cholesterol lowering effects in the egg from feeding sitosterol or a mixture of plant sterols could not be demonstrated in several research studies.

There has been an interest in fiber and its relationship to cholesterol in the gastrointestinal tract. Certain types of fibers have been shown to bind with sterols, resulting in increased amounts of them being excreted in the feces and preventing enterohepatic circulation of these sterols. Excessive energy levels in the diet may cause increased cholesterol production. The energy content of the diet may be lowered by addition of fiber, and this limited energy intake may result in reduced cholesterol production, especially if energy intake was previously excessive. Therefore fiber may affect cholesterol metabolism in different ways, depending on the source and level of fiber in the diet (McNaughton, 1978; Vargas and Naber, 1984).

When laying hens were fed varying levels of crude fiber from alfalfa meal, ground oats, sunflower meal, rice mill feed and wood shavings, a statistically significant reduction in egg yolk cholesterol of 6 to 11% was observed from the higher fiber levels employed (McNaughton, 1978). Ground oats and wood shavings seemed to be most effective (9 to 10% reduction). Fractions of barley kernels, including high-protein barley flour, may contain substances which inhibit hepatic cholesterol synthesis. When these feeds were fed to chicks (Beyer, 1991) and laying hens, those that were fed barley produced eggs with less cholesterol that a corn-fed control group (Qureshi et al., 1986).

Yolk cholesterol was correlated to feed intake with body weight gains exceeding 100 g, but was not correlated when weight gains were less than 110 g per day (Beyer, 1991). In egg yolks, there is a physiologically minimum concentration of cholesterol. Increases in this minimum cholesterol level may occur when there is insufficient energy intake to support egg production or when there is excess energy retained in the body. Egg cholesterol concentration can be altered by the energy balance, but the extent of this alteration depends on the magnitude and direction of energy balance change. Thus, when the bird is in positive energy balance, the concentration of egg yolk cholesterol increases. When the hens are losing weight or consuming less than 340 kcal/day, yolk cholesterol is then inversely related to body weight (Vargas et al., 1986).

Other studies have indicated that fatty acid composition of the egg can be substantially changed through the diet of the hen. One study found that wheat to triticale-based diets gave good production of eggs of lower cholesterol content, and that soybean oil supplementation gave eggs with a high unsaturated to saturated fatty acid ratio (Hargis, 1990; Hargis et al., 1991). Several recent studies have shown that feeding hens a diet high in fish oils or fish meal will increase the omega-3 fatty acids (Adams et al., 1989).

5. Effect of processing on yolk composition

Research studies emphasize processing innovations for modification of the yolk's composition. Formulation, organic solvent extraction, enzymatic treatments, use of absorbents, blending of components and super critical fluid extraction are some of the processes that have been studied. Use of organic solvents to remove cholesterol and lipids from the eggs has been attempted. When a hexane: isopropanol (2:1) solvent was used to extract egg oil from the yolk, the cholesterol content was reduced by 40% (Larsen and Froning, 1981). Various organic solvents could extract lipid components from dried egg yolk (Warren and Ball, 1990). Solvents which were tested in this project were hexane, hexane: isopropanol (2:1) and chloroform: methanol (2:1). The results suggested that the more polar solvents removed more of the cholesterol and carotenoid pigments.

The use of cholesterol reductase has been used to generate a low-cholesterol or cholesterol-free food (Beitz, 1990). Cholesterol reductase is found in many biological sources such as alfalfa, cucumbers, peas, young corn, etc. It catalyzes the conversion of cholesterol to coprostanol, which is not absorbed well by humans.

Increased pressure and temperatures enabled the removal of more lipids and cholesterol. Two-thirds of the cholesterol was removed when extraction conditions were elevated (306 atm/45°C or 374 atm/55°C) (Froning et al., 1990). In this study, phospholipids were concentrated under super critical conditions.

In a series of works, scientists (Smith et al., 1995; Awad and Smith, 1996; Awad et al., 1997) have reported that beta-cyclodextrin (CD) could be used to produce a low cholesterol egg product with compositional and functional properties similar to control egg yolks. In previous works, surface methodology was used to optimize a CD process for extraction of cholesterol from liquid egg yolk based on the dissociation and solubilization of the granular fraction at an alkaline pH. CD are cyclic oligosaccharides comprised of seven glucose units that have been found to form complexes with cholesterol (Saenger, 1984).

6. Changing egg cholesterol with drugs and other chemicals

The hypocholesterolemic drugs such as triparanol, azasterols, alpha-ketoisocaproic acid (KIC), and olvastatin are potent inhibitors of the last step of cholesterol synthesis and its inclusion in laying hen diets causes the replacement of cholesterol in yolks with its immediate precursor, desmosterol (Elkin and Rogler, 1989; Luhman et al., 1990). Desmosterol cannot act as a precursor for hormone synthesis as does cholesterol, and as a result the hens rapidly stop laying. Lovastatin acts as an inhibitor of the regulatory coenzyme for cholesterol biosynthesis (3-hydroxy-3-methylglutaryl coenzyme A reductase or HMG-CoA reductase) (Elkin and Rogler, 1989). Even though lovastatin reduces egg cholesterol by 3 to 12% in a dose dependent matter, egg cholesterol reduction by HMG-CoA reductase inhibitiors and KIC has yielded inconsistent results (Elkin and Rogler, 1989; Beyer and Jensen, 1992).

7. Genetic selection to control egg cholesterol

Egg cholesterol levels have been shown to vary with species of bird, breed or strain, as well as age of fowl. One report showed that 3 generations of selection for lower yolk cholesterol of a White Leghorn population was successful and that egg cholesterol levels were reduced 5.4% (or 9 mg/egg) by the third generation (Ansah et al., 1985). In practical terms, these reductions in egg cholesterol of 9 to 10 mg are not significant if an average daily consumption of approximately 250 mg of cholesterol is to be adhered to. The response of several production traits to 5 generations of selection for high and low plasma cholesterol levels was examined in a population of Single Comb White Leghorn hens (Marks and Washburn, 1977). Yolk cholesterol concentrations were significantly reduced (approximately 7%, again not a significant reduction in practical terms) by selection for low plasma cholesterol but were not affected by selection for increased plasma cholesterol.

Selection for lower egg cholesterol has been modest with only a 5 to 7% reduction possible (Hargis, 1993). Some progress may be made through production changes, but this small reduction is unlikely to satisfy the consumers.

8. Manipulation of egg cholesterol content

Manipulation of the cholesterol concentration in the egg yolk is generally unsuccessful since the cholesterol can only be changed to a small extent. In persons that need to reduce their dietary cholesterol, this amount may not contribute significantly to this reduction. Drugs have been shown to be the most consistent in reducing egg cholesterol levels, but these reductions are small. These drugs may potentially harm the chicken, alter the nutrient composition of the egg, lead to drug residues remaining in the egg and increase production costs.

Most people consume a diet that contains 400 to 600 mg of cholesterol per day. In the U.S., the average egg consumption from all sources was 0.67 eggs per person per day in 1988. This means that eggs provide 140 mg of dietary cholesterol per day. If egg cholesterol could be decreased by 10% through any of the methods described previously, the average daily intake would be reduced by only 14 mg, which is insignificant. Changes made to decrease cholesterol levels in eggs will remain meaningless unless the hen could be made to radically reduce the cholesterol levels in her eggs (Froning, 1991).

In patients with artherosclerotic heart disease, total energy intake and saturated fat intake have been shown to affect the blood cholesterol levels. Dietary cholesterol levels appear to have little or no effect on blood cholesterol levels in normal humans, within reasonable limits. Even though egg consumptions per week in three countries (U.S., France and Japan) were 4.2, 4.7, and 6.1 eggs each, the rate of heart problems was lowest in Japan (Poultry Digest, 1997). Dietary changes that contribute most to lowering blood cholesterol levels are first restricting energy intake, then reducing saturated fat intake and finally reducing dietary cholesterol intake would make a relatively insignificant contribution.

Other criticism on the eggs as a contributor of cholesterol is not based on the relative proportion of cholesterol in yolk or on the gross amount of cholesterol provided through the consumption of egg fat, but rather on the gross amount of cholesterol within an arbitrary egg of yolk weight. The mode of presentation of compositional data enables different interpretations to be placed on the cholesterol content of the egg. There are many instances where it has been concluded that the eggs should be considered as a rich source of cholesterol when compared with a range of other common dietary constituents. For example, whereas it has been reported that there are 504 mg of cholesterol in 100 g egg, the figure has also been expressed as 1480 mg cholesterol per 100 g yolk (Findlay and Silberner, 1989). Expressed in either of these ways, the egg appears to provide more cholesterol than all the major red meats of our diet. In the main, however, it is whole eggs that are consumed and when the cholesterol contents of a range of foods are based on average daily dietary consumption, the relative rating of the egg is entirely different (Naber, 1976).

EGG YOLK PIGMENTATION

One of the factors of economic importance to the egg industry is the egg yolk color. Yellow corn, corn gluten meal, dehydrated alfalfa meal, grasses and marigold meal are the most important traditional sources of pigmentation. Synthetic pigments can be added to fed in small quantities to achieve the color desirable to consumers.

Factors which may affect the degree of pigmentation of the yolk include the type of xanthophyll and its concentration in the feed, the feed composition, and the health of the hen. Pigmentation can be altered by respiratory infections and other diseases, and there are certain feed bone meal that can inhibit the formation of pigments. Certain storage conditions can also cause the deterioration of yellow xanthophylls in corn (Braeunlich, 1974).

1. Classification of carotenoids

Carotenoids have been classified into two groups: (1) hydrocarbons containing only hydrogen and carbon, which are called carotenes, and (2) oxygen containing derivatives, called xanthophylls and oxycarotenoids (Henken, 1974).

Carotenoids have also been classified as follows (Martusich and Bauernfeind, 1981):

  a. Vitamin A precursors that do not pigment, such as alpha and beta-carotenes;
  b. Vitamin A precursors that pigment, such as cryptoxanthin, beta-apo-8'-carotenal, and beta-apo-8'-carotenoic acid ethyl ester;
  c. Nonvitamin A precursors that either do not pigment or pigment poorly, such as wiolaxanthin and neoxanthin; and
  d. Nonvitamin A precursors that pigment, such as lutein, zeaxanthin and canthaxanthin.

Carotenoids of type b and d are of significant economic interest in the pigmentation of egg yolks.

Beta-carotene is structurally split at the $15 = 15'$ carbon atoms by the enzyme, beta-15, 15'-dioxygenase yielding two molecules of vitamin A for each molecule of beta-carotene (Goodman and Hyan, 1965). Beta-carotene, which is transformed into vitamin A in the bird body, has no pigmenting activity (Braeunlich, 1974). This scientist also stated that pigmenting carotenoids are mainly found in groups which have no vitamin A activity at all, they are transferred unchanged to the yolk or to the skin.

Carotene ($C_{40}H_{56}$) is a highly unsaturated hydrocarbon. In the yolk it is found in two isomeric forms known as alpha-and beta-carotene (Kim *et al.*, 1995). It is soluble in chloroform and ether, but insoluble in water, acid or alkali. Xanthophylls usually contain at least two hydroxy groups. They are closely related to carotene structurally. Unlike carotene, xanthophylls dissolve readily in alcohol and ethyl ether, but only slightly in petroleum ether. Cryptoxanthin ($C_{40}H_{56}$) is a monohydroxy derivative of beta-carotene. It is difficult to distinguish from beta-carotene and zeaxanthin. Lutein and zeanthin ($C_{40}H_{56}$) are isometric dihydroxy derivatives of alpha-and bera-carotene, respectively. They can be differentiated by lutein's greater solubility in boiling methanol. The various carotenoids differ in their color values (Martusich and Banernfeind, 1981). The xanthophylls, especially lutein and zeaxanthin, are approximately twice as intense in color as the carotenes.

2. Sources of xanthophyll pigments

Green alfalfa, clover and pasture grasses contain a number of xanthophyll pigments in addition to the chlorophyll that gives them their green color. When chlorophyll is removed or destroyed from these leaves, as during exposure to frost in autumn, the yellow and red xanthophylls appear since they are no longer masked by the green of chlorophyll. The most common carotenoid rich plants are corn (mainly zeaxanthin) and grasses (carotene and lutein) (NRC, 1994).

Carotenoids are the red, orange and yellow pigments found in the chloroplasts (chlorophyll granule). The molecules of carotenoids are long and have many conjugated double bonds, which are the chemical basis of color in organic compounds along with other patterns of unsaturation. Even though many carotenoids have been isolated from plants, only a few are found in the yolk of eggs (Karunajeeewa, 1980).

Besides the two carotenes (alpha-and beta-) and the three xanthophylls (cryptoxanthin, lutein and zeaxanthin), traces of other carotenoid pigments have been found in egg yolks, i.e. lycopene (Karunajeewa *et al.*, 1984), flavoxanthin-like compounds and neoxanthin (Chung, 1991). The usual ratio of carotene to xanthophyll in the egg yolk is 1:10.

Of all the common poultry feedstruffs, only dehydrated alfalfa, lucerne meal, yellow corn and yellow corn gluten meal contain significant quantities of xanthophyll. Many naturally occurring plant contain carotenoids, as lutein (grass, lucerne), zeaxanthin (maize), canthaxanthin (chanterelle), violaxanthin (pumpkin), capsanthin (paprika), and lycopene (tomato) (Hencken, 1974).

A recent work has shown the contents of natural xanthophylls in various feed ingredients (Liu, 1997). Minimum levels of xanthophyll exist in wheat. Corn and corn gluten are a rich source, but variation is substantial, depending on many factors such as corn variety, growing conditions and storage.

Natural forms of xanthophyll are highly unsaturated lipids and therefore readily oxidized, their pigmenting power is then lost. They can be bleached by photo-oxidation from sunlight and by classical lipid autoxidation. In the gastrointestinal tract, any factors affecting intestinal absorption will have an impact on pigmentation. Moldy corn has poor pigmentation in that microorganisms consume fat with carotenoids and mycotoxins further affect intestinal absorption as proven by many researchers (Liu, 1997).

3. Metabolism of carotene

1) Effect of ration ingredients on pigmentation

Certain feed components can interfere with metabolism of the carotenoid pigments. Vitamin E or antioxidants such as butylanted hydroxy toluene (BHT) enhance pigmentation of the vitellus of the egg and stabilize the pigments (Bartov and Borentein, 1976). Carotene metabolism can also be affected by cereals, rice bran, fatty acids and vitamin A.

2) Digestive transport and intestinal absorption

Absorption of beta-carotene takes place through a process similar to the absorption of fatty acid. Prior to absorption from the intestine, beta-carotene is dispersed in micellar form. The micelles are composed of bile salts, monoglycerides and long-chain faty acids, and together with vitamin D, E and K they facilitate transfer of beta-carotene to the intestinal cells. Much of the beta-carotene is converted to vitamin A here (El Boushy and Raterink, 1989).

Other carotenes are transported through the fatty acids in the intestinal mucosa of the chicken to the blood stream through the liver to their final target in the ovary and ovum of the adult laying hen. Zeaxanthin and lutein were at higher concentrations in the serum, adipose tissue, liver and egg yolk than beta carotene (Scott et al., 1982).

The yolk color depends on the extent to which carotenoids in the feed are absorbed by the digestive system and deposited in the yolk. The site of absorption of xanthophylls is the jejunum-ileum. A small amount, if any, is absorbed in the duodenum and large intestine, and that takes place in the cecum (Littlefield et al., 1972).

4. Metabolism of apo-8'-carotenoic acid, ethyl ester

In the chicken, apocarotenoic ester occurs as a metabolite of apo-8'-carotenal, which is found in many plants such as lucerne, alfalfa meal, grass, green vegetables and citrus fruits. The beta-apo-8'-carotenal has been shown to be an effective pigmentor for coloring egg yolks in vivo (Glover and Redfearn, 1954). Beta-apo-8'-carotenal reduces to vitamin A aldehyde, which in turn is reduced to vitamin A (Glover and Redfearn, 1954). Echinenone, crytoxantin, beta-apo-8'-carotenal, beta-apo-8'-carotenoic acid ethyl ester and citranaxanthin act not only as vitamin A precursors, but also as egg yolk pigments (Henken, 1974).

1) Pigmentation measurement and practical utilization

The evaluation of egg yolk color is based on an "optimal-yellow", which must be "appetizingly pretty" as determined by the "corruptible" human eye (Borentein and Bartov, 1966). The visual impression of the consumer does not always correspond to the chemical concentration of yolk pigments because:

- The human eye is not sensitive to the darker shades of yellow;
- The standard colorimetric method (AOAC, 1992) is not sensitive to reddish pigments, which deepen the visual color of yolks (Bartov and Borentein, 1967); and
- The color of the broken egg yolk is not the same as the whole yolk (Ashton and Fletcher, 1962).

The color fan of Hoffman-LaRoche is used presently is many countries in its new form with 15 different color shades. The feed industry must be able to determine which pigments deposit in the egg yolk and produce certain colors. The ability of certain carotenoids in the diet to influence yolk color has been investigated by measuring the light (at 514 nm) reflected by the egg yolk. Yolk color was not influenced by beta carotene and bixin, but the pigments carotenal and carophyll improved the color significantly. Cantaxanthin and capsanthin should not be used alone since they produce an unnatural red tinge to the yolk, but may be used together with yellow pigments of natural or synthetic origin. Equal amounts of red and yellow pigments are deposited in the egg yolk by using a combination of beta-apo-8'-carotenoic acid ester and canthaxanthin (Fletcher and Halloran, 1981).

Pigmentation is an inherited characteristic that is also influenced by feed ingredients and light. Pigmentation has been attributed to variations in feed ingredients, availability of xanthophylls, oxidation during storage and health factors. The genetic ability to absorb and deposit xanthophylls has been found to vary among hens within stains and between breeds (Braeunlich, 1974).

Xanthophyll varies in its ability to produce dominant wavelength depending on the natural ingredients used. Xanthophylls from corn and corn gluten meal, for example, produce a greater wavelength than xanthophyll from alfalfa meal. Consequently, alfalfa meal and marigold meal are used to produce lightly colored broilers and egg yolks, but if more deeply colored birds or yolks are desired, corn or corn gluten meal should be fed as these impart a higher dominant wavelength (Fletcher, 1982).

In formulating rations, the dominant wavelength of the pigment and the amount of biologically available pigment in the ingredient must be considered in determining the color influence sought. Birds grown in windowless buildings do not express pigment as well as birds grown in open houses; and among birds exposed to natural diurnal light cycles, those birds restricted by pens or other means to the inside did not pigment as well as those birds to the outside (Janky, 1983).

Broiler chickens respond to pigments in much the same way as laying hens. Dietary pigments are absorbed and are carried in the serum proportional to the dietary levels. A combination of red and yellow pigments greatly enhances the visual egg yolk scores and broiler skin scores (Couch et al., 1971).

5. Factors influencing pigmentation

Several feed ingredients interact with carotenoid pigment to improve or reduce their deposition rates in yolks.

1) Rice bran

Inclusion of 60% non-autoclaved rice bran led to an adverse effect on laying hen egg yolk color, reducing the intensity of the Roche color fan score (Majun and Payne, 1977). They suggested that non-autoclaved rice bran contains some factors that cause changes within the lipid fraction which in turn affects the yolk color.

2) Cereals

Yellow maize is high in pigments, which in turn leads to production of eggs with reasonable yolk color. Wheat is superior to barley in contributing to egg yolk color when using the same concentrations (Karunajeewa, 1980). Some samples of barley which have the absence or deficiency in a fungal enzyme (endo-beta-glucanase) give rise to a highly viscous state of the glucans in the gut and this probably inhibits the absorption of nutrients and xanthophylls (Burnett, 1966). Triticale, a cross between wheat and rye, also has been shown to inhibit the transfer of oxy-carotenoids from the diet to the egg yolks. Replacement of maize or wheat in layer diets with triticale reduced pigmentation of egg yolks by 7 to 11% (Choudhary and Netke, 1976). The deposition of carotenoid pigments is inhibited also by some feedstuffs such as meat scraps, fish meal and soybean meal (Culton and Bird, 1941).

3) Fats

Dietary fat supplementation may effect egg yolk color, depending on the degree of saturation of the fatty acids (Abu-Serewa, 1976).

4) Antibiotics

Antibiotics added to layer diets have been shown to increase yolk color significantly (Scott et al., 1982).

5) Vitamin A content

Extremely high levels of vitamin A markedly depress egg yolk color, while normal levels have little effect. As the vitamin A content increased, the amount of xanthophylls decreased. A competition between vitamin A and xanthophyll absorption and/or transport occurs under conditions of low lipid intake, but no competition exists under conditions of adequate dietary fat levels (Scott *et al.*, 1982).

6) Vitamin E and antioxidants

Vitamin E or antioxidant supplementation to poultry diets enhances egg yolk pigmentation. Antioxidants are normally added to feeds to prevent oxidation of fats, fat soluble vitamins, xanthophylls and other components. Copper, iron, and other metal ions can enhance the rate of oxidation and increase the demand for antioxidants.

Feeding 125 ppm ethoxyquin resulted in a statistically higher level of yolk pigmentation at each level of alfalfa meal (1.25 to 6.25% of the corn-soy diet) fed (Anjaneyain *et al.*, 1963). These scientists reported that analyses of dietary xanthophylls in mixed feed indicated a less of 24% of xanthophyll components within three weeks without antioxidant protection, compared to a 6% less with antioxidants during high temperature period (35.5 to 39.8℃). Studies conducted during cooler months (20.0 to 23.0℃) indicated an improvement of 19.2 to 23.5% in yolk pigmentation with 125 ppm ethoxyquin. There was little less in dietary xanthophylls during the cooler weather. However, a minimum of 150 ppm is necessary to provide protection to the xanthophylls of alfalfa meal (Chung, 1991).

7) Aflatoxin

Dietary aflatoxin has been shown to raise the yolk and plasma carotenoid concentrations (Huff *et al.*, 1975).

8) Source, harvesting and storage conditions of the feedstuffs

Xanthophyll content from different sources of yellow corn cannot be considered to be equally available for egg yolk pigmentation (Bartov and Borentein, 1967). This may be caused by different carotenoid patterns, the presence of labile factors such as tocopherols of the effects of dietary free fatty acids.

Considerable loss of carotenoid pigments can be caused by improper storage. During unfavorable storage conditions, there was particularly a marked decrease in the xanthophyll concentration of maize (Bartov and Borentein, 1967). In one study, corn lost 25% of its pigment content after drying to reduce its moisture content from 11% to 3%, concluding that stored corn for one year at 25℃ lost 50% of its pigment content due to xanthophyll and carotene xanthophyll content is decreased by sun curing (Miettinen, 1971).

9) Stability

Natural xanthophyll sources are usually found in a dry form. Destruction of xanthophylls occurs through exposure to heat, light and air. The use of antioxidants like ethoxyquin helps to stabilize xanthophylls (Bartov and Borentein, 1976).

10) Breeds and strain variation

The ability to absorb and deposit carotenoids in egg yolks varies with different breeds and hybrids. Yolk color is also influences by genotype and the rate of egg production in hens. There is some variation between breeds, strains and individual hens in their ability to absorb and deposit oxycarotenoids in egg yolks (Karunajeewa et al., 1984).

11) Health conditions

Any disease that reduces the efficiency of absorption of nutrients from the alimentary tract (jejunum-ileum) can reduce the uptake of carotenoids. The following summarizes the action that disease has in reducing yolk color in commercial layers (Scott et al., 1982; Nahm and Chung, 1995).
- Ingestion of pigments: Reduction in food consumption causes lack of pigmentation through insufficient supplies of pigments.
- Digestive transit: Changes in transit time affect intestinal absorption and serum transport of pigments.
- Plasmatic pigmentation: Oocytes of the parasite *Eimeria tenella* cause a plasmatic discoloration that results in decreased pigmentation in the egg yolk.
- Deposit in the vitellus: Inoculation with *Eimeria acervulina* caused a discoloration of the egg yolk.

12) Age of birds and feed intake

Old layers (53-week-old) showed 10 to 20% lower efficiency in depositing beta-apo-8'-carotenoec acid ethyl ester in egg yolks than those which were 32 to 38 weeks old. This may be due to the absorptive power of the gut declining in older layers (Karunajeewa, 1980).

13) Housing system

Birds housed in cages laid eggs with higher yolk color than those of hens housed on deep litter; the differences were equivalent to 2 units on the Roche color fan in favor of the caged birds (Fletcher et al., 1978). The cause may be a result of differences in feed intake and consequent differences in pigment intake. High calcium levels in diets also reduced egg yolk color and droppings of hens housed on deep litter were found to be rich in minerals, mainly calcium and phosphorus (El Boushy and Vink, 1977).

6. Variations in biological availability of xanthophylls

The source and level of natural dietary pigmenting ingredients determines the pigmentation of the egg yolk. Formulation of layer diets for specific yolk color is difficult due to variances in xanthophyll content and variations in the biological availability of certain feedstuffs. When the beta-apo-8'-carotenal is used as a standard, the relative availability values of xanthophylls from alfalfa, yellow corn and corn gluten meal were 57.4, 75.5 and 107.9%, respectively (Fry and Harms, 1975). This means that a chemical assay of xanthophyll content of a given feedstuff cannot be used directly to estimate the value of that material for pigmenting egg yolk (Scott *et al.*, 1982). Some other sources of xanthophyll pigments suggested for use by some researchers are algae meal and marigold petal meal. Non-conventional feedstuffs fed up to certain percentages for sources of pigment include cirtrus pulp (apocarotenal), tomato waste (lycopene), paprika waste (capsanthin) and lobster waste (astaxanthin) (Scott *et al.*, 1982).

Marigold petal meal produced by drying and grinding of marigold flowers contains up to 17 different carotenoids. The pigments are mainly present in the esterified form. Lutein-diester, a yellow carotenoid, makes up 70 to 90% of the total carotenoid content. Zeaxanthin-diester, a red carotenoid, is the second most important carotenoid present and makes up about 10 to 25% of the total carotenoids. All other xanthophylls are present in traces and contribute insignificantly to the total pigmenting efficacy of marigold products (El Boushy and Raterink, 1985). Marigold petal meal normally contains 0.6 to 1% xanthophylls, and marigold concentrate products have been developed from extraction of the xanthophylls from marigolds. These concentrates contain 1 to 4% xanthophylls and contain varying levels of ethoxyquin as an antioxidant. The richest sources of xanthophylls are marigold petal meal (6,000 to 10,000 mg/kg), algae (4,000 mg/kg), dehydrated clover meal (490 mg/kg), corn gluten meal 41% protein (90 to 180 mg/kg) and yellow corn (20 to 25 mg/kg)(Fletcher, 1982; El Boushy and Raterink, 1989).

7. Synthetic carotenoids

A few carotenoids have been synthesized and tested as supplements for egg yolk pigmentation.

Canthaxanthin (beta, beta-carotene-4,4'-dione) is the red pigment of chanterelle mushrooms, and when added to the natural yellow pigments of yellow corn and alfalfa, it helps to produce an orange-yellow color (Fletcher *et al.*, 1978). Only 2 to 10 g of canthaxanthin per ton of feed is needed to supplement the natural xanthophylls in the yolk in the normal rations (Scott *et al.*, 1982).

Beta-apo-8'-carotenal or preferably the ethyl ester of beta-apo-8'-carotenoic acid (8'-apo-beta-carotene-81ft-al) is also used as a feed supplement (Fletcher *et al.*, 1978). They are yellow pigments that act as a provitamin A. They have been isolated from grass, lucerne, green vegetables and citrus fruits. Addition of 2 to 8 grams per ton of feed supplements the natural pigments to produce higher quality yolk color (Scott *et al.*, 1982).

Synthetic carotenoids are added as small particles in which the carotenoid pigments are finely distributed in a gelatin base to prevent oxidation. They may be mixed into compound feeds, concentrates and mineral mixtures and are highly stable during storage due to their gelatin coating.

8. Levels of carotenoids in layer rations

Alfalfa (lucerne) meal which is commonly used in layer rations is rich in xanthophylls (150-310 mg/kg), but its use is limited due to its high fiber content (Scott *et al.*, 1982). Synthetic carotenoids must be used to achieve the required yolk color to satisfy both the consumer and the industry.

The consumer of each country prefers different levels of pigmentation. For example, the yellow pigments in layer feed are much lower in Sweden than in Germany. In Sweden, 0.5 mg canthaxanthin per kilogram of feed is used to improve the color of the yolk to 4 degrees on the Roche color fan. In Germany, a minimum of 13 is required to satisfy consumers. The manufacturers use top quality maize at the highest levels possible. The yellow pigments alone are not able to increase the color beyond 11 Roche, so a red synthetic carotenoid is added to improve color further(Braeunlich, 1974).

CONTROLLING EGG WEIGHT BY DIET AND MANAGEMENT

Egg producers have always faced the problem of getting their flocks to lay table eggs with market weight, and at the same time controlling egg size once it starts to increase excessively. Egg weight is mainly determined by the size of the egg yolk. The size increases as the hen ages because the yolk size increase. Other components such as albumin and shell are proportional to the yolk size but this proportion decreases with age of the hen and is influenced by components of the blood.

1. Early egg size

Various factors such as genetics, body weight and shank length of pullets, season of maturity, environmental temperature and lighting programs have influences on egg weight (Scott *et al.*, 1982; Lesson and Summers, 1992; Nahm and Chung, 1995).

2. Dietary manipulation

1) Energy

In early maturing pullets, low feed intake for the first two to three months of production is a problem. It also undoubtedly contributes to small egg size. Egg weight was significantly reduced by 15% feed restriction, but it has also been reported that egg production is reduced by any restrictions greater than 5% (Kim *et al.*, 1995).

2) Protein and amino acids

Dietary protein and amino acid levels, especially methionine, have been reported to influence egg size under different environmental and dietary situation. At the peak of production, a layer should receive 18 g of protein and 400 mg of methionine daily to meet requirements for egg output, body maintenance and growth. In field trials when pullet were consuming 100 g daily of an early lay ration with less than 0.4% methionine, addition of 451 to 908 g (l to 2 lb.) of DL-methionine per ton improved early egg size. The weight of eggs from pullets was not affected by increases in dietary levels of methionine, linoleic acid or protein above the established requirements (Aghir, 1991).

Most of the beneficial effects of a high protein level (17, 19 and 21%) or supplemental fat (2 or 4% tallow, blended fat of corn oil) on early egg weight (18 to 38 weeks of age) discontinued upon changing the feeds of a 16.5% protein diet (Keshavarz, 1995). This research pointed out that egg weight of the heavy-weight groups remained greater that the light-weight groups.

After peak egg mass, dietary protein and methionine level manipulation is used to control egg weight. A reduction of only 0.5% protein and methionine level manipulation is used to control egg weight. A reduction of only 0.5% protein at any one time with intervals between subsequent reductions of at least 3 to 4 weeks is recommended (Daghir, 1991). If production decreases occur beyond the predicted age, this scientist suggests a safer procedure is to reduce dietary methionine rather than protein. Methionine reductions of 0.01% at any one time with intervals between reductions of 3 to 4 weeks can reduce the terminal egg weight by up to 2g. Attempts at reducing or tampering with egg size later in the production cycle by phase feeding of protein or methionine have met with only limited success (Daghir, 1991).

3) Low protein diets (after peak egg mass)

Most research studies have shown that laying hens must be fed a diet containing at least 16% protein to maintain maximum egg weight. Low protein diets may support maximum egg production but usually fail to support maximum egg weight when compared to diets with 16% protein or more. When the protein intake is low (less than 14 to 15 g/day), there may be a reduction of egg size when energy levels are increased. The response of the layer to protein is most likely associated with the sulfur containing amino acids, especially methionine. When the intake of methionine daily is lower than 255 mg, egg size is reduced but egg production rate is not changed (Summers and Leeson, 1984; Leeson and Summers, 1989).

An experiment comparing a 16% crude protein practical diet with a 13% crude protein diet and various additions of amino acids to the 13% crude protein diet was conducted (Jensen and Penz, 1990). This study showed that egg yolk as a percentage of total egg was generally higher for diets based on the 13% crude protein while albumin weight as a percentage of the total egg weight was usually lower. Synthesized amino acid supplementation did not influence albumin or yolk percent. The reduction in egg weight appeared to be the result of a reduced albumin. These researchers noted that the protein deposited in the yolk is synthesized in the liver and accumulates continuously in the ovum over a period of several days until ovulation occurs. On the other hand, albumin is synthesized in the oviduct and must be supplied to the egg during a 3 to 3.5 hour period of time when the ovum is in the magnum of the oviduct (Jensen and Penz, 1990). The level of amino acids, originating from the diet and not from synthesized amino acids, circulating in the blood during the time when albumin is being actively synthesized and deposited in the magnum may have an effect on the amount of albumin synthesized. This need for additional amino acids during albumin synthesis suggests that feeding a high-protein diet at this time may improve egg weight.

4) Linoleic acid

Linoleic acid is known to be a requirement for maximum, egg size, but the optimum of maximum requirement for birds has been debated. It has been recommended that layer diets contain 1.4% linoleic acid with a gradual reduction starting after peak egg mass (Daghir, 1991). Another study showed that increasing the level of dietary linoleic acid from 0.6 to 4.3% increased the egg weight during the first 14 weeeks of production: however, average egg yield was not affected (March and MacMillan, 1990).

5) Dietary fat

The addition of fats to diets of laying hens has been shown by several investigators to increase production and egg size. Incorporation of 1 to 2% feed grade animal fat to the layer diet has been shown to be effective in decreasing the percentage of small plus medium-sized egg and increasing the percentage of large and extra-large eggs during 22 to 28 weeks of age. In another study, addition of up to 5% vegetable oils such as corn oil to layer diets increased egg weight (Jensen *et al.*, 1958). This effect was attributed to a specific property of the oil rather than to its energy content, since replacement of the oil by starch to provide the same amount of energy depressed egg size (Kennedy and Vevers, 1975). Increasing the ME of laying hen diets by adding 4% animal tallow also increased egg production and egg size (Reid, 1983).

Egg size was increased with the fat supplementation regardless of the dietary energy levels. The increase in egg size was observed with the addition of poultry fat, corn oil and tallow. However, the addition of fat to pullet rations during the rearing stages had no effect on egg production, irrespective of the fat content in the laying diet (Whitehead, 1981). Three major effects of added fats to poultry diets were recognized. The first of these is still improvement in feed conversion, which accrues from the increased caloric density of the diet and can result in substantial savings in feed costs. The second benefit from fat has been termed the "extra-caloric effect" that apparently results from improved nutrient availability in ingredients and mixed diets. Many studies designed to measure the metabolizable energy(ME) of fat have found values that are higher that the gross energy(GE) of the fat. The third major benefit of fat involves the "extra-metabolic effect" that is noted as improved performance and increased energetic efficiency.

6) Ingredient quality

Early egg size can also be influenced by ingredient quality. Differences in the digestibility and available amino acid levels are most responsible for these effects. Decreasing the dietary energy level, as may occur when sorghum or barley is substituted for corn, may decrease egg weight (Coon *et al.*, 1988).

7) Age and limiting amino acids

Older laying hens produce a high proportion of extra-large eggs for which the monetary returns often do not offset the costs of production. When formulators wish to reduce the weight of eggs laid by older hens, the most limiting amino acid level is lowered below the required level, which results in proportional reductions in egg weight and rate of egg production. For example, weight of eggs produced by hens more than 38 weeks of age was reduced by limiting methionine intake to 270 mg per hen daily, compared with feeding 300 mg methionine per hen daily (Peterson *et al.*, 1983).

ORGANIC EGGS

The egg industry is constantly being challenged to sell more eggs. Eggs need to be promoted as a versatile commodity and new processed egg items need to be developed. The entire industry must join with the poultry science community in this effort. Organic produce and / or produce that has been tested pesticide residue free by an independent company has shown promise as a new area of interest in the U. S. and other countries for the retail grocery business (Ernst, 1993; Nahm and Chung, 1995).

1. Production of organic eggs

Hens that are used to produce organic eggs need to be raised without chemicals or drugs to stimulate or regulate growth or tenderness and without drugs or antibiotics, except for treatment of specific disease malady. These hens are fed a ration formulated from ingredients produced, harvested, stored, processed and packaged free from the application of synthetically compounded fertilizers, pesticides or growth regulators.

2. Difficulties in producing organic eggs

Finding a source of organic poultry feeds has been the most difficult problem to overcome in producing organic eggs. Feed mill operators have reported that it was virtually impossible for them to find sources of organic grains when they were asked to produce organic feeds. They thought farmers would find it too expensive to raise organic grains and they could not believe that a grain was actually organic just based on the word of the broker. Synthetic vitamins at normal levels and minerals of rock origin need to be supplemented in the organic feed. Labeling on the feed should state that organically grown corn and soybeans were used to formulate the organic ration.

The cost of the organic grains is the greatest expense incurred by farmers wishing to produce organic eggs. Despite the increased cost of producing these eggs organically over the conventional methods, consumers seeking organic products are willing to pay significantly higher prices for the eggs. Producers considering the production of organic eggs should consider all the production changes necessary before attempting to switch from conventional or traditional production methods. A market survey should also be carried out if necessary before this change is done.

CONCLUSION

Eggs have to compete with other foods since a wide variety of products are becoming available to consumers. The disadvantages of egg consumption are becoming more relevant, because the consumer is demanding guarantees for quality. The quality of an egg is a complex relationship between internal quality of the egg, cholesterol content, egg size, eggshell strength and shell color. Internal quality of the egg is of great importance for commercial producers, processors and traders, as well as consumers. It is measured through the visible characteristics of the egg, its freshness and nutrition. Public concern about the emergence of Salmonella contamination of the egg has led to changes in egg production methods.

Dietary cholesterol, blood cholesterol and their relationship has been a high profile health issue for many years. The manipulation of the cholesterol concentration in the egg yolk, however, is generally unsuccessful since the cholesterol can only be alter to a small extent. New information and research data about the role of dietary cholesterol should take the pressure and attention off of eggs in recommendations to the general public.

Consumers generally prefer eggs with well pigmented yolks. Pigmentation is inherited, but is also influenced by feed ingredients and light. Variations in carotene and xanthophyll contents in feed ingredients, availability of xanthophyll, oxidation during storage and other dietary or health factors may alter pigmentation. Feed manufacturers should insist that ingredient suppliers provide ingredients that have been properly treated with antioxidants and stored properly.

Egg size classifications are used throughout the marketing system to determine egg price. Factors such as body weight of the hen, housing temperature, lighting programs and dietary manipulation affect egg size. There is no doubt that the egg size can be controlled. The most common methods used for this are limiting protein intake, limiting total sulfa-amino acid (TSAA) intake, limiting methionine intake and practicing feed restriction. It is important that egg weight control begins before excessive egg weight occurs.

Organic eggs laid by hens raised in chemical and drug free environments are a area of interest in the U. S. and other countries for the retail grocery business because the egg industry is constantly being challenged to sell more eggs. There are still difficulties in producing these eggs due to the availability of organic poultry feeds and the cost of organic grains. Despite the increased cost of producing organic eggs, the consumers appear willing to pay more money for these eggs according to market survey research. Further research is needed before increasing the organic egg production.

ACKNOWLEDGMENTS

I would like to thank Dr. T. Savage (Dept. of Animal Science, Oregon State Univ.), Dr. R. Blair (Dept. of Animal Science, The University of British

Columbia), and Dr. B. Winselman-Nahm (Lincolnway Animal Hospital, Matteson, IL) for their criticism and corrections of this manuscript.

REFERENCES

Abu-Serewa S 1976 Effects of source and level of fat in the hen's diet on the deposition of dietary oxycarotenoids in egg yolks. Aust. Exp. Agric. Anim. Husb. 16:204-208.

Adams RL, Pratt DE, Lin JH, Stadelman UJ 1989 Introduction of omega-3 unsaturated fatty acids in eggs. Poultry Sci 68(Suppl. 1):166.

Anjaneyaly YY, Kurick AA, Reid BL 1963 Ethoxyquin and egg yolk pigmentation. Proc. Soc. Exp. Biol. Med. 113:275-278.

Anonymous 1989 Fear of eggs. Consumer Reports. Oct., pp. 650-652.

Association of Official Agricultural Chemists 1992 Official Methods of Analysis, 12th ed. Washington D. C.

Ansah GA, Chan CW, Touchburn SP, Buckland RB 1985 Selection for low yolk cholesterol in Leghorn-type chickens. Poultry Sci 64:1-5.

Ashton HE, Fletcher DA 1962 Development and use of color standards for egg yolk. Poultry Sci 41:1903-1909.

Award AC, Smith DM 1996 Method for reduction of cholesterol in egg materials. US Patent 5, 482, 624. Jan. 16.

Award AC, Bennink MR, Smith DM 1997 Composition and functional properties of cholesterol reduced egg yolk. Poultry Sci 76:649-653.

Balnave D 1970 Essential fatty acids in poultry nutrition. World's Poultry Sci J 26:442-460.

Band HO, Dyerburg J 1972 Plasma lipids and liporproteins in Greenlandic west coast Eskimos. Acta Med Scand 192:85-94.

Bartov I, Borentein S 1967 Studies on egg yolk pigmentation. Poultry Sci 46:796-805.

Bartov I, Borntein S 1976 Effect of degree of fattiness in broilers on other Carcass characteristic; relationship between fatness and the composition of carcass fat. Br Poult Sci 17:17-27.

Beitz DC 1990 The use of cholesterol reductase. Proceedings of fat and cholesterol reduced foods. March 22-24. New Orleans, LA, IBC USA Inc., 8 Pleasant St., Bldg. D, South Natick, Mass. 01760.

Beyer RS 1991 Naturally occurring substances which reduce cholesterol in meat and eggs. Georgia Nutrition Conf. Proc. Nov. 21. pp. 24-30.

Beyer RS, Jensen LS 1992. Cholesterol concentration of egg yolk and blood plasma and performance of laying hens as influenced by dietary alpha-ketoisocaproic acid. Poultry Sci 71:120-127.

Blair R 1996 Future of feeding poultry to vary by region. Feedstuffs, Dec 16 pp. 17-20, 31.

Borentein S, Bartor I 1966 Studies on egg yolk pigmentation. Poultry Sci 45:287-296.

Braeunlich K 1974 The chemistry and action of pigmenters in avian diets. Proc. 15th World Poultry Congress. New Orleans, U. S. A., pp. 236-239.

Burnett GS 1966 Studies of viscosity as the probable factor involved in the improvement of certain barleys for chickens by enzyme supplementation. Br. Poultry Sci. 7: 55-61.

Canter AH, Pescatore AJ, Widjazanti P, Johnson TH, Straw ML 1992 Sterols in layer feed fail to lower cholesterol levels. Feedstuffs, Jan. 20. pp. 50-56.

Choudhary KS, Netke SP 1976 Incorporation of triticale in layer diet. Br. Poultry Sci 17:361-371.

Chung DH 1991 Textbook of Biochemistry. Sun Jin Pub. Co., p. 217, 222-224.

Clarenburg R, Kim IA, Wakefield LM 1971 Reducing the cholesterol level by including emulsified sitosterol in standard chicken diet. J. of Nutrition 101: 289-298.

Coon CN, Obi I, Hamre ML 1988 Use of barley in laying hen diets. Poultry Sci 67:1306-1311.

Couch JR, Camp AA, Farr FM 1971 The supplementary effect of adding canthaxanthin to a diet containing natural sources of pigmenting compounds on the pigmentation of broilers. Br Poultry Sci 12:205-211.

Culton TJ, Bird HR 1941 Effect of certain protein supplements in inhibiting pigment deposition in growing chicks. Poultry Sci 20:432-437.

Daghir NJ 1991 How egg size is influenced by environment and nutrition. Shaver Focus. pp. 13-16.

El Boushy AR, Raterink R 1985 Eggshell strength: The causes of egg breakage in relation to nutrition, management and environment. Feedstuffs, Aug. 12. pp. 7-9.

El Boushy AR, Raterink R 1989 Various aspects of egg yolk pigmentation explored. Feedstuffs, Jan. 30. pp. 41-48.

El Boushy AR, Vink FWA 1977 The value of dried poultry waste as a feedstuff in broiler diets. Feedstuffs. Dec. 9, pp. 24, 26.

Elkin RG, Rogler JC 1989 Effect of lovastation on laying hen performance and egg cholesterol content. Poultry Sci 68(Suppl. 1):49(Abstract).

Ernst M 1993 Egg processing: Where will we be in the year 2000? Poultry Int., Jan., pp. 82, 84.

Farrell DJ 1997 The importance of eggs in a healthy diet. Poultry Int. 36:72, 74, 76, 78.

Findlay S, Silberner J 1989 The truth about cholesterol. US News and World Report. Nov. 27, pp. 82-90.

Fletcher DL, Harms RH, Janky DM 1978 Yolk color characteristics, xanthophyll availability and a model system for predictiong egg yolk color using beta-apo-8 -carotenal and canthaxanthin. Poultry Sci 57:624-629.

Fletcher DL, Janky DM, Christmas RB, Arafa AS, Harms RH 1977 Strain differences in egg yolk pigmentation. Poultry Sci 56:2061-2068.

Fletcher DL, Halloran HR 1981 An evaluation of commercially available marigold concentrate and paprika oleoresin on egg yolk pigmentation. Poultry Sci 60: 1846-1851.

Fletcher DL 1982 Current research in evaluation of pigment sources for poultry. Proceedings 1982 Maryland Nutrition Conference, pp. 21-26.

Froning GW 1991 Charges in hen diet, egg yolk processing could reduce cholesterol. Feedstuffs, Aug. 28. pp. 47-49, 51.

Froning GW, Wehling RL, Cuppett SL, PierceMM, Niemann L, Siekman DK 1990 Extraction of cholesterol and other lipids from dried egg yolk using supercritical carbon dioxide. J. of Food Sci 55(1):95-101.

Fry JL, Harms RH 1975 Yolk color, candled egg grade and xanthophyll availability from dietary natural pigmenting ingredients. Poultry Sci 54:1094-1101.

Glover J, Redfearn ER 1954 The mechanism of the transformation of beta-carotene into vitamin A In Vivo. Biochem J 58:XV.

Goodman De WD, Hyan HS 1965 Biosynthesis of vitamin A with rat intestinal enzymes. Science 149:879-882.

Griffin HD 1990 Modifying egg yolk cholesterol in the domestic fowl-a Review. World's Poultry Sci J 44(1):17-32.

Hargis PS 1990 Dietary modification of fatty acid composition of shell eggs. Proceedings of fat and cholesterol reduced foods. Mar. 22-24. New Orleans, LA, IBC USA. Inc., 8 Pleasant St., Bldg. D, South Natick, Mass. 01760.

Hargis PS, Van Elswyk ME and Hargis BM 1991 Dietary modification of yolk lipid with menhaden oil. Poultry Sci 70:874-879.

Hargis PS, Van Elswyk ME 1993 Manipulating the fatty acid composition of poultry meat and eggs for the health conscious consumer. World's Poultry Sci J 49: 251-264.

Henken H 1974 The chemistry and distribution of pigmenting carotenoids in nature and their use for pigmentation of animal products. Seminar for the feed industry. pp. 29-46.

Huff WE, Wyat RD, Hamilton PB 1975 Effects of dietary aflatoxin on certain egg yolk parameters. Poultry Sci 54:2014-2018.

Janky DM 1983 Broiler: Better pigmentation. Broiler Industry. Feb., pp. 6, 8.

Jensen LS, Allred JB, Frey RE, Meginnis J 1958 Evidence for an unidentified factor necessary for maximum egg weights in chicken. J of Nutrition 65:219-233.

Jensen LS, Penz AM 1990 Low protein diets for laying hens to sustain maximum egg weight. Georgia Nut. Conf. p. 24-36.

Johnson ED 1967 Effect of dietary fat and D-thyroxin on the incorporation of acetate. J of Nutrition 93:153-160.

Karunajeewa H 1980 The deposition of synthetic oxycarotenoids in egg yolks. World's Poultry Sci J. 36:219-226.

Karunajeewa H, Hughes RJ, McDonald MW, Shenstone FS 1984 A review of factors influencing pigmentation of egg yolk. World's Poultry Sci J. 40:52-65.

Keshavarz K 1995 An overview of calcium and phosphorus nutrition of growing pullets and laying hens. Proceedings 1995 Cornell Nut. Conf, Oct 24-26 pp. 161-170.

Kennedy GY, Vevers HG 1975 A survey of avian eggshell pigments. Compar. Biochemistry and Physiology. 558:117-123.

Kim DJ, Myang WJ, Nahm KH, Ko YD, Chang MB 1995 A Textbook of Feed Resources (Korean edition). Hang Mun Pub. Co., Seoul, Korea. pp. 229-251.

Kuit AR 1984 Egg's interior quality. Feedstuffs, Sept. 24. pp. 14-16.

Larson JE, Froning GW 1981 Extraction and processing of various components from egg yolk. Poultry Sci 60:160-164.

Lesson S, Summers JD 1992 Commercial Poultry Production. The University of Guelf Press, ON, Canada.

Lesson S, Summers JD 1989 Response of Leghorn pullets to protein and energy in the diet when reared in regular or hot-cyclic environments. Poultry Sci 68:546-551.

Littlefield LH, Bletner JK, Shirley HV, Goff OE 1972 Locating the site of absorption of xanthophylls in the chicken by a surgical techniques. Poultry Sci 51:1721-1725.

Liu K 1997 Cereal-based pigments vary widely. Asian Poultry Magazine. Sept./ Oct., pp. 47-48.

Luhman CM, Miller BG, Beitz DC 1990 Research note: The effect of feeding lovastatin and colestipol on production and cholesterol content of eggs. Poultry Sci 69:852-855.

Majun GK, Payne CG 1977 Autoclaved rice bran in layer's diets. Br Poultry Sci 18:201-203.

March BE, MacMillan C 1990 Linoleic acid as a modificator of egg size. Poultry Sci 69:634-640.

Marks HL, Washburn KW 1977 Divergent selection for yolk cholesterol in laying hens. Br Poultry Sci 18:179-188.

Martusich WL, Bauernfeind JC 1981 Oxycarotenoids in poultry feeds. Edited by J. C. Bauernfeind, Academic Press N. Y., London, Toronto, Sydney, San Francisco, CA.

McNaughton JL 1978 Effect of dietary fiber on egg yolk, liver and plasma cholesterol concentrations of the laying hen. J of Nutrition 108:1842-1848.

Miettinen TA 1971 Cholesterol production in obesity. Circulation 44:842-849.

Moats WA 1978 Egg washing-A review. J Food Prot 41:919-925.

Moats WA 1979 Effect of washing eggs under commercial conditions on bacterial loads on eggshells. Poultry Sci 58:1228-1231.

Moats WA 1981b Factors affecting bacterial loads on commercially washed eggs. Poultry Sci 60:2084-2090.

Moats WA 1981a Antimicrobial activity of compounds containing active chlorine and iodine in the presence of egg solids. Poultry Sci 60:1834-1840.

Moore TJ 1989 The cholesterol myth. The Atlantic Monthly. Sept., pp. 37-70.

Naber EC 1976 The cholesterol problem, the egg and lipid metabolism in the laying hen. Poultry Sci 55:14-30.

Naber EC 1983 Nutrient and drug effects on the cholesterol metabolism in the laying hen. Federation Proc 42:2486-2493.

Nahm KH 1996 Korean research direction for animal science and technology in the 21st century. The Proceedings of the Korean Association of Animal Science. June 25-27. pp. 129-167.

Nahm KH, Chung SB 1995 A textbook of Chicken Production (English version). Mun Un Dang Pub. Co., Seoul, Korea

Nahm KH, Chung KK, Go YD, Kim DH, Kim YK 1997 Animal Nutrition (Korean version), Yu Han Pub. Co., [cited in Yvore (1974)]

National Research Council 1994 Nutrient Requirements of Poultry. 9th Revised Ed. National Academy Press, Washington, D. C..

Peterson CF, Sauten EA, Steele EE, Parkinson JF 1983 Use of methionine intake restriction to improve eggshell quality by control of egg weight. Poultry Sci 62: 2044-2050.

Poultry Digest 1997 News Views. March. p. 8.

Qureshi AA, Peterson DM, Dim ZZ, Elson CE, Bitgood JJ 1986 The independent roles of genetics and dietary factors in determining the cholesterol status of laying hens. Nut Rep Int 34:457-464.

Reid BI 1983 Tallow for laying hens examined. Feedstuffs. Mar. 14. p. 32-34, 36.

Richardson P, Jimenez-Flores R 1990 Absorption of cholesterol. Proceedings fat and cholesterol reduced foods-Technologies and strategies symposium, March 22-24. New Orleans, LA., IBC, USA.

Saenger W 1984 Structural aspects of cyclodextrins and their inclusion complexes. pp. 231-259. In: Inclusion complexes. J. L. Atwood, J. E. D. Davis and D. D. MacNiol, ed. Academic Press, London, UK.

Scott ML, Nesheim MC, Young RJ 1982 Nutrition of the Chicken. 3rd ed. Ithaca, NY., USA.

Shafer DJ, Carey JB, Prochaska JF 1996 Effect of dietary methionine intake on egg component yield and composition. Poultry Sci 75:1080-1085.

Sim JS, Kitts WD, Bragg DS 1980 Influence of dietary oil, cholesterol and soysterols on the fecal neutral and acidic steroid excretion in laying hens. Poultry Sci 59: 325-327.

Sim JS, Bragg DS 1977 Effect of dietary factors on serum and egg yolk cholesterol levels of laying hens. Poultry Sci 56:1616-1621.

Smith DM, Award AC, Bennink MR, Grill JL 1995 Cholesterol reduction in liquid egg yolk using beat-cyclodextrin. J. Food Sci 60:691-694, 720.

Summers JD, Leeson S 1984 Poultry Nutrition Handbook. The University of Guelf, ON. Canada.

Vargas RE, Allred JB, Biggert MB, Naber EC 1986 Effect of dietary 7-ketocholesterol, pure and oxidant cholesterol on hepatic 3-hydroxy 3-methylglutaryl-co-enzyme A reductase activity, energy balance, egg cholesterol concentration and C14-acetate incorporation into yolk lipids of laying hens. Poultry Sci 65:1333-1342.

Vargas RE, Naber EC 1984 Relationship between dietary fiber and nutrient density and its effect on energy balance, egg yolk cholesterol and hen performance. J. Nutrition 114:646-652.

Warren DC, Ball HR 1990 Yolk or white: which is the more important to egg flavor. Egg Industry Sept./Oct. pp. 24, 26.

Weiss JF, Johnson RM, Naber EC 1967 Effect of dietary fat and other factors on egg yolk cholesterol. Archives of Biochemistry and Biophysics. 105:521-526.

Whitehead CC 1981 The response of egg weight to the inclusion of different amounts of vegetable oil and linoleic acid in the diet of laying hens. Br Poultry Sci 22:525-532.

A strategy to solve the environmental concerns caused by poultry production

K. H. Nahm

Feed and Nutrition Laboratory, College of Natural Resources, Taegu University, Gyong San, 712-714, South Korea

Poultry manure and litter have the potential to be either land resources or pollutants of surface and ground water as well as giving rise to unpleasant odors. Provided proper attention is paid to nutrient management, they can be used as fertilisers, soil amendments and feed ingredients. Furthermore, the contents of nitrogen, phosphorus and other minerals in poultry manure and litter can be reduced by paying careful attention to diet composition- for example, by applying the concept of ideal protein, supplementation with synthetic amino acids, the addition of various types of enzymes including phytase, lowering of the protein and phosphorus contents and the use of highly available sources of supplementary phosphorus and vitamin D. Good nutrient management also depends on obtaining representative sample of feed, manure, litter, water and soil from each handling system and having these analysed on a regular basis in a reliable laboratory. This not only ensures that proper quantities of nutrients are added to the native soil on which the crops that are ultimately to be used as feed sources are to be grown, but also means that lower amounts of nitrogen, phosphorus and other elements are present in the feed. One outcome of the latter effect is that the poultry manure and litter excreted contains fewer pollutants and reduces the criticism leveled at the poultry industry that it runs roughshod over environmental concerns. It would be beneficial if all of these analytical procedures were handled by one laboratory specializing in animal agriculture with specialists advising farmers on how best to apply the analytical data.

Keywords: Analytical laboratory; dietary manipulation; feed; litter; manure; pollutant; soil; water

Introduction

Sustainability of livestock farming in the world is dependent on both environmental and economic viability (Fretz *et al.*, 1993; Francis, 1995). There are many situations in which environmental and financial goals are in direct conflict. Analyses of nutrient inputs and outputs from South Korean livestock farms have shown that inputs are consistently 3.5 to 9 times higher than outputs (Kim *et al.*, 1995). The excess nutrients remain in the soil, run off into the surface or ground water or, in the case of nitrogen, escape into the atmosphere where they often result in unpleasant odours.

Much of the previous research on nutrient management related to animal agriculture, particularly in the poultry operations, has focused on altering the impact of specific components such as poultry manure management (Moor *et al.*, 1995), soil conservation (Gordillo and Cabrera, 1997), crop production (Vanotti and Bundy, 1994) or poultry density (Edwards and Daniel, 1992). The objectives of this work are to improve the overall efficiency of nutrient utilization and to reduce losses. Because agricultural scientists have tended to specialize in parts of the production process rather than taking an integrated approach, it has been difficult to demonstrate the overall effects on the environment of management decisions taken at the level of the whole farm. Particular areas of concern to poultry and egg producers include confined poultry feeding operations, and nutrient management for manure, litter and soil (water). Studies have shown that poultry manure and litter compete economically with commercially available fertilisers if properly used and transportation costs are not too great (Weaver and Sounder, 1990; Patterson, 1993). The nutrient content of poultry manure and litter is higher than usual protein supplements when used as feed (Ko, 1992; Kim *et al.*, 1993). The concept of the interaction between feed, animals, manure, soil, water and feed production in animal agriculture establishes the need for an analytical laboratory.

Recycling nutrients in ecological systems

Nutrients enter the poultry farm in the feed. These nutrients then pass from the animal into the manure, and then from the manure into the soil. Food sources such as plants grow in the soil and obtain their nutrients from the soil. These plants are then consumed as feed to begin the cycleis repeated as shown in Figure 1. This cycle will continue as long as the poultry industry remains.

The cycle occurs because only portions of the nutrients are digested by poultry, with the remainder of the undigested nutrients passing into the manure. Because poultry operations are frequently concentrated in localized areas, the amounts of nitrogen (N) and phosphorus (P) generated in the litter and manure often exceed the fertilizer requirements for crop production on adjacent farms. When the continual application of poultry manure and litter exceeds the nutrient requirements

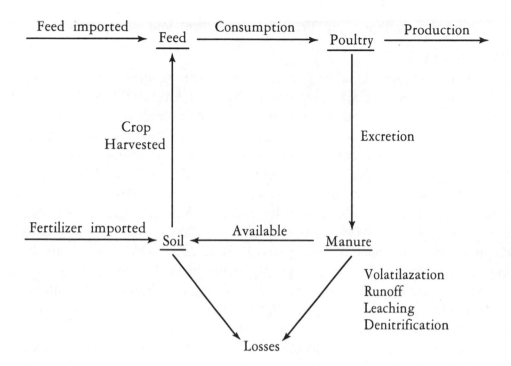

Figure 1. Recycling of nutrients in the environment

of crops, enrichment of nitrates in ground water and phosphorus in surface water can occur (Heathman *et al.*, 1995; Sharpley *et al.*, 1996).

Nutrients in poultry manure and litter

Twenty-one trace, minor and major elements including aluminum, barium, calcium, cadmium, chromium, copper, iron, potassium, magnesium, molybdenum, sodium, nickel, phosphorus, lead, rubidium, sulfur, stronium, titanium, vandium and zinc have been detected in poultry manure and litter (Ihnat and Fernandes, 1996). Vodela *et al.* (1997) selected arsenic, boron, cadmium, lead and trichloroethylene (TCE) for their research into general performance and immune function in broiler chickens because they believed these elements are the most common contaminants near hazardous waste sites. However, concerns about the impacts of N, P, and pathogens on the quality of surface and ground water has forced the poultry industry to implement voluntary waste management guidelines for use by poultry growers (Chapman, 1996). Although poultry manure and litter are valuable sources of N and P as plant nutrients (Beegle, 1990), saturation of the soil with them may cause problems because of the nature of some soils (Narrod *et al.*, 1994).

Impact of poultry manure and litter on water, soil and air quality

WATER QUALITY

Nitrogen (as nitrate) in the ground water near poultry farming operations normally range from generally accepted background levels of less than 3 mg/l to high concentrations of more than 10 mg/l. Up to a third of the sampled water wells in poultry growing areas of Delaware and Florida have been reported to have nitrate N concentrations of more than 10 mg/l (Darling, 1994; Zygmunt, 1994). However, in the Jackson Purchase area of Kentucky poultry farming was found to have had no effect on the quality of well water. Pescatore et al. (1998) reported that the nitrate levels in samples collected from the Jackson Purchase area averaged 1.41 ppm in 1990/91 and 1.37 ppm in 1996/97. The nitrite content was 0.005 ppm and 0.001 ppm for the years 1990/91 and 1996/97, respectively. This finding demonstrated that there had been no change in the ammonia concentration or in the conductivity of ground water. Furthermore, although the chloride and sulfate concentrations had changed slightly, they were found to be within the ranges normally associated with surface water.

There has also been some disagreement as to what represents an acceptable content of phosphorus (P) in the soil in order to release excess soluble P from eutrophic lakes and streams. Research has shown that the higher soil P level, the greater the amount or P that runs off (Sharpley et al., 1993), and the concentration of P in runoff increases in direct proportion to the P loading rate but decreases rapidly with successive storms (Edwards, 1993a: Edwards and Daniel, 1993).

Water quality is affected by many factors such as the nature of the soil, the geology of the area, the depth to water table, well construction and manure application rates, handling methods, and timing (Chapman, 1996). Barton (1995) suggested that the water supply in regions where poultry are grown should by analyzed for mineral and microbial content to determine suitability for consumption.

SOIL CONTAMINATION

With proper management and controlled transportation costs poultry manure and litter can be sold and used as fertilizers, feed or as sources of energy (Chipperfield, 1994; Nicholson and de Bode, 1994). However, if proper procedures are not followed for managing the litter or manure after removal from the chicken house, there is potential to lose valuable nutrients. Methods involving stockpiling uncovered manure during the winter season before application on cropland in the spring can result in up to five fold reductions in the N content of the manure (Savage, 1986).

N and P may pollute the soil after application of manure. If an excessive amount of manure and litter is applied to crops that are unable to fully utilize the N, the residual large nitrate content may leach through soils into ground water after harvesting and cause problems (Shepherd, 1993). The volatility of the N source is important when selecting the mode of application of the fertilizer. Some scientists (Noll, 1991; Schmitt and Rehm, 1992; Carter, 1993) have reported that when poultry litter and manure is surface applied, about one-half of the N and other components are available for the plants to utilize. Excess P presents a special problem because, as a result of its low solubility, it tends to be immobile in the soil. Consequently, it does not leach but adheres to the soil particles, contaminates surface water and causes erosion (Green, 1996).

Poultry growers frequently do not appreciate the large amounts of N being applied to the soil when spreading the manure and take little or no account of its nutrient content when planning application rates of manure, litter and subsequent inorganic fertilizer (Shepherd, 1993). This occurs because nutrient contents are variable, depend on many factors, and because of difficulties in estimating the actual amount of manure applied to a field (Shepherd, 1993) unless the quantities of N, P and potassium in manure, litter, and soil of a particular moisture content are determined by analysis (Beegle, 1988; Bitzer and Sims, 1988).

AIR QUALITY

Decomposition of poultry manure results in the release of volatile (VOC) and reactive organic compounds (ROC) into the air. Currently there is much concern about the release of ROC and their effect on the ozone layer. Hydrocarbon radicals, which oxidize nitrous oxide (emitted from the burning of gas and oil at high temperatures) to nitrogen dioxide, are provide from ROC. Sunlight causes the nitrogen dioxide to be converted back to nitrous oxide, releasing O^- ions which react with oxygen to form ozone. This reaction occurs where there is a high rate of production of nitrous oxide as occurs in metropolitan areas. Raised ozone concentrations at ground level are detrimental and can cause an increase in the incidence of respiratory problems in very young children, asthmatics and the elderly (Morse, 1996).

Minimizing the emissions of ammonia from manure also reduces the impact of agriculture on the environment. A high atmospheric concentration of ammonia can result in acidification of land and water surfaces, causing damage to plants and reducing plant biodiversity in natural systems (McGinn and Janzen, 1998). Ammonia emissions from manure were found to coincide with odours, which are a nuisance in areas of intensive livestock operations. Reducing ammonia emissions by altering manure management will also reduce problems caused by unpleasant odours.

Analytical results of 60 broiler manure samples submitted to the University of Arkansas Agricultural Diagnostic Service Lab showed that average N and potassium contents were 2.55% and 1.71%, respectively, at 22.1% moisture (Chapman and Snyder, 1992), but as much as half of this N may be subject to loss to the atmosphere by volatilization (Chapman, 1996). The loss of N would tend to increase with the length of time over which the manure is stored (Patterson, 1994). Sharpley *et al.* (1996) reported that increasing the time between litter application and rainfall from 1 to 35 days also caused a reduction of total N from 7.54% to 2.34%, ammonium-N (NH_3-N) from 5.53% to 0.11%, dissolved phosphorus (DP) from 0.74% to 0.45%, bioavailable phosphorus (BAP) from 0.99 to 0.65mg/l, by leaching and volatilization of N and adsorption of P. The main factors affecting N and P run-off from land to which manure has been applied include the rate, method and timing of application (Pionke *et al.*, 1996).

Laboratories for animal agriculture

FUNCTIONS AND FORMATION OF LABORATORIES

A key to successful waste management is good nutrient management which takes account of the nutrients present in animal diets, excreted nutrients, loss of nutrients during storage, transportation and application to the land, and use of the nutrients by the plants (Coffey, 1992; Clanton, 1993). Scientists (Jackson, 1958; Baldwin, 1985; Nahm, 1989; Morse, 1996) have suggested that a summary of the nutrient resources should be available to the producer, which at minimum, should include: (a) soil tests for pH, N, P and potassium; (b) nutrient analysis of manure, sludge, mortalities and effluent; (c) N contribution to the soil; and (d) N contribution to irrigation water. Chapman (1996) recommended that soil tests should be done at least once every two years. Analytical methods for poultry manure and litter will differ depending on whether these materials will be used for fertilizer or for feed (Nahm, 1989, 1992; AOAC, 1992). Chapman and Snyder (1992) developed guidelines on the basis of analytical results to help chicken growers to maintain a balanced fertility program using both animal manures and commercial fertilizer.

The nutrient content of poultry diets should also be analyzed whenever poultry feed formulations are developed. It is generally recognized that the chemical composition of feed ingredients is variable, especially those in by-products, poultry manure and litter which depend primarily on the original plant material, weather, soil conditions, and manufacturing processes. In fact, some of the older tabulated nutritional data becomes unacceptable because of the modern processes and efficiencies associated with newer manufacturing facilities and environmental regulations. Analytical values allow the laboratory to calculate the nutrient content of the feed ingredients, by-products, manure, litter, soil and the amount that should be spread on the crop (Nahm, 1995).

Universities and national research centres have operated separate analytical laboratories for different types of analyses, such as those evaluating diets and feed ingredients and those testing soil, water sources and pesticides. Private laboratories have also become involved. However, there are two factors tat can easily be overlooked by scientists and farmers (Nahm, 1995): (1) very few livestock farmers have any idea which is the best laboratory to use to analyse their samples of poultry feed, manure or litter, soil, or water and (2) these laboratories must be able to interpret the results for the farmers. Not many farmers can understand how these values obtained from the laboratory can best be applied to improve their enterprise, and not many laboratories have specialist who can advise farmers on how best to use poultry manure and litter without it having an adverse impact on the environment.

Dietary manipulation with the objective of reducing the concentrations of nutrients in manure and litter

For optimum growth and maintenance animals require to be fed on diets containing certain concentrations of essential nutrients such as amino acids, fatty acids, carbohydrates, water, minerals and vitamins. Areas involving livestock and poultry that are considered critical in an ecological context include odor, N and P output and feed digestibility (Scott, 1991; Coelho, 1994). Altering dietary formulations to protect the environment is possible provided that reliable analytical data are available (Nahm and Sung, 1995).

The primary function of dietary protein is to supply the amino acids required by the animal for structural and functional purposes. A large part of the N losses is a consequence of imbalance in the amino acid make up of the dietary protein or of inefficiencies of digestion and absorption. It therefore follows that the excretion of N in feces and urine can be influenced by dietary manipulation. For example, in one study in which the protein content of a diet fed to 24-week-old laying hens was reduced from 17% to 13%, fecal N excretion was shown to be reduced as much as one third without affecting production (Summers, 1993). Other researchers (Moran et al., 1992; Moran, 1994) have reduced dietary protein contents to 10 and 15%, while maintaining the proper amino acid levels for each age group of broilers and reduced litter N content by approximately 24% (percentage dry matter) without affecting weights gained by the birds. Recently, Blair et al. (1999) reported that reducing the dietary crude protein content resulted in a 10-27% decrease in the total amount of N excreted during the six week broiler rearing period, while there was a 30-35% reduction in daily N output from layers. To apply this policy successfully in practice it is necessary to supplement the diets with limiting amino acids.

The use of synthetic amino acids and the application of the concepts of ideal protein and digestible amino acids could reduce both the dietary protein concentration and N excretion by poultry and ammonia production from their manure (Baker, 1995; Parsons, 1995) without compromising the performance of the poultry flock. In a review of the topic Nahm and Carlson (1998) have suggested that the possible minimum protein requirements for replacement pullets are, respectively 16%, 13.5% and 11.5% for the 0-6, 7-12 and 13-18 week periods of development. The corresponding recommendations for 0-3 and 4-7 week old broilers are 18% and 16.5%, respectively.

One of the mineral elements which constitutes the inorganic part of plant and animal tissues is P, essential for formation and maintenance of bones. It also plays an important role in the body's metabolic functions during growth, maintenance and laying (Khan, 1994). P exists in both organic or inorganic forms. Significant amounts of P are present in cereal grains and vegetable protein. Between 50 to 80% of the P is stored in plant feed sources as phytin/phytic acid and is largely unavailable to monogastric animals (Scott, 1991). This so called "phytate P" also constitutes a significant portion of the P in animal waste. Up to 75% of P excreted by animals is in the form of phytate (O'Dell and de Boland, 1976). Before the animal can use this P the phytate molecule must be broken down.

Phytase is one enzyme that assists in increasing the available P content of plant sources and decreases the need for supplemental dietary P. This, in turn, leads to a reduction in P excretion. Simons and Varsteegh (1993) reported that chicks fed phytase excreted 40% less P than those receiving P from a mixture of dicalcium phosphate and mono-ammonium phosphate. Supplemental microbial phytase is effective in improving not only the availability of P in plant ingredients, but also the availabilities of Ca, Zn and amino acid N (Kornegay, 1996; Kornegay *et al.*, 1996). Nahm and Carlson (1998) have suggested that the minimal concentrations of P (shown as available P) required for pullets, layers and broilers, respectively, are 0.25%, 0.09% and 0.25%, provided phytase is added to the diet.

Other potential methods for reducing P excretion are feeding highly available sources of P, and not providing supplemental limestone or other forms of inorganic P to broilers during the last week of growth (42-49 days of age; Skinner *et al.*, 1992). Another effective strategy is to include hydroxylated vitamin D in the diet to improve P utilization (Edwards, 1993b).

Feeding enzymes such as carbohydrases, lipases and proteases can also modify feed ingredients by improving dietary nutritive values and thereby reducing manure production. Wyatt and Harker (1995) have shown that the feeding of wheat or wheat/barley-based broiler diets supplemented with such enzymes resulted in the production of 17-28% less fresh manure, equivalent to 12-15% (by weight) less waste dry matter.

Evaluating poultry manure and litter as feed sources in the laboratory

Poultry manure and litter have been used as feed ingredients (Ko, 1992; Kim *et al.*, 1993; Kim and Ko, 1995). These studies illustrated the wide variation that exists in nutrient contents of poultry manure and litter and this variability is attributed both to the planes of nutrition applied to the birds and the nature of the waste management systems used. Kim *et al.*(1993) showed that, when hens were fed on diets high in protein (and other nutrients), the amount of N, ash, calcium, P and other nutrients in the droppings were also high. Ko and Ahn (1987) reported that cage layer manure contained (on a dry matter basis) 28% crude protein, 12.7% crude fiber, 8.8%. calcium, and 2.5% P. However, when the same manure was analyzed on an air dry basis (Kim, 1993), the chemical composition was 24.5% crude protein, 10.1% crude fiber, 10.6% calcium and 2.7% P. Patterson (1997) reported that the crude protein and crude fiber contents of cage layer manure were 28.1% and 13%, respectively. It is not advisable, however, to apply these values universally to cage layer manure because many factors such as feed types, loss of N during storage and the moisture content of the manure can affect their compositions (Patterson, 1994). Recently, Xin and Lorimor (1998) reported that the N content of manure from a layer facility was actually 53% less than that estimated by the state, while the amount of phosphate was 30% greater. They concluded that effective nutrient management plans and feed quality programs are becoming ever more important as the animal production industry continues to grow.

Conclusion

Some of the nutrients present in poultry pass through the birds and end up in the manure which is then spread on the soil. Many of these then pass into the plants which grow on the soil and are frequently used as dietary ingredients. Poultry manure and litter contain N as well as 21 trace elements. Among these, N and P are the main causes of pollution of water, soil and air after application of excess amounts of manure and litter to the soil.

However, there is disagreement as to the amounts of N, P and other nutrients found in the water, soil and air depending on the nutrient management methods of animal diets, excreted nutrients, nutrient loss in storage, transportation and land application. Samples of feed, poultry manure and litter, soil and water must be regularly sent to animal agricultural laboratories to obtain reliable estimates of their N, P, and potassium concentrations, pH of the soil, as well as the nutrient contents for protecting the environmental concerns and for promoting the use of poultry manure and litter as feeds and fertilizers.

References

AOAC (1992). *Official Methods of Analysis. 15th edition.* Association of Analytical Chemists. Washington, D.C.

Baldwin, C. S. (1985) Poultry should utilize more of manure's trade value. *Newsletter for Ontario Egg Producers.* pp. 12-16.

Baker, D. H. (1995) Ideal protein in broilers. *Poultry Digest* (November). pp. 8-14.

Barton, L. (1995) Relevance of water quality to broiler and turkey performance. *Poultry Science* **75**:854-856.

Beegle, D. B. (1990) Manure nutrient management plans for new crops. In: *Proceedings of 1990 National Poultry Waste Management Symposium.* pp. 214-222. J. P. Blake and R. M. Hulet, ed. Auburn University, Auburn, AL.

Beegle, D. B. (1988) Fertilizer value of poultry manure and commercial fertilizer. In: *Proceedings of National Poultry Waste Management Symposium.* pp. 120-124. April 18-19. Columbus OH., The Ohio State University, Columbus, OH.

Bitzer, C. C. and Sims, T. J. (1988) Estimating the availability of nitrogen in poultry manure through laboratory and field studies. *Journal of Environmental Quality* **17**(1):47-54.

Blair, R., Jacob, J. P., Ibraham, S. and Wang, P. (1999) Diets for nitrogen use to minimize nitrogen pollutions from poultry waste. *Journal of Applied Poultry Research* **8**:25-47.

Carter, T. (1993) *Soil facts-poultry manure as a fertilizer source.* N. C. Cooperative Extension Service, N. C. State University, Raleigh, NC.

Chapman, S. L. (1996) Soil and solid poultry waste nutrient management and water quality. *Poultry Science* **75**:862-866.

Chapman, S. L. and Snyder, C. S. (1992) Poultry manure as a substitute for commercial fertilizer. *Soils and Fertilizers Information Article 2-92.* University of Arkansas, Cooperative Extension Service, Little Rock, AR.

Chipperfield, K. (1994) Fraser Valley poultry industry waste management survey. *Sustainable Poultry Farming Group Final Report and Resource Binder 1991-1994.* Project SCP 1109, Abbotsford, BC, Canada.

Clanton, P. E. (1993) Nutrient characteristics of manure. *Livestock Waste Management Conference.* pp. 73-75. Minnesota Experimental Service, University of Minnesota, Minneapolis, MN.

Coelho, M. B. (1994) Ecological nutrition: A costly or smart move? *Feedstuffs* (June 10) **66**:13-15.

Coffey, M. T. (1992) An industry perspective on environmental and waste management issues: Challenge for the feed industry. *Proceedings Georgia Nutrition Conference.* pp. 144-148. University of Georgia, Athens, GA.

Darling, W. A. (1994) Groundwater pollution prevention regulations from the state and local perspective. In: *Proceedings of 1994 National Poultry Waste Management Symposium*. pp. 10-18. P. H. Patterson and J. P. Blake, ed. Auburn University, Auburn, AL.

Edwards, D. R. (1993a) Transport of phosphorus from land areas treated with animal manures. In: *Proceedings of 1993 AWRC Research Conference*. p. 25. University of Arkansas, Fayetteville, AR.

Edwards, D. R. and Daniel, T. C. (1992) Environmental impacts of on-farm boiler waste disposal-A review. *Bioresource Technology* **41**:9-93.

Edwards, D. R. and Daniel, T. C. (1993) Effect of poultry litter application rate and rainfall intensity on quality of runoff from fescue grass plots. *Journal of Environmental Quality* **22**:361-365.

Edwards, H. M., Jr. (1993b) Dietary 1,25-Dihydroxycholecalciferol supplementation increases natural phytate phosphorus utilization in chickens. *American Institute of Nutrition* 568-577.

Francis, C. (1995) What is sustainability? In: *Proceedings of Agriculture and People-Building a Shared Environment*. pp. 70-71. Ithaca, NY. Oct 9-10. University of Nebraska, Lincoln, NE.

Fretz, T. A., Keeney, D. R. and Sterrett, S. B. (1993) Sustainability: Defining the new paradigm. *Horticulture Technology* **3**:118-126.

Gordillo, R. M. and Cabrera, M. L. (1997) Mineralizable nitrogen in broiler litters: I. Effect of selected litter chemical characteristics. *Journal of Environmental Quality* **26**:1672-1679.

Green, L. W. (1996) Effects of trace mineral manipulation on animal performance, waste management. *Proceedings of the Plains Nutrition Council Waste Management Seminar*. pp. 32-43.

Heathman, G. C., Sharpley, A. N., Smith, S. J. and Robinson (1995) Poultry litter application and water quality in Oklahoma. *Fertilizer Research* **40**:165-173.

Ihnat, M. and Fernandes, L. (1996) Trace elemental characterization of composted poultry manure. *Bioresource Technology* **57(2)**:143-156.

Jackson, M. L. (1958) *Soil Chemical Analysis*. Prentice-Hall, Inc. Englewood Cliffs, NJ.

Khan, N. (1994) Phosphorus: The essential element. *Feed Mix* (Special Issue). pp. 4-6.

Kim, J. H. (1993) Studies on nutrition and feed value of the whole crop corn ensiled with cage layer manure for ruminants. *A thesis for the Doctorate Degree*, Gyong San National University, South Korea.

Kim, J. H., Yokota, Y., Ko, Y. D., Okajima, T., and Ohshima, M. (1993) Nutritional quality of whole crop corn ensiled with cage layer manure. I. Quality, voluntary feed intake and digestibility of the silage in goats. *Asian-Australian Journal of Animal Science* **6(1)**:45-51.

Kim, J. H. and Ko, Y. D. (1995) Body weight gain, feed conversion and feed cost of Korean native goats fed corn-manure silages. *Asian-Australian Journal of Animal Science* **8(5)**:427-431.

Kim, K. S., Choi, H. L. and Kang, S. M. (1995) The improvement of animal manure systems and their utilization. *Korean National Livestock Research Report*. pp. 24-32.

Ko, Y. D. (1992) A study on corn and broiler litter utilization. *Korean Journal of Grassland Science* **14(2)**:132-141.

Ko, Y. D. and Ahn, B. G. (1987) A study on the corn-layer manure silage about digestibility and silage fermentation. *Korean Journal of Animal Science* **29(11)**: 501-508.

Kornegay, E. T. (1996) Nutritional, environmental and economical considerations for using phytase in pig and poultry diets. In: *Proceedings International Symposium. Management of Food Animals to Enhance the Environment*. June 4-7. Blacksburg, VA.

Kornegay, E. T., Denhow, D. M., Yi, Z. and Ravindran V. (1996) Response of broilers to graded levels of Natuphos phytase added to corn-soybean meal based diets containing three levels of nonphytate phosphorus. *British Journal of Nutrition* (In Press).

McGinn, S. M. and Janzen, H. H. (1998) Ammonia sources in agriculture and their measurement. *Canadian Journal of Soil Science* **78(1)**:139-148.

Moor, Jr., P. A., Daniel, T. C., Sharpley, A. N., and Wood, C. W. (1995) Poultry manure management: environmentally sound options. *Journal of Soil and Water Conservation* **50(3)**:321-327.

Moran, E. T., Jr. (1994) Significance of dietary crude protein to broiler carcass quality. *Proceeding Maryland Nutrition Conference for Feed Manufacturers*. pp. 1-11. University of Maryland, College Park, MD.

Moran, E. T., Jr., Bushong, R. D. and Bigili, S. F. (1992) Reducing dietary crude protein for broilers while satisfying amino acid requirements by least-cost formulation: Live performance, litter composition and yield of fast-food carcass cuts at six weeks. *Poultry Science* **71**:1687-1694.

Morse, D. (1996) Impacts of water and air quality legislation on the poultry industry. *Poultry Science* **75**:857-861.

Nahm, K. H. (1989) *The Complete Agricultural Lab Manual* (English Edition). Taegu University Press. pp. 3-5.

Nahm, K. H. (1992) *Practical Guide to Feed, Forage and Water Analysis* (English Edition). Yoo Han Publishing Co. pp. 22-36.

Nahm, K. H. (1995) Future direction for the livestock production in Korea. *Proceedings of the Korean Animal Production Conference*. pp. 32-63.

Nahm, K. H. and Carlson, C. W. (1998) The possible minimum chicken nutrient requirements for protecting the environment and improving cost efficiency. *Asian-Australian Journal of Animal Science* **11(6)**:755-768.

Nahm, K. H. and Sung, C. H. (1995) Improving management on layer farms through utilization of a checklist: A field report. *Korean Journal of Animal Nutrition and Feed* **19(4)**:261-272.

Narrod, C. A., Reynnells, R. D. and Wells, H. (1994) Poultry waste utilization issues; a focus on the Delmare Peninsula. pp. 249-255. In: *Proceedings of 1994 National Poultry Waste Management Symposium.* P. H. Patterson and J. P. Blacke, ed. Auburn University, Auburn, AL.

Nicholson, R. J. and de Bode, M. (1994) Environmental regulations affect in poultry production in Europe. pp. 52-61. In: *National Poultry Waste Management Symposium.* Auburn, AL.

Noll, S. (1991) *Turkey manure handling. Ag-Fo-5653-B.* Minnesota Extension Service, University of Minnesota, St. Paul, MN.

O'Dell, B. L. and de Boland, A. (1976) Complexation of phytate with proteins and cations in corn germ and oilseed meals. *Journal of Agricultural Food Chemistry* **24**:804-808.

Parsons, C. M. (1995) Nutrient utilization and methods of assessment-An environmental perspective. *Degussa Technical Symposium.* May 17. pp. 1-5.

Patterson, P. H.(1993) Nutrient management poultry manure utilization. *Lancaster Farming* **38(33)**:A-22.

Patterson, P. H. (1994) Estimating manure production based on nutrition and production: laying hens. In: *Proceedings of 1994 National Poultry Waste Symposium.* pp. 90-96. P. H. Patterson and J. L. Blake, ed. Auburn University, Auburn, AL.

Patterson, P. H. (1997) Nutrient contents in caged layer manure. In: *Proceedings of 1997 National Poultry Waste Symposium.* pp. 67-78. P. H. Patterson and J. L. Blake, ed. Auburn University, Auburn, AL.

Pescatore, A. J., Cocanougher, J. B., Henken, K., Green, W. H., Potts, J. and Rasnake, M. (1998) Poultry farms did not affect well water. *Southern Poultry Science Meeting.* Atlanta, GA. pp. 72-74.

Pionke, H. B., Gburek, W. J., Sharpley, A. N. and Schnabel, R. R. (1996) Flow and nutrient export patterns for an agricultural hill-land. *Water Resources Research* **32**:1795-1804.

Savage, S. (1986) Laying hen numbers need to be balanced with available land. *Feedstuffs* (November 24):15, 22.

Schmitt, M. and Rehm, G. (1992) *Fertilizing cropland with poultry manure. Ag-Fo-5885-C.* Minnesota Extension Service, University of Minnesota, St. Paul, MN.

Scott, T. A. (1991) Nutritional effects of waste production from monogastrics. *Canadian Society of Animal Science Meetings.* Chilliwack, BC.

Sharpley, A. N., Daniel, T. C. and Edwards, D. R. (1993) Phosphorus movement in the landscape. *Journal of Production Agriculture* **6**:492-500.

Sharpley, A. N., Meisinger, J.J., Breeuwsma, A. Sim., T., Datiid, T. C. and Shepers (1996) Impact of animal manure management on ground and surface water quality. pp. 173-242. In J. Hatford (ed). *Effective management of animal waste as a soil resource.* Lewis Publication, Boca Raton, FL (in press).

Shepherd, M. A. (1993) Poultry manure and nitrate leaching. *World Poultry Science Journal* **49**:171-172.

Simons, P. C. M. and Varsteegh, H. A. J. (1993) Role of phytase in poultry nutrition. In: *Enzymes and Animal Nutrition.* Wenk, C. and Boessinger, M., ed. Kartause-Ittingen, Switzerland, October 13-16. p. 192.

Skinner, J. T., Izat, A. Z. and Waldrop, P. W. (1992) Studies on calcium and phosphorus requirements of finishing broilers. *Journal of Applied Poultry Science* 1:42.

Summers, J. D. (1993) Reducing nitrogen excretion of the laying hen by feeding lower crude protein diets. *Poultry Science* **72**:1473-1478.

Vanotti, M. B. and Bundy, L. G. (1994) Corn nitrogen recommendations based on yield response data. *Journal of Production Agriculture* **7**:249-256.

Vodela, J. K., Renden, J. A., Lenz, S. D., Mcelhenney, W. H. and Kemppainene (1997) Drinking water contaminants (Arsenic, Cadmium, Lead, Benzene and Trichloroethylene). 1. Interaction of contaminants with nutritional status on general performance and immune functions in broiler chickens. *Poultry Science* **76**:1474-1492.

Weaver, W. D., Jr., and Sounder, G. H. (1990) Feasibility and economics of transporting poultry waste. In: *Proceedings of 1990 National Poultry Waste Management Symposium.* pp. 123-129. J. P. Blake and R. M. Hulet, ed. Auburn University, Auburn, AL.

Wyatt, C. L. and Harker, A. (1995) Application of feed enzymes to commercial wheat and barley based poultry feeds. *Proceedings California Nutrition Conference.* pp. 203-211. University of California, Davis, CA.

Xin, H. and Lorimor, J. C. (1998) Research may lead to more accurate manure management plans. *Feedstuffs* (May 8):15, 48-49.

Zygmunt, H. (1994) Groundwater pollution prevention regulations from the state and local perspective. In: *Proceedings of 1994 National Poultry Waste Management Symposium.* pp. 7-9. P.H. Patterson and J. P. Blake, ed. Auburn University, Auburn, AL.

Journal of Science and Technology, Taegu University Vol. 8(1): 41-52 (2001) 197

Evaluating the Nitrogen Content in Animal Manure with the Conventional Kjeldahl Method

K. H. Nahm

Feed and Nutrition Laboratory, College of Natural Resources, Taegu University, Gyong San, 712-714, South Korea. E-mail: nahmkh@daegu.ac.kr

INTRODUCTION

Poultry litters and manures or livestock manures (hereafter referred to as animal manures) used as feed sources (Ko and Ahn, 1987; Kim et al., 1993) and added to both pastures and crops sources of plant nutrients (Kirchman, 1985; Sutton et al., 1986) can also contribute to the pollution of the natural environment by volatilization of ammonia and leaching of nitrate (Pratt et al., 1976; Prins and Snijders, 1987). Both the beneficial and harmful effects of manure application depend mainly on the total quantity of nitrogen (N) and the forms in which it is added (Faassen and van Dijk, 1987).

With increasing emphasis on accurate feeding or agronomic land application of nutrients from animal manures, greater demands are being placed on the analytical processes associated with animal manures' characterization. Significant amounts of N in animal manures can be in volatile forms (Azevedo and Stout, 1974; Kirchmann, 1985) making it difficult to quantify the total N content.

Silage or other types of feeds which contain animal manures or animal manures for fertilizers will likely be fed to livestock animals or land applied the form in which it was sampled. Therefore, it is critical to use values in the report that are based on the "As Received" basis (SD-NRCS-FS-38, 1999).

New analytical methods and laboratory equipment for N analysis methods have been introduced by several research reports. Whenever these new analytical methods are used it is necessary to compare the results with the results of the conventional Kjeldahl method to determine if these new analytical methods are accurate or not. However, many of these methods are not useful in the practical laboratory when animal feed which contains animal manure or animal manure for fertilizer are to be analyzed to determine N content. This may be one of the reasons why many laboratories still have kept their conventional Kjeldahl digestion and distillation apparatus.

In the following sections, some of the published information about factors influencing the content of N in the process of laboratory analysis and available information regarding the laboratory techniques for animal manures are reviewed. Within this context, attention is focused on the accurate laboratory processes for the analysis of animal feeds which contain animal manures or animal manures for fertilizer with minimal laboratory equipment and one standard solution.

COMPARISON OF CONVENTIONAL KJELDAHL N METHODS TO MODIFIED PROCEDURES

Nitrogen in organic materials such as soil, plant materials and animal manure is generally measured by the Kjeldahl method (Bremner and Mulvaney, 1982; Bremner and Yeomans, 1988; Nelson and Sommers, 1980; Nahm, 1992) and expressed as total Kjeldahl N. Kjeldahl N includes mostly the organic and ammoniacal N (Bremner and Mulvaney, 1982).

Research scientists have developed various modified procedures of the Kjeldahl N procedure. However, there were no significant differences between N content in fresh manures measured by the Kjeldahl methods alone and modified methods (Haynes, 1980; Mahimairaja *et al.*, 1990; Cabrera and Beare, 1993). This indicates that most of the N in fresh manures is present in organic and ammoniacal forms and was recovered by standard Kjeldahl digestion alone (Table 1).

Rapid methods for determining major nutrients in livestock manures were evaluated for accuracy and possible on farm use (Chescheir *et al.*, 1985). Methods are: (a) correlation of nutrients with specific gravity (measured with a soil hydrometer), (b) ammonia electrode, (c) water analysis field kits, and (d) a 'nitrogen meter' that measures nitrogen gas pressure in a reaction chamber. These scientists say, however, that rapid methods should not replace periodic laboratory analysis by approved standard methods, but they can be used to improve accuracy of land application rates.

FACTORS AFFECTING THE N CONTENT IN LIVESTOCK MANURE

Several research reports have shown that drying animal manure before chemical analysis resulted in reducing the content of N in the manure (Witter and Lopez-Real, 1987; Mahimairaja *et al.*, 1990; Gale *et al.*, 1991; Wood and Dall, 1991; Robinson and Sharpley, 1995) (Table 2).

However, there are also various research studies that compare difference in breeds, various drying techniques and temperatures, pH of the manure, moisture content of the manure and others as to their impact on animal manure N content. The major reduction in total N during drying may be due to the loss of volatile

N compounds such as ammonia and amincs. Mahimairaja *et al.* (1990) showed that there was a corresponding release in NH_3 which accounted for more than 95% of the loss of total N. They reported that the extent of reduction in the total N due to drying decreased as follows: poultry manure > pig slurry > dairy slurry. Drying has almost no effect on the total N content of horse and sheep manure. Whereas the former three manures contain both feces and urine (or uric acid) the latter two contained mainly feces. This report suggested that most of the N loss

Table 1. Nitrogen contents(g Kg^{-1}; expressed on a freeze dried weight basis) of fresh animal manures measured by the standard Kjeldahl and its modified methods (Mahimairaja *et al.*, 1990)

| | Kjeldahl | Pretreatment[1] | | | | | | |
	alone	Salicylic $Na_2S_2O_3$	Aqueous $Na_2S_2O_3$	Devarda's alloy	Zn-$CrK(SO_4)_2$	$KMnO_4$ -Fe	H_2O_2 -Fe	NaOCl -Fe
Poultry	62.6[3]	63.2	64.2	64.6	64.3	64.3	63.9	58.6
Poultry[2]	35.7	43.6	41.6	42.8	44.8	44.0	43.7	36.0
Pig	46.3	45.8	46.2	46.0	46.1	46.9	46.8	41.4
Dairy	33.6	34.6	34.7	33.8	33.2	34.0	34.6	30.0
Horse	27.6	28.0	27.7	28.3	27.6	28.2	28.2	28.2
Sheep	21.3	22.0	21.8	22.0	21.0	21.5	21.0	22.6

[1] Pretreatment was followed by standard Kjeldahl digestion.
[2] Composted with wood chips.
[3] The standard deviation values for triplicate samples ranged from 0.82 to 3.72.

Table 2. Animal manure total N loss rate (%) as affected by oven drying temperature and length of time

Types of Manure	Total N loss rate	Drying temperature and Time length
Poultry manure	8	
Pig slurry	9	
Dairy slurry	9	105℃ for 48 hrs[1]
Horse manure	0	
Sheep manure	4	
Broiler litter (Hardwood shavings)	12	60℃ for 3 days[2]
Hen manure	19	66℃ for 48 hrs[3]

[1] Mahimairaja *et al.* (1990)
[2] Wood and Hall (1991)
[3] Gate *et al.* (1991)

occurred from urinary compounds (urea and uric acid). The major N component of poultry manure is uric acid, which readily decomposes to ammoniacal N forms (Schefferle, 1965; MacMillan *et al.*, 1972; Siegel *et al.*, 1975; Reddy *et al.*, 1980; Gale *et al.*, 1991). Most of the N in fresh poultry and animal manure is present mainly as urea or uric acid and during drying most of the NH_3 is released through chemical and/or biological decomposition of these compounds (Burnett and Dondero, 1969; Azevedo and Stout, 1974; Krogdahl and Dalsgard, 1981).

Slow drying of animal manures at low temperatures (air drying or room temperature drying) has been shown to cause increased losses of N than fast drying at high temperatures (oven drying) (Adriano *et al.*, 1974; Giddens and Rao, 1975). This difference in N loss suggest that uric acid and urea hydrolyzing microorganisms or extracellular hydrolases are denatured or destroyed by high temperatures or that the rapid loss of moisture with oven drying resulted in greater conservation of N than did air drying. Microorganisms also are inactivated by freezing followed by freeze drying and therefore there is less decomposition of uric acid (Schefferle, 1965).

The magnitude of losses of N is a function of drying time. Scientists (Westerman *et al.*, 1983; Edwards and Daniel, 1993) reported that concentration of N and NH_3-N decreased with decreasing drying time between application and simulated rainfall. Thus the influence of drying time on the N content in animal manure should be considered when determining the optimum time in the laboratory analysis.

Acidification of manure is an effective means of reducing volatilization of ammonia from manure during storage, application and drying (Stevens *et al.*, 1989; Frost *et al.*, 1990; ten Have, 1993). Since the behavior of most volatile compounds depends upon pH, those losses may vary from sample to sample (Derikx *et al.*, 1994). These scientists proved the loss of ammonia and volatile fatty acids from pig, cattle and poultry manure was a function of pH. It was shown that above pH 8, all ammonia was volatilized and below pH 5 all volatile fatty acids evaporated. Total fixation of ammonia was achieved below pH 4. pH of poultry houses and litter also significantly affects nitrogen loss due to ammonia volatilization (Burgess *et al.*, 1998).

Animal manures in laboratories are typically oven-dried prior to N analysis without accounting for the ammonia loss from the manure during this process. Samples should not be dried prior to analysis (Gale *et al.*, 1991). When laboratory analysis values that have experienced N loss are used to calculate animal manure to the amount of feed or land application, it is likely that more nitrogen is being applied or fed than is estimated. In a study involving manures, broiler litter, sewage sludge and soil amendments, Douglas and Magdoff (1991) and Gordillo and Cabrera (1997) found a good relationship between the function of organic N mineralized and N released.

THE KJELDAHL METHODS FOR ANALYZING N CONTENT IN ANIMAL MANURES

Crude protein analysis (AOAC 1980; AOAC, 1984; Nahm, 1989; Nahm, 1992)

Reagents

1) Sulfuric acid: concentrated reagent grade, 95-98% H_2SO_4
2) Copper catalytic salt mixture (15 g K_2SO_4 and 0.04 g anhydrous $CuSO_4$)
3) Sodium hydroxide solution (45%)
4) Boric acid (4%)
5) Tashiro's indicator
6) Zinc-mossy
7) Standard hydrochloric acid (N/14 HCl)

Apparatus

1) Macro Kjeldahl nitrogen digestion and distillation apparatus
2) Kjeldahl flasks (800 ml or 1,000 ml)
3) Erlenmeyer flasks (500 ml)
4) Two burettes

Procedure

1) Sample pretreatment

 (1) Freeze a representative portion of the sample upon receipt

  A. If wet soil, manure, sewage or sludge and silage or other feeds containing manure or being treated with ammonia:

    a. To prevent the loss of organic N and NH_4-N, prepare the samples while frozen, one at a time, chop small portions in a blender for about 15 seconds each. Combine and thoroughly mix portions.

    b. Weigh about 5 g of silage samples or other feed (1 to 2 g for soil, manures, sewage or sludge) of the sample, recording the exact weight, in tared filter paper that has been decreased into a quarter fold. At the same time prepare a flask to be run as a blank.

    c. Carefully fold the paper around the sample to avoid loss.

  B. If liquid manure:

    a. Place a numbered Kjeldahl flask on a cork ring on a top-loader balance that reads to 0.01 g. Obtain the tare weight.

    b. Place contents in a blender and blend at a speed to keep the particle throughout the sample. While blending, withdraw an aliquot using a serological pipette with the tip cut off.

    c. Pipette more than 10 g of sample into the Kjeldahl flask. Record the sample weight. At the same time prepare a flask to be run as blank.

d. Use water to wash down any sample that may have adhered to the neck. Use as small of an amount of water as possible.

C. If liquid samples which contain some solid particle with urine only:

a. Tare a small beaker on an analytical balance that read to 0.01 g.

b. Using a glass rod or pipette with the tip cut off, throughly mix the sample.

c. Weigh 1 to 2 g of sample to the exact amount. At the same time prepare a flask to be run as a blank.

d. Quantitatively transfer the sample to a number Kjeldahl flask, rinsing the beaker with water from a water bottle. Use as small of an amount of water as possible.

2) Digestion

(1) Add K_2SO_4 (15 g) and anhydrous $CuSO_4$ (0.04 g) with 40 ml concentrated H_2SO_4 and two glass boiling beads.

(2) Turn on the exhaust fan to the digestion rack.

(3) Digest at a warm temperature for 30 minutes after the digest clears(about 1 and a half hours).

(4) Turn the flask frequently during digestion, using a glove.

(5) Allow the exhaust fan to run after digestion until the flasks are cool.

(6) When the flasks are cool, slowly add about 300 ml of deionized water to each. Swirl to mix. Allow to cool before distilling.

3) Distillation

(1) Add 80 ml of 4% boric acid to the appropriate number of Erlenmeyer flasks and place of the lower shelf of the distillation apparatus. Insert the condenser tube into the flasks.

(2) Turn on the condenser water.

(3) Slowly add 80 ml of 45% NaOH to the Kjeldahl digest by allowing it to run down the neck and layer at the bottom of the Kjeldahl flask.

(4) Add a few pieces of zinc to the flask to prevent bumping.

(5) Place the flask on the distillation heater inserting the rubber stopper into the mouth of the flask to insure a tight seal.

(6) Quickly swirl the flask vigorously to mix the content and place the flask back on the heater. Immediately raise the Erlenmeyer flask up to the upper shelf so the condenser tube is submerged beneath the boric acid.

(7) Turn the heater switch to high temperature (HI).

(8) Allow the flasks to distill until about 250 ml of distillate has been collected in the Erlenmeyer.

(9) Remove the Erlenmeyer when the volume of distillate reaches 250 ml and place on a plastic beaker on deionized water under the condenser tip. Shut

the heater switch off.

4) Titration
  (1) Add 0.4 ml of Tashiro's indicator to each Erlenmeyer flask.
  (2) Insert the magnetic stirring bar into flask, place on the stirring plate and turn on the plate.
  (3) Titrate the N/14 HCl to a neutral gray end point. Color change sequence: green(basic) - gray(neutral) - purple(acidic).
  (4) Read the burette to the nearest 0.1 ml and record.
5) Calculation
  Sample (ml N/14 HCl) - Blank (ml N/14 HCl) = ml N/14 HCl

$$\frac{A \times 6.25}{10 \times SW} = \%\ \text{protein}$$

  A: ml N/14 HCl titrated   SW: Sample Weight

Total nitrogen determination (AOAC, 1980; AOAC 1984; Nahm, 1989; Nahm, 1992)

Reagents
  1) Salicylic acid
  2) Sodium thiosulfate ($Na_2S_2O_3 \cdot 5H_2O$)
  3) Other reagents are the same as in the protein determination.
Apparatus
  All of the apparatus are the same as in the protein determination.
Procedure
  1) Sample pretreatments
    Sample pretreatments are same as in the protein determination.
  2) Analytical procedure
  (1) Weigh out about amount of samples depending on sample types into a Kjeldahl flask as crude protein determination. At the same time, prepare a flask to be run as a blank.
  (2) Dissolve 1 g of salicylic acid in 40 ml H_2SO_4 and then add to Kjeldahl flask.
  (3) Let the flask stand for about 30 minutes. Shake the solution several times while you are waiting.
  (4) Add 5 g of $Na_2S_2O_3 \cdot 5H_2O$ (Sodium thiosulfate) to each flask. Add 2 glass bead to each flask. Immediately place the flask on the digestion rack and turn on the fan. Warm gradually until fumes begin to appear.
  (5) Add K_2SO_4 (15 g) and anhydrous $CuSO_4$ (0.04 g).
  (6) Digest the 1 and 1/2 or 2 hour as in Kjeldahl determination (Without

adding K_2SO_4 and anhydrous $CuSO_4$, 1 and half hours digestion is maximum for urine sample).

(7) After digestion, let flasks cool and add 300 ml deionized water to each flask.

(8) Continue as in Kjeldahl protein determination subsequent to digestion, distillation and titration.

3) Calculation

Sample (ml N/14 HCl) - Blank (ml N/14 HCl) = ml N/14 HCl

$$\frac{A}{SW \ X \ 10} = \text{Total Nitrogen}$$

A: ml N/14 HCl titrated   SW: Sample Weight

4) For urine samples, do not add K_2SO_4 and anhydrous $CuSO_4$.

Sample weight (ml N/14 HCl) - Blank (ml N/14 HCl) = ml N/14 HCl

$$\frac{A}{\text{ml sample}} = \text{Total Nitrogen}$$

A: ml N/14 HCl titrate

CONCLUSION

Recently, new methods and equipment for determination of protein and total nitrogen contents in animal feeds have been developed. These methods and equipment, however, are sometimes inappropriate for analyzing animal feed containing manure of animal manure used for fertilizer. Because much of the nitrogen is lost in the pretreatment or analytical process of these materials, the animal feed containing manure or manure used for fertilizer should be analyzed on an "As Received" Basis.

The conventional Kjeldahl method is recommended for analyzing animal feed containing animal manure or animal manure used for fertilizer because the analytical results obtained from the Kjeldahl method are not different from those obtained from newly developed methods and can be done accurately in practical laboratories. This method also utilizes only one standard solution in the analysis for crude protein and total nitrogen determination.

Journal of Science and Technology, Taegu University Vol. 8(1): 41-52 (2001)   205

ABSTRACT

Accurate amounts of crude protein total nitrogen (N) contents must be analyzed in samples which contain animal manure for animal feed and animal manure or sludge or sewage used for land fertilizer. This process requires that sample must be pretreated by freezing or all samples be analyzed on an "As Received" basis. Recently new analytical methods and lab equipment have been introduced by several scientists, but some of them are not practical in analyzing these samples in laboratories. The analytical results obtained from the conventional Kjeldahl method are different from those obtained from newly developed methods and equipment, and one standard solution for crude protein and total nitrogen determination is utilized in the conventional Kjeldahl method.

(Key words: nitrogen, manure, sludge, lab equipment, Kjeldahl method)

REFERENCES

Association of Official Analytical Chemists, 1980. Official Methods of Analysis. 13th ed.

Association of Official Analytical Chemists, 1984. Official Methods of Analysis. Sec. 7.033-7.037. 14th ed. Association of Official Analytical Chemists, Washington, DC.

Adriano, D. C., Chang, A. C., Sharpless, R., 1974. Nitrogen loss from manure as influenced by moisture and temperature. J Environment Qual, 3(3), 258-261.

Azevedo, J., Stout, P. R., 1974. Farm animal manures: An overview of their role in the agricultural environment. Manual 44. California Agric Exp Sta Ext Ser, Berkeley, CA.

Bremner, J. M., Mulvaney, C. S., 1982. Nitrogen-Total. In: Page, A. L. (Ed.) Methods of Soil Analysis, Part 2, 2nd Edition. Am Soc Agron, Madison, WI, pp. 595-624.

Bremner, J. M., Yeomans, J. C., 1988. Laboratory techniques for determination of different forms of nitrogen. In: Wilson, J. R. (Ed), Advances in Nitrogen Cycling in Agricultural Ecosystems. CAB International, Willingford, UK, pp. 399-414.

Burgess, R. P., Carey, J. B., Shafer, D. J., 1998. The impact of pH on nitrogen retention in laboratory analysis of broiler litter. Poultry Sci 77, 1620-1722.

Burnett, W. E., Dondero, N. C., 1969. Microbiological and chemical change in poultry manure associated with decomposition and odor generation. Cornell Ann Waste Management Conf, Syracuse, NY. pp. 271-291.

Cabrera, M. L., Beare, M. H., 1993. Alkaline-persulfate oxidation for determining total nitrogen in microbial biomass extracts. Soil Sci Am J 57, 1007-1012.

Chescheir, G. M., Westerman, P. W., Safley, Jr., L. M., 1985. Rapid methods for determining nutrients in livestock manures. Am Soc of Ag Eng 28(6), 1817-1824.

Derikx, P. J. L., Willers, H. C., ten Have, P. J. W., 1994. Effect of pH on the behaviour of volatile compounds during dry-matter determination. Bioresource Technology 49, 41-45.

Douglas, B. F., Magdoff, F. R., 1991 An evaluation of nitrogen mineralization indices for organic residues. J Environ Qual 20, 368-372.

Edwards, D. R., Daniel., T. C., 1993. Effect of poultry litter application rate and rainfall intensity on quality of runoff from Fescue grass plots. J Environ Qual 22, 361-365.

Faassen, H. G., van Dijk, T. A., 1987. Manure as a source of nitrogen and phosphorus in soils. In: van der Meer, G., Unwin, R. J., Van Dijk, T. A., Ennik, G. C. (Eds.) Animal Manure on Grassland and Fodder Crops: Fertilizer or Waste. Martinus Nijhoff Publishers, Dordrecht, Netherlands, pp. 27-45.

Frost, J. P., Stevens, R. J., Laughlin, R. J., 1990. Effect of separation and acidification of cattle slurry on ammonia volatilization and on the efficiency of slurry nitrogen for herbage production. J Agric Sci 15, 49-56.

Gale, P. M., Phillips, J. M., May, M. L., Wolf, D. C., 1991. Effect of drying on the plant nutrient content of hen manure. J Prod Agric 4(2), 246-250.

Giddens, J., Rao, A. M., 1975. Effect of incubation and contact with soil on microbial and nitrogen changes in poultry manure. J Environ Qual 4, 275-278.

Gordillo, R. M., Cabrera, M. L., 1997. Mineralizable nitrogen in broiler litter: I. Effect of selected litter chemical characteristics. J Environ Qual, 26, 1672- 1679.

Haynes, R. J., 1980. A comparison of two modified Kjeldahl digestion techniques for multi-element plant analysis with conventional wet and dry ashing methods. Commun in Soil Science and Plant Analysis 11(5), 459-467.

Kim, J. H., Yokota, Y., Ko, Y. D., Okajima, T., Ohshima, M., 1993. Nutritional quality of whole crop corn ensiled with cage layer manure. I. Quality, voluntary feed intake and digestibility of the silage in goats. Asian-Australian J Anim Sci 6(1), 45-51.

Kirchman, H., 1985. Losses, plant uptake and utilization of manure nitrogen during a production cycle. Acta Agric Scandinavia, 24, 1-77.

Ko, Y. D., Ahn, B. G., 1987. A study on the corn-layer manure silage about digestibility and silage fermentation. Korean J Anim Sci 29(11), 501-508.

Krogdahl, A., Dalsgard, B., 1981. Estimation of nitrogen digestibility in poultry. 1. Content and distribution of major urinary compounds in excreta. Poultry Sci 60, 2480-2485.

MacMillan, K., Scott, T. W., Bateman, T. W., 1972. A study of corn response and soil nitrogen transformations upon application of different rates and sources of chicken manure. In: Loehr, R. C. (Ed.), Proc Cornell Agric Waste Management Conf, Rochester, NY. Graphics Management Corp, Washington, DC, pp. 481-494.

Mahimairaja, S., Bolan, N. S., Hedley, M. J., Macgregor, A. N., 1990. Evaluation of methods of measurement of nitrogen in poultry and animal manures. Fertilizer Research 24, 141-148.

Nahm, K. H., 1989. The Complete Agricultural Lab Manual (English Edition). Yoo Han Pub. Co., Seoul, Korea, pp. 8-12, 24-25.

Nahm, K. H., 1992. Practical Guide to Feed, Forage and Water Analysis (English Edition). Yoo Han Pub. Co., Seoul, Korea, pp. 30-35, 47, 58-60.

Nelson, D. W., Sommer, L. E., 1980. Total nitrogen analysis of soil and plant tissues. J Assoc Off Anal Chem 63, 770-778.

Pratt, P. F., Davis, S., Scharpless, R. G., 1976. A four year field trial with animal manures. 1. Nitrogen balances and yields. Hilgardia 44, 99-125.

Prins, W. H., Snijders, P. J. M., 1987. Negative effects of animal manure on grassland due to surface spreading and injection. In: van der Meer, G., H., Unwin, R. J., Van Dijk, T. J., Ennik, G. C. (Eds.), Animal Manure on Grassland and Fodder Corps: Fertilizer or Waste. Martinus Nijhoff Publishers, Dordrecht, Netherlands, pp. 119-135.

Reddy, K. R., Khaleel, R., Overcach, M. R., 1980. Nitrogen, phosphorus and carbon transformations in a coastal plain soil treated with animal manures. Agric Wastes 2, 225-238.

Robinson, J. S., Sharpley, A. N., 1995. Release of nitrogen, phosphorus and carbon transformations in a coastal plain soil treated with animal manures. Agric Wastes 2, 225-238.

Schefferle, H, E., 1965. The decomposition of uric acid in built up poultry litter. J Appl Bacteriol 28, 412-420.

SD-NRCS-FS-38, 1999. Country Extension Agent; Natural Resources Conservation Service (NRCS) Field Office of the South Dakota Department of Agriculture, Pierre, SD.

Siegel, R, S., Hafez, A. A. R., Azevedo, J., Stout, P. R., 1975. Management procedures for effective fertilization with poultry manure. Compos Sci 16, 5-9.

Stevens, R, J., Laughlin, R. J., Frost, J. P., 1989. Effect of acidification with sulfuric acid on the volatilization of ammonia from cow and pig slurries. J Agric Sci 113, 389-395.

Sutton, A. L., Nelson, D. W., Kelly, D. T., Hill, D. L., 1986. Comparison of solid vs. liquid manure application on corn yield and soil composition. J Environ Qual 15, 370-375.

ten Have, P. J. W., 1993. Nitrogen and the industrial processing of pig manure. In: Verstegen, M. W. A., den Hartog, L. A., Van Kempen, G. J M., Metz, J. H.

M. (Eds.) Proc. Symp. Nitrogen Flow in Pig Production and Environmental Consequences, Doorwerth, The Netherlands, June 8-11, 1993, EAAP Publ. no. 69, pp. 404-409.

Westerman, P. W., Donnelly, T. L., Overcash, M. R., 1983. Erosion of soil and poultry manure a laboratory study. Trans ASAE 26, 1070-1078.

Witter, E., Lopez-Real, J. M., 1987. The potential of sewage sludge and composting in a nitrogen recycling strategy for agriculture. Biol. Agri. Host 5, 1-23.

Wood, C. W., Dall, B. M., 1991. Impact of drying methods on broiler litter analysis. Commun in Soil Sci and Plant Anal 22 (15 & 16), 1677-1678.

Korean Journal of Poultry Science Vol. 28(3): 215-224 (2001)   209

Causes of Nitrogen Loss During Animal Manure Analysis[1]

K. H. Nahm

Feed and Nutrition Laboratory, College of Natural Resources, Taegu University, Gyongsan, 712-714, South Korea

ABSTRACT: Since nitrogen (N) is a volatile compound affected by many environmental factors, determining the N content of manure tends to be difficult. Upon arrival in the laboratory, the manure should be moist and refrigerated. Manure samples will have variable N contents due to drying temperature, and the presence of soil in the sample will affect N content. Acidification of the sample prevents ammonia volatilization and should be done before drying. It is recommended that manure samples be pretreated with a strong oxidizing agent, $KMnO_4$, followed by digestion under reduced conditions (reduced $Fe-H_2SO_4$), which achieves a complete recovery of both NO_3-N and NO_2-N, without a low recovery of NH_4-N, resulting in a more accurate determination of N content. Accuracy of results for N content determined by recently developed rapid analysis techniques in the field should be tested by comparison with results obtained at laboratories using approved standard methods. Most commonly, the Kjeldahl system is used to determine manure N content. More research is needed on the effects of species, breed, age and individuals on the nutrient contents of manure. The procedures for manure sampling on the farm, shipping and handling of the sample until it reaches the laboratory, and the methods of sampling of the manure at the laboratory must be studied. Development of animal agricultural laboratories where feed, manure, soil, and water are all analyzed by appropriate specialists is needed.

(Key words: Animal agricultural laboratory, Digestion, Kjeldahl system, manure, nitrogen)

[1]This research was supported (in part) by the Taegu University Research Grant.

INTRODUCTION

Poultry litter and manures, or livestock manures and urine (hereafter referred to as animal manure or livestock manure) used as feed sources (Ko and Ahn 1987; Kim *et al*, 1993) and added to both pastures and crops as sources of plant nutrients (Kirchmann, 1985; Sutton *et al*, 1987) can also contribute to the pollution of the natural environment by volatilization of ammonia and leaching of nitrate (Pratt *et al*, 1976). The value of animal manure as a feed or a fertilizer is usually based on its macronutrient content, especially nitrogen (N) (Dou *et al*, 1996). In most of the European countries, the guidelines on the number of animals maintained per unit area are based on the amount of N produced in the manure (Faassen and Dijk, 1987).

With increasing emphasis on accurate feeding or agronomic land application of nutrients from animal manures, greater demands are being placed on the analytical processes associated with animal manures' characterization. Laboratories typically oven- dry manure prior to N analysis are not accounting for ammonia loss during the process (Nahm, 1992). Scientists (Kirchmann, 1985; Wood and Hall, 1991) reported that significant amounts of N in animal manures can be in volatile forms, making it difficult to quantify the total N content leading to considerable errors in mass balances. Silage or other types of feeds which contain animal manures or animal manures for fertilizers will likely be fed to livestock animal or land applied in the form in which they are sampled. Therefore, it is critical to use values in the report from laboratories that are based on the "As Received" basis (South Dakota Cooperative Extension Service, 1999).

Animal manures have physiological properties suitable for rapid microbiological growth (Enwezor, 1976), ammonification and loss of N via NH_3 volatilization (Nodar *et al*, 1990). Because nitrification in animal manure is inhibited due to high biological oxygen demand and limited O_2 availability (Nodar *et al*, 1990), NH_3 volatilization is enhanced because the NH_3 gas-liquid equilibrium is proportionally related to the concentration of NH_3 in solution and the partial pressure of NH gas in the atmosphere (Witter and Lopez-Real, 1987).

The following section includes information on factors that affect the N content of animal manure as determined by laboratory analysis in order to enable laboratories to determine manure N content as accurately as possible.

FACTORS AFFECTING N CONTENT DURING LABORATORY ANALYSIS

1. Drying Temperature

Dry determination by drying at 105℃ is one of the most widespread methods used in the characterization of manure and loss of volatile compounds during dry matter determination using the mass-balance may lead to considerable error (Derikx et al, 1994). Mass balance has been used in most laboratories, especially in the large-scale manure treatments plants.

To determine the application rates necessary for optimum crop growth and minimal nitrate leaching, estimates of the N content in livestock manure are necessary to protect available N in livestock manure (Bitzer and Sims, 1988). Parker et al. (1959) reported N losses during processing of 11.6 and 17.0% in broiler and layer manure, respectively. Wood and Hall (1991) compared various drying methods and reported N loss during drying ranged from 12 to 15%. Research results of Gale et al.(1991) indicated that oven drying reduced estimates of total N from 5.65 to 4.01% in wet and dry manure, respectively. They showed that from a practical standpoint, the microwave drying at 40℃ might be a more desirable alternative than no drying, or air drying for 10 days, or drying at 40℃ in a forced air laboratory oven for 3 days, or drying at 60℃ in a forced air laboratory oven for 3 days, drying at 60℃ in a micro-wave oven for 20 minutes. Studies (Parker et al, 1959; Tinsley and Nowakowski, 1959) also showed that drying in forced air ovens at temperature near 80℃ decreased the content of total N in poultry manure by much as 17%. These results also show that the ammonia is lost during normal dry-matter determination of untreated manure originating from pigs, cattle, or poultry.

The N content in poultry manure can decrease from the time the manure is excreted to the time of application which influences the manure application rate recommended (Overcash et al., 1975). Giddens and Rao (1975) reported that poultry manure lost 47.6% of the total N upon air-drying for 10 days but only 23.6% after drying in a boiling water bath. They suggested that the difference in N lost is that heat killed the uric acid hydrolyzing microorganisms or that loss of moisture by heating resulted in greater conservation of N than air-drying. It was observed that slow drying of animal manures at low temperature caused greater losses of N than fast drying at higher temperatures (Giddens and Rao, 1975; Adriano et al., 1974). The difference in N lost between air dried and oven dried samples suggests that uric acid and urea hydrolyzing microorganisms or extracellular hydrolases are killed or denatured at higher temperature or that the rapid loss of moisture at high temperature resulted in greater conservation of N than with air drying. Freezing followed by freeze drying inactivates microorganisms and results in loss through decomposition of uric acid (Schefferle, 1965). Research results (Mahimairaja et al., 1990) suggest that the major reduction in total N during drying may be due to the loss the volatile N compounds such as ammonia and amines. This may lead to considerable errors of the dry-matter determination in using mass-balance because an unknown part of the volatile substances is included in the dry-matter determination and attention is focused on ammonia and volatile fatty acid in dry matter results (Derikx *et al.*, 1994).

Total N loss (%) in fresh manures by the modified Kjeldahl method after electric oven drying is presented in Table 1. The magnitude of N losses is a function of drying temperature (Robinson and Sharpley, 1995), drying method of analysis (Overcash *et al*, 1975) and drying time length (Chao and Kroontje, 1964; Westerman *et al.*, 1983). The effects of drying method and length also results in different N values in Table 1. Research results (Wood and Hall, 1991; Mahimairaja *et al.*, 1990) demonstrated that maintaining broiler litter in a moist, refrigerated state before chemical analyses was more desirable than drying.

2. Animal Manure Mixed with Soil

Microbial and chemical changes in animal manure as affected by contact with soil have been studied. Manure and litter mixed soil contained greater numbers of bacteria and fungi than manure alone, and total coliform bacteria decreased more rapidly when manure was mixed with soil than when not mixed (Giddens and Rao, 1975). Incorporation of manure into the soil greatly increased the amount of N oxidized to NO_3, and air drying of manure in soil resulted in greater N loss than rapid drying with heat. Litter samples with soil also contain more bacterial counts than fresh poultry droppings (Schefferle, 1965; Hallbrook *et al.*, 1951).

Ammonia formation, presumed to be from uric acid, was dependent upon the activity of microorganisms and temperature and humidity of the litter and soil(Ivos *et al.*, 1966), and ammonia emissions in soil manure during composting of animal

Table 1. Total N loss rate (%) of animal manure as affected by oven drying and different lengths of time

Types of manure	Total N loss rate time	Oven temperature and drying time
Poultry manure	8	
Pig slurry	7	105 ℃ for 48 hrs[1]
Dairy slurry	3	
Horse manure	0	
Sheep manure	4	60 ℃ for 3 days[2]
Broiler litter (Hardwood shavings)	12	
Hen manure	5.6 − 4.0	66 ℃ for 48 hrs[3]
Broiler manure	11.6	78 ℃ for 10 hrs[4]
Hen manure	17	

[1] Mahimanraja *et al.* (1990); [2] Wood and Hall (1991);
[3] Gale *et al.* (1991); [4] Parker *et al.* (1959)

manure can be significant and decrease the fertilizer value of manure (Kithome *et al.*, 1999).

3. Effect of pH on the N Loss from animal manure

Acidification of manure is an effective means of reducing volatilization of ammonia from manure during storage, application or drying (Frost *et al.*, 1990; ten Have, 1993). Since the behavior of most volatile compounds depends upon pH, these losses may vary sample to sample. It was shown that above pH 8 all ammonia was volatilized and below pH 5 all volatile fatty acids evaporated in pig, cattle and poultry manure (Derikx *et al.*, 1994). They found that total fixation of ammonia was achieved below pH 4, and above pH 10 all volatile fatty acids were fixed in the residue after drying. It has been shown that the pH of broiler litter influences ammonia levels in poultry facilities (Reece *et al.*, 1979). At a litter pH below 7, ammonia release was negligible. As the pH became closer to 7, the ammonia began to be released. To summarize, as the pH of the litter decreases, the ammonia loss also decreases.

Loss of volatile substances from manure is not a constant factor. Considerable error may result in the laboratory since an unknown part of the volatile substances is included in results of the dry matter determination (Derikx *et al.*, 1994). It is believed that control of ammonia loss during drying processes may provide a more accurate measure of litter N and therefore allow more accurate application of the litter in practical agricultural settings.

Burgess *et al.* (1998) reported that treatment (small - 10g, large - 100g) of litter samples with $Al_2(SO_4)_3$ (ammonium sulfate) prior to drying resulted in more accurate quantification of N in litter, which can ultimately result in more accurate utilization of litter in agronomic application. Ammonium sulfate and numerous other acidic compounds are also effective in lowering litter pH and reducing ammonia volatilization in commercial broiler houses (Moore *et al.*, 1995). In another report, Moore *et al.*, (2000) indicated that ammonium sulfate applications lowered the litter pH, particularly during the first 3 to 4 weeks of each grow out. Reduction in litter pH resulted in less NH_3 volatilization, which led to reduction in atmosphere NH_3 in the ammonium sulfate-treated house.

4. N loss due to using different chemicals in processing

Animal manures vary in their total N contents and N forms because of differences in feed, feed conversion by different animal species age of animal bedding materials and water intake (Ministry of Agriculture, Fisheries and Food, 1992). The total N content in animal manure may be difficult to quantify since significant amounts of N may be in volatile forms (Kirchmann, 1985).

Kjeldahl digestion is generally used to determine the total N in organic materials such as soils, plant materials and animal manures (Nahm, 1992; Bremner and Yeomans, 1988; Nahm, 1989) and this is usually referred to as total Kjeldahl N. The organic ammoniacal N makes up most of the Kjeldahl N and measurement of the inorganic forms of N may be done after extraction with 2M KCl solution (Bremner and Mulvaney, 1982). The total N may be calculated by adding the Kjeldahl N to the nitrate (NO_3) N and nitrite (NO_2) N in the KCl extract (Bitzer and Sims, 1988; Sims, 1986; Tyson and Cabrera., 1993). Chadwick et al. (2000) reported that the organic N fraction varied between manure types and represented from 14% to 99% of the total N content after refluxing 40 g (fresh weight) of slurry or manure with 200 ml of 2M KCl for 4 hour following the method of Gianello and Bremmer (1986) for organic N and Kjedahl digestion for total N.

Total N may be measured alternatively by pretreating samples with oxidizing and reducing agents to include NO_3-N and NO_2-N during the Kjeldahl digestion. Scientists (Bremner and Yeomans, 1988; Haynes, 1980) have studied the effect of some of these oxidizing and reducing agents on NO_3-N and NO_2-N recovery. Mahimairaja et al. (1990) compared these methods for the measurement of Total N in organic materials. They measured total N, Kjeldahl N using a standard micro-Kjeldahl digestion technique (Bremner and Mulvaney, 1982) and inorganic forms of N (NH_4, NO_3 and NO_2) in poultry and animal manures. The pretreatments prior to Kjeldahl digestion for recovering NO_3-N and NO_2-N were: 1) Salicylic acid thiosulfate (Bremner and Mulvaney, 1982), 2) Aqueous $NO_2S_2O_3$ (Dalal et al., 1984), 3) Devard's alloy and H_2SO_4 (Liao, 1981), 4) Zinc and acidified (H_2SO_4) solution of $CrK(SO_4)_2$ (Pruden et al., 1985), 5) Hydrogen peroxide (H_2O_2) + acidified (H_2SO_4) reduced Fe (Mahimairaja et al., 1990), 6) Alkaline sodium hydrochlorite (NaOCl) + acidified (H_2SO_4) reduced Fe (Mahimairaja et al., 1990), 7) Potassium permanganate ($KmnO_4$) + acidified (H_2SO_4) reduced Fe (Bremner and Mulvaney, 1982). Mahimairaja et al. (1990) indicated that the Permanganate method has been found suitable for the analysis of total N and inorganic forms of N in soils, sediments and plant samples. They said that pre-treatment with a strong oxidizing agent, $KMnO_4$, followed by digestion under reduced conditions (reduced Fe-H_2SO_4), achieved a complete recovery of both NO_3-N and NO_2-N without causing a low recovery of NH_4-N (Bremner and Mulvaney, 1982).

Since Kjeldahl introduced a method for determining total N, many studies have been made to improve accuracy, shorten digestion time, and improve recovery of N from a wide range of samples with a modification of the conventional Kjeldahl method (Haynes, 1980; Dalal et al, 1984; Liao., 1981; Goh., 1972). However, there is still some disagreement about the effectiveness of these methods in recovering NO_3-N and NO_2-N, as well as other problems with the methods (Mahimairaja et al, 1990).

5. N loss due to in rapid analysis and automated techniques

For determining the nutrient contents of some animal manures such as dairy and swine slurries, taking samples and sending them to a laboratory may not be the easiest or most accurate method. When slurry is stored, stratification and crusting may make representative sampling questionable without complete agitation. To improve the farmer's ability to properly land apply livestock slurries, a rapid field test to estimate nutrient contents on site immediately prior to application would be useful.

The relationship between N and total solid (TS) has been discussed widely in literature. Specific gravity (SG) measured with a soil hydrometer correlated well with TS content of slurries and a quadratic relationship with TS for N has been demonstrated for swine and cattle slurries (Tunney, 1979). The slopes of the linear regression equations for N and TS for cattle and swine slurries were found to be different (Chescheir et al., 1986).

Stewart (1968) utilized a water analysis kit which determined NH_4-N content to analyze weak acid extracts of swine slurries in the field. When compared to estimating soluble N through weak acid extraction using Kjeldahl digestion and steam distillation of the extract, the results were very similar (Hoyle and Mattingly 1954). A device called the "Nitrogen Meter" for estimating nitrogen in manure was introduced in Sweden (AGROS, Ovagen 1, S-5333 03 Kallby, Sweden) in 1983. The device consists of a stainless steel reaction chamber with a pressure gauge. In order to oxidize the ammonia to N gas (N_2), the manure is mixed with a strong oxidizing agent (calcium hypochlorite, $CaCOCl_2$, 30-37% available chloride). Oxidation of urea also occurs, but its extent depends on the pH according to the developer of this device. The increase in pressure due to formation of N gas is measured by the pressure gauge and is calibrated to units of N per unit of manure volume.

The Auto-Analyzer which was originally designed for the purpose of clinical chemistry has been adapted to soil analysis (Flannery and Steckel, 1964). Improvements in automated techniques were evaluated by Flannery and Markus (1980). This new analyzing system was critically evaluated by Kane et al. (1981). Markus et al. (1985) introduced the micro-processor-based Auto-Analyzer for analyzing NO_3-N, NO_2-N and NH_4-N in soils. They reported that this new system provided improvement in accuracy and precision of results and has the potential for more rapid chemical determination. For the measurement of total N, they used salicylic acid thiosulfate ($NO_2S_2O_3$) for pretreatment to recover NO_3-N and NO_2-N in a semimicro-Kjeldahl procedure (Bremner and Mulvaney 1982). These semimicro-Kjeldahl procedures were used by Robinson and Sharpley (1995) for measuring the content of NO_3-N and NH_4-N with colorimeter, and the content of NO_2-N was measured using indophenol blue procedure after being reduced with

Cd (Keeney and Nelson, 1982).

To summarize, there have been several new, quick methods developed to measure the N content of manure. It has been reported that these methods should not replace regular laboratory analysis by standard methods (Chescheir et al., 1986). These methods are best used to improve land application rates since they provide a rapid indication in changes in manure slurries when storage facilities are unloaded or they estimate some nutrients when it is not possible to use laboratory analysis.

6. Future research on N loss

There are still inadequacies in our knowledge about the nutrient contents of the manure of each species along with analytical techniques for determining these nutrients, especially the N content. The total N content and N forms vary in animal manures due to differences in feed, feed conversion by different animal species, age of animal, bedding material and water intake (Ministry of Agriculture, Fisheries and Food). For example, urea in bovine uric reacts rapidly with urease in the feces which results in a high pH and loss of NH_4 gas (Lauer et al., 1976) and The total N content of fresh manures varies as follows: poultry > pig > horse = sheep. Whereas poultry manure, pig slurry and dairy slurry samples were composed of both feces and urine (or uric acid), horse and sheep manure samples were composed mainly of feces. This may be one of the reasons for the higher content of total N in the former than in the latter (Mahimairaja et al., 1990). It has been shown that most of the N in fresh animal manure is present mainly as urea or uric acid (Azevedo and Stout, 1974; Krogdahl and Dalsgard, 1981). Further research should be done for determining the nutrient content of manure depending on different animal species, age of animal, bedding material, water intake and other factors in the future.

Pretreatment steps that are important in the results of analysis include sampling, sample handling and sample management before analysis. Representative sampling will be very questionable unless there is complete agitation of the manure and slurry storage area. Samples should be transported to the laboratory as soon as possible in proper containers and kept at temperatures below 0℃ (Nahm, 1992). Upon arrival at the laboratory, a portion at the sample should be set aside immediately in case the sample must be analyzed again and the rest of sample must be reduced to a proper size that adequately represents the content of the total sample. There are few reports, however, on proper manure sample pretreatment for each type of manure.

There are two factors that can easily be overlooked by scientists and farmers (Nahm, 1995): 1) Very few livestock farmers have any idea which is the best laboratory to use to analyze their samples of animal feed, manure, litter, soil or water and 2) These laboratories must be able to interpret the results for the farmers. It would be beneficial if all of these analytical procedures were handled in one laboratory specializing in animal agriculture with specialists advising farmers on how best to apply the analytical data (Nahm, 2000).

CONCLUSION

There are many factors to consider when determining the N content of manure. The N content of manure is affected by the drying temperature and length of time, the presence of soil in the sample, the pH of the manure, the chemicals used in the analysis and the use of rapid or automated analytical techniques. N is an important component of manure used as fertilizer or feed, but its volatility makes it an environmental concern as well.

Further research is needed on how the N content of manure may be affected by animal breed and age, season and feed or water sources. Appropriate management of the sample from sampling on the farm to analysis in the laboratory should be developed. Establishment of animal agricultural laboratories where feed, manure, soil, water are analyzed in one laboratory and qualified specialists then advise farmers should be a priority in the future research.

REFERENCES

Adriano DC, Chang AC, Sharpless R 1974 Nitrogen Loss From Manure as Influenced by Moisture and Temperature. Journal of Environmental Quality 3(3), 258-261.

Azevedo J, Stout PR 1974 Farm Animal Manures: An Overview of Their Role in the Agricultural Environment, Manual 44; California Agricultural Experimental Station in Extension Service: Berkeley, CA, USA.

Bitzer CC, Sims JT 1988 Estimating the Availability of Nitrogen in Poultry Manure through Laboratory and Field Studies. Journal of Environmental Quality 17, 47-54.

Bremner JM, Mulvaney CS 1982 Nitrogen-Total. In Methods of Soil Analysis, Part 2, 2nd edition; Page, A.L., American Society of Agronomy: Madison, WI, USA, 595-624.

Bremner JM, Yeomans JC 1988 Laboratory Techniques for Determination of Different Forms of Nitrogen, In Advances in Nitrogen Cycling in Agricultural Ecosystems; Wilson, J.R., Ed.; CAB International, Wallingford, UK, 399-414.

Burgess RP, Carey JB, Shafer DJ 1998 The Impact of pH on Nitrogen Retention in Laboratory Analysis of Broiler Litter. Poultry Science 77, 1620-1622.

Chao T, Kroontje W 1964 Relationship between Ammonia Volatilization, Ammonia Concentration and Water Evaporation. Soil Science Society of America Proceeding 28, 393-395.

Chadwick DR, John F, Pain BF, Chambers BJ, Williams J 2000 Plant Uptake of Nitrogen from the Organic Nitrogen Fraction of Animal Manures; A Laboratory Experiment. Journal of Agricultural Science 134, 159-168.

Chescheir GMIII, Westerman PW, Safley LM 1986 Laboratory Methods for Estimating Available Nitrogen Manures and Sludges. Agricultural Wastes 18, 175-195.

Dalal RC, Sahrawat KL, Myers RJK 1984 Inclusion of Nitrate and Nitrate in the Kjeldahl Nitrogen Determination in Soils and Plant Internals Using Sodium Thiosulphate. Communications in Soil Science and Plant Analysis 15, 1453-1461.

Derikx PJL, Willers HC, ten Have PJW 1994 Effects of pH on the Behavior of Volatile Compounds in Organic Manures During Dry-Matter Determination. Bioresource Technology 49, 41-45.

Dou Z, Kohn RA, Ferguson JD, Boston RC, Newbold JD 1996 Managing Nitrogen on Dairy Farms an Intergrated Approach. I. Model Description. Journal of Dairy Science 79, 2071-2080.

Enwezor WO 1976 The Mineralization of Nitrogen and Phosphorus in Organic Materials of Varying C:N and C:P Ratios. Plant Soil 44, 237-240.

Faassen HG, van Dijk H 1987 Manure as a Source of Nitrogen and Phosphorus in Soils. In Animal Mmanure on Grassland and Fodder Crops: Fertilizer or Waste; Van der Meer, H.G., Unwin, R.J., van Dijk, T.A., and G.G. Ennik, G.G., Eds.; Martinus Nijhoff Publishers: Dordrecht. The Netherlands 27-45.

Flannery RL, Steckel JE 1964 Simultaneous Determination of Calcium, Potassium, Magnesium and Phosphorus in Soil Electrodialyzates by Autoanalysis. In Soil Testing and Plant Analysis: Part 1; Hardy, G.W., Ed.; Soil Science Society of America: Madison, WI, USA, 137-150.

Flannery RL, Markus DK 1980 Automated Analysis of Soil Extracts for Phosphorus, Potassium, Calcium and Magnesium. Journal of Association Official Analytical Chemists 63, 779-787.

Frost JP, Stevens RJ, Laughlin RJ 1990 Effect of Separation and Acidification of Cattle Slurry on Ammonia Volatilization and on the Efficiency of Slurry Nitrogen for Herbage Production. Journal of Agricultural Science 15, 49-56.

Gale PM, Phillips JM, Wolf DC 1991 Effect of Drying on the Plant Nutrient Content of Hen Manure. Journal of Production Agriculture 4(2), 246-250.

Gianello C, Bremner JM 1986 A Simple Chemical Methods of Assessing Potentially Available Organic Nitrogen in Soil. Communication in Soil Science and Plant Analysis 17, 195-214.

Giddens J, Rao AM 1975 Effect of Incubation and Contact with Soil on Microbial and Nitrogen Changes in Poultry Manure. Journal of Environmental Quality 4(2), 275-278.

Goh KM 1972 Comparison and Evaluation of Methods for Including Nitrate in the Total Nitrogen Determination of Soils 23, 275-284.

Hallbrook ER, Winter AR, Sutton TS 1951 The Microflora of Poultry House Litter and Droppings. Poultry Science 30, 381-388.

Haynes RJ 1980 A Comparison of Two Modified Kjeldahl Techniques for Multielement Plant Analysis with Conventional Wet and Dry Ashing Techniques. Communications in Soil Science and Plant Analysis 11, 457-467.

Hoyle DA, Mattingly GEG 1954 Studies on Composts Prepared from Waste Materials. 1. Preparation, Nitrogen Losses and Changes in "Soluble Nitrogen". Journal of Science and Food Agriculture 5(1), 54-64.

Ivos I, Asaj A, Marjanovic LI, Madzirov Z 1966 A Contribution to the Hygiene of Deep Litter in the Chicken House. Poultry Science 45, 676-683.

Kane PF, Bennett BR, Gulik S 1981 Data Handler/ Controller System with Application to P_2O_5 and K_2O in Fertilizer. Journal of Association Official Analytical Chemists 65, 1322-1328.

Keeney DR, Nelson DW 1982 Nitrogen-Inorganic Forms. In Methods of Soil Analysis: Part 2, 2nd Edition; Page, A.L., Ed.; ASA and SSSA: Madison, WI, USA, 643-698.

Kim JH, Yokota Y, Ko TD, Okajima T, Ohshima, M 1993 Nutritional Quality of Whole Crop Corn Ensilaged with Cage Layer Manure. I. Quality, Voluntary Feed Intake and Digestibility of the Silage in Goats. Asian-Australian Journal of Animal Science 6, 45-51.

Kirchmann H 1985 Losses, Plant Uptake, Utilization of Manure Nitrogen during a Production Cycle. Acta Agricultural Scandinavica 24, 1-77.

Kithome M, Paul JW, Bomke AA 1999 Reducing Nitrogen Losses During Simulated Composting of Poultry Manure Using Adsorbents or Chemical Amendments. Journal of Environmental Quality 28, 194-201.

Ko YD, Ahn BG, 1987 A Study on the Corn-Layer Manure Silage about Digestibility and Silage Fermentation. Korean Journal of Animal Science 29, 501-508.

Krogdahl A, Dalsgard B 1981 Estimation of Nitrogen Digestibility in Poultry. I. Content and Distribution of Major Urinary Nitrogen Compounds in Excreta. Poultry Science 60, 2480-2485.

Lauer DA, Bouldin DR, Klausner SD 1976 Ammonia Volatilization from Dairy Manure Spread on the Soil Surface. Journal of Environmental Quality 5(2), 134-141.

Liao CFH 1981 Devarda's Alloy Method for Total Nitrogen Determination. Soil Science Society of American Journal 45, 852-855.

Mahimairaja S, Bolan NS, Hedley MJ, Macgregor AN 1990 Evaluation of Methods of Measurement of Nitrogen in Poultry and Animal Manures. Fertilizer Research 24, 141-148.

Markus DK, McKinnon JP, Buccafuri AF 1985 Automated Analysis of Nitrate, Nitrite and Ammonium Nitrogen in Soils. Soil Science Society of America Journal 49, 1208-1215.

Ministry of Agriculture, Fisheries and Food 1992. Fertilizer Recommendations. IN MAFF Reference Book 209, 6th Edition; HMSO: London UK.

Moore PA, Jr Daniel TC, Edwards DR, Miller DM 1995 Effect of Chemical Amendments on Ammonia Volatilization from Poultry Litter. Journal of Environmental Quality 24, 293-300.

Moore PA, Jr Daniel TC, Edwards DR 2000 Reducing Phosphorus Runoff and Inhibiting Ammonia Loss from Poultry Manure with Aluminum Sulfate. Journal of Environmental Quality 29, 37-49.

Nahm KH 1989 The Complete Agricultural Lab Manual (English Edition). Taegu University Press: Taegu, South Korea.

Nahm KH 1992 Practical Guide to Feed, Forage and Water Analysis (English Edition). Yoo Han Pub. Co.; Seoul, South Korea.

Nahm KH 1995 Future Direction for the Livestock Production in Korea. In Proceedings of the Korean Animal Production Conference; Korean Animal Science Association: Seoul, Korea 32-63.

Nahm KH 2000 A Strategy to Solve Environmental Concerns Caused by Poultry Production. World's Poultry Science Journal 56, 379-388.

Nodar R, Acea MJ, Carballas T 1990 Microbial Populations of Poultry Pine-Sawdust litter. Biological Wastes 33, 295-306.

Overcash MR, Hashimot AG, Reddell DL, Day DL 1975 Evaluation of Chemical Analyses for Animal Wastes. In Standardizing Properties and Analytical Methods Related to Animal Waste Research; ASAE: St. Joseph, MO, USA, 333-355.

Parker MB, Perkins HP, Fuller HL 1959 Nitrogen, Phosphorus, and Potassium Content of Poultry Manure and Some Factors Influencing its Composition. Poultry Science 38, 1154-1158.

Pratt PF, Davis S, Sharpless RG 1976 A Four Year Field with Manures. Hilgardia 44, 99-125.

Pruden G, Kalembasa SJ, Jenkinson DS 1985 Reduction of Nitrate Prior to Kjeldahl Digestion. Journal of Science and Food Agriculture 36,

Reece FN, Bates BJ, Lott BD 1979 Ammonia Control in Broiler Houses. Poultry Science 58, 754-755.

Robinson JS, Sharpley AN 1995 Release of Nitrogen and Phosphorus from Poultry Litter. Journal of Environmental Quality 24, 62-67.

Schefferle HE 1965 The Decomposition of Uric Acid in Buildup Poultry Litter. Journal of Applied Bacteriology 28, 421-420.

Sims JT 1986 Nitrogen Transformation in a Poultry Manure Amended Soil: Temperature and Moisture Effects. Journal of Environmental Quality 15(1), 59-63.

South Dakota Cooperative Extension Service 1999 Using Results from a Manure Analysis. SD_NRCS_FS-38; South Dakota Cooperative Extension Service: Brookings, SD 57007, USA, 1-4.

Stewart TA 1968 A Rapid method for Estimating the Soluble Nitrogen Content of Animal Slurries. Ministry of Agriculture, Northern Ireland. 17, 91-96.

Sutton AL, Nichols SR, Jones DD, Kelly DT, Scheidt AB 1987 Survey of Seasonal Atmosphere changes in Confinement Farrowing Houses. In Proceedings of the 2nd Seminar Technical Selection CIGR. on Latest Developments in Livestock Housing; Auburn University, AL, USA, 106-107.

ten Have PJW 1993 Nitrogen and the Industrial Processing of Pig Manure. In Proceedings of Symposium on Nitrogen Flow in Pig Production and Environmental Consequences, Doorwerth, The Netherlands, June 8-11; Verstegen, M.W.A., den hartog, L.A., van Kempen, G.J.M., Metz, J.H.M., Eds.; EAAP, Doorwerth, The Netherlands, 69, 403-409.

Tinsley J, Nowakowski TZ 1959 The Composition and Manurial Value of Poultry Excreta, Straw-Droppings Compost and Deep Litter. II-Experimental Studies on Composites. Journal of Science and Food Agriculture 10, 150-167.

Tunney H 1979 Dry Matter, Specific Gravity, and Nutrient Relationships of Cattle and Pig Slurry. In Engineering Problems with Effluents from Livestock; Hawkins, J.C., Ed.; Luxembourg, 430-447.

Tyson SC, Cabrera ML 1993 Nitrogen Mineralization in Soils Amended with Composted and Uncomposted Poultry Litter. Communications in Soil Science and Plant Analysis 24(17 & 18), 2361-2374.

Westerman PW, Donnelly TL, Overcash MR 1983 Erosion of Soil and Poultry Manure - A Laboratory Study. Transactions of the American Society of Agricultural Engineers 26, 1070-2078, 1084.

Witter E, Lopez-Real JM 1987 The Potential of Sewage Sludge and Composting in a Nitrogen Recycling Strategy for Agriculture. Biological Agricultural Horticulture 5, 1-23.

Wood CW, Hall BM 1991 Impact of Drying Method on Broiler Litter Analyses. Com. Soil Sci. Plant Anal. 22, 1677-1688.

Efficient feed nutrient utilization to reduce pollutants in poultry and swine manure

K. H. Nahm

Feed and Nutrition Laboratory, College of Natural Resources Taegu University, Gyong San, 712-714, South Korea. E-mail: nahmkh@daegu.ac.kr

ABSTRACT: High density livestock facilities leads to concentration of livestock wastes and subsequent leakage of pollutants into the environment, resulting in public concern about their effects. Nitrogen (N) and phosphorus (P) are the most harmful components of animal manure, but odor from the manure itself and the livestock facilities is also a problem. Improving the nutrient efficiency of the livestock helps to decrease excretion of these environmental contaminants. Pigs and chickens are the main animals used in studies to improve nutrient efficiency to reduce excretion of environmental contaminants. Addition of feed supplements and modifying feeding programs to improve nutrient efficiency can result in significant decreases in the N, P, odor and dry matter (DM) weight of manure. Examples of these methods include the following. 1) Addition of synthetic amino acids and reducing protein contents resulted in N reductions of 10-27% in broilers, 18-35% in chicks and layers, 19-62% in pigs, and a 9-43% reduction in odor from pigs. 2) Enzyme supplementation resulted in a 12-15% reduction in DM weight of broiler manure. 3) Phytase supplementation resulted in P reductions of 25-35% in chickens and 25-60% in pigs. 4) Use of growth promoting substances resulted in a 5-30% reduction in N and a 53-56% reduction in odor from pigs. 5) Formulating diets closer to requirements (diet modification) reduced N and P by 10-15% each in chickens and pigs, and odor by 28-79% in pigs. 6) Phase feeding reduced N and P excretion by chicken and pigs from 10-33% and 10-13% each, as well as odor in growing and finishing pigs by 49-79%. 7) Use of highly digestible raw materials in feed reduced N and P excretion by 5% in chickens and pigs. Certain feed manufacturing techniques (grinding feed grains and proper particle size, feed uniformity in rations, or expanding and pelleting) when done properly can significantly reduce N, P and odor contents and DM weight of chicken and pig manure. Feed with proper grinding reduced 27% of N in finishing pigs and 22-23% reduction of N in piglet fed with pelleting, 60% reduction of NH_3

emission fed with finely ground Zeolites in pig and 26% reduction of DM weight in finishing pigs fed with proper grinding were reported, but further research is needed in this area. Coordinating actual feed analytical results with production technique modifications is needed to reduce environmental contamination by animal manure, but specialists may need to be consulted for successful implementation of these efforts.

Keywords: Enzymes; Feed manufacturing; Manure; Nutrient efficiency; Phase feeding; Pollutants; Protein levels

I. INTRODUCTION

Public concern about environmental pollution from intensive swine and poultry production is increasing. Environmental pollution is defined as contamination with poisonous or harmful substances to human beings, animal production and other organisms (Williams, 1995).

The primary livestock excreta of concern in agriculture is manure. Animal manure is primarily a mixture of urine and feces, and it contains undigested dietary components, endogenous end products, and indigenous bacteria from the lower gastrointestinal tract (GIT), which contain a variety of organic compounds, complex to simple in nature, inorganic compounds, and potentially, feed additives, depending upon the make-up of the diet (Sutton *et al.*, 1999).

Much of the concern for pollution from animal manure involves nitrogen (N) pollution of ground water and run off into surface water and phosphorus (P) pollution of ground and surface water via soil erosion and run off. Although odors are generally considered a swine problem, all livestock producers may have to address the changing public attitude toward rural air quality eventually (Hamilton and Arogo, 1999). N, P, and some metals in livestock manure are feed nutrients, but environmental pollutants are caused by feed nutrients in the manure. Nutrient excretion is a result of the inefficiencies associated with digestion and metabolism (Coffey, 1996).

Without appropriately addressing these critical eco-nutritional issues, the livestock and poultry industries will be faced with major public opinion and regulatory problems that could limit the potential for growth. There are many methods of reducing environmental pollution by reducing excreta N, P, and odor contents and dry matter weight of manure. The focus of this paper is on improving manufacturing techniques along with feed testing to improve feed nutrient efficiency and therefore reducing manure pollutants. Various feed supplements and modified feeding systems that have been developed for the same purpose are also introduced here.

II. STRATEGIES TO IMPROVE FEED NUTRIENT EFFICIENCY FOR REDUCING POLLUTANTS IN MANURE

A. Ways to increase feed nutrient efficiency

More attention should be placed on feeding diets with minimal nutrient excesses. Until recently, diets have been often formulated with relatively large excesses of nutrients with little attention being paid to the excretion patterns of non-utilized nutrients (Farrell *et al.*, 1998; Morse *et al.*, 1992). Provided proper attention is paid to nutrient management, animal excreta can be used as fertilizers, soil amendments and feed ingredients (Nahm, 2000). Furthermore, the contents of N, P, odor and dry matter contents in livestock manure can be reduced by paying careful attention to diet composition - for example, by applying the concept of ideal protein, supplementation with synthetic amino acids, addition of various enzymes including phytase, lowering the protein and P contents, and use of highly available sources of supplementary P and vitamin D (Nahm, 2000).

Scientists have reported the potential reduction of N, P, odor (measured by NH_3 emission reduction), and excreta weights in chickens and pigs (Table 1). Methods have mainly involved adding supplements to the feed and modifying the feeding programs. Supplements that have been found to be beneficial include: synthetic amino acids and reduced protein levels, enzymes, phytase, and growth promoting substances. Modifications to feeding programs that have been studied include: formulations closer to requirements (including diet modification), phase feeding, and use of highly digestible raw materials in the ration.

When feed rations were formulated to maintain the appropriate levels of each amino acid rather that just the total protein content, there was improved feed efficiency as well as reductions in manure pollutants. For example, in one research study (Blair *et al.*, 1999), there was a reduction of 10-27% of the N content of broiler manure by using synthetic amino acids and reducing protein content. A similar reduction of 18-35% was seen in chicks and layers (Blair *et al.*, 1999; Farrell, 2000; Summers, 1993) and in pigs there was a reduction of 19-62% (Bridges *et al.*, 1995; Carter *et al.*, 1996; Cromwell and Coffey, 1995; Hobbs *et al.*, 1996; Pierce *et al.*, 1994).

By supplementing rations with enzymes, a reduction in manure dry matter content of 12-15% (broiler) could be expected (Wyatt and Harker, 1995). Phytase supplementation reduced P contents of manure up to 25-35% in chicken (Federation Europeenne des Fabricants d'Adjuvants pour la Nutrition Animale - FEFANA, 1992; Lobo, 1999) and up to 25-60% in pigs (Cromwell and Coffey, 1995; FEFANA, 1992; Jongbloed *et al.*, 1992; Kornegay and Harper, 1997; Michel and Frosoth, 1999). When somatotrophin was used as a growth promotant, N content of pig manure was reduced 5-30% (FEFANA, 1992; Williams *et al.*, 1987). The

Table 1. Reducing concentration of various pollutants in animal manure through supplements and feeding programs

| Factors | % reduction of pollutants in manure (dry matter) | | | | Experimental animal used | References |
	N	P	Odor (NH$_3$ emission)	Dry matter		
Supplements						
Synthetic amino acids	18-35				chicks and layers	2, 9, 23
and reduced protein	10-27				broilers	2
Intake	19-62				pigs	4, 7, 8, 13, 22
			9-43		pigs	1, 25
		2-37			chickens & pigs	10
Enzymes, General	5				chickens &	10
				12-15	pigs broilers	31
				5	pigs	20
Phytases	5	25-35			chickens	10, 19
		25-60			pigs	8, 10, 14, 18, 21
		20			turkeys	16
Growth promotants	5-30	5			chickens & pigs	10, 30
or chemicals			53-56		pigs	24
Programs						
Formulation closer to requirements	10-15	10-15			chickens & pigs	10
Diet modification	41				pigs	15
			28-79		pigs	5, 6, 11, 15, 27
Phase feeding	10-33	10-13			chickens & pigs	10, 12, 17, 26
			49-79		pigs	3, 26, 28, 29
Use of highly digestible raw materials	5	5			chickens & pigs	10

1. Aarnick *et al.* (1993); 2. Blair *et al.* (1999); 3. Boisen *et al.* (1995); 4. Bridges *et al.* (1995); 5. Cahn *et al.* (1998a); 6. Cahn *et al.* (1998b); 7. Carter *et al.* (1996); 8. Crumwell and Coffey (1995); 9. Farrell (2000); 10. FZTANA (1992); 11. Hankins *et al.* (2000); 12. Henry and Dourmad (1993); 13. Hobbs *et al.* (1996); 14. Jongbloed *et al.* (1992); 15. Kay and Lee (1997); 16. Khan (2000); 17. Koch (1990); 18. Kornegay and Harper (1997); 19. Lobo (1999); 20. Lobo (2000); 21. Michel and Frosoth (1999); 22. Pierce *et al.* (1994); 23. Summers (1993); 24. Sutton *et al.* (1992); 25. Sutton *et al.* (1996); 26. Sutton *et al.* (1997); 27. Sutton *et al.* (1999); 28. Turner *et al.* (1996); 29. Vander Peet - Schwering and Voermans (1996); 30. Williams *et al.* (1987); 31. Wyatt and Harker (1995).

amount of ammonia gas cmission of pig manure was reduced by 53-56% when sarsaponin extracts were fed to pig (Sutton *et al.*, 1992).

When feeding systems were adopted to provide formulations that were closer to the nutrient requirements, a 10-15% reduction of N and P contents of chicken manure resulted (FEFANA, 1992). Recent research into dietary modification has resulted in the reduction of NH_3 emission of 28-79% in pig manure (Canh *et al.*, 1998a; Canh *et al.*, 1998b; Hankins *et al.*, 2000; Kay and Lee, 1997; Sutton *et al.*, 1999).

Phase feeding in chicks and pigs reduced N content 10-33% (FEFANA, 1992; Henry and Dourmad, 1993; Koch, 1990; Sutton *et al.*, 1997) and NH_3 emission in growing and finishing pig manure by 49-79% (Boisen *et al.*, 1995; Sutton *et al.*, 1997; Turner *et al.*, 1996; Van der Peet-Schwering *et al.*, 1996). According to scientists (FEFANA, 1992; Henry and Dourmad, 1993; Koch, 1990; Sutton *et al.*, 1997), phase feeding also resulted in a 10-13% reduction in the P content of pig manure. Use of highly digestible raw materials in chicken and pig formulations has resulted in an 5% reduction each in manure N and P contents (FEFANA, 1992).

B. Odor in animal agriculture and diet manipulation

Odor has been described as the number one problem associated with animal pollution (Lyons, 1995). And odor and N pollution are closely related since both are mainly produced by crude protein (CP) (Coelho, 1994). Offensive odors from livestock facilities consist of many (ranging from 30 to more than 200) volatile odorous compounds including hydrogen sulfide and ammonia (Hobbs *et al.*, 1995; O'Nell and Phillips, 1992; Shurson *et al.*, 1999; Spoelstra, 1980). Sutton *et al.* (1999) reported that primary odor-causing compounds evolve from excess degradable proteins and lack of specific fermentable carbohydrates during microbial fermentation.

Solutions to odor control have been studied in masking agents, enzyme and bacterial preparations, feed additives, chemicals, oxidation processes, air scrubbers, biofilters and new ventilation systems, but research relating the effects of the swine diet on manure odors has been scarce (Sutton, 1999). However, dietary manipulation is an opportunity for improvement to reduce nutrient excretion as well as to improve odor control (Coffey, 1992).

A large part of the N losses is associated with inefficiencies of digestion and absorption, so providing diets with highly digestible amino acids may reduce the amount of N excretion. Hobbs *et al.* (1996) demonstrated that reducing dietary protein concentration reduced several of the odor producing compounds. When nutritionally adequate, low sulfur starter diets are fed, total sulfur and sulfate excretion can be reduced approximately 30% without compromising energy and N digestibility or pig performance (Shurson *et al.*, 1999). Furthermore, this study shows that a reduction in total sulfur consumption and excretion can lead to a reduction in hydrogen sulfide gas and odor, but not affect ammonia levels in nursery facilities. Sutton *et al.* (1999) reported that ammonia emissions were reduced by 28 to 79% through diet modification and limited research on reduction of other odorous volatile organic compounds through diet modifications is promising. They added that continued nutritional and microbial research to incorporate protein degradation products, especially sulfur-containing organics, with fermentable carbohydrates in the lower gastrointestinal tract of pigs will further control odors from manure.

III. IMPROVING NUTRIENT EFFICIENCY THROUGH MANUFACTURING STRATEGIES TO REDUCE POLLUTANTS

Decreasing the excretion of excess nutrients may be achieved by determining the content of nutrients in feedstuffs and improving feed manufacturing techniques. Determining the nutrient content in feedstuffs will be discussed in the section on testing of the complete feed. Feed processing, especially grinding, increases the surface area of the feed that is exposed to the animal digestive system. Processing is also known to facilitate mixing, improve feed density, reduce dustiness, improve palatability, extend "shelf life" and alter nutrient makeup (Jensen *et al.*, 1965; Nahm *et al.*, 1998; Peisker, 1994; Wilson and Beyer, 1997).

A. Effect of grinding and particle size on feed efficiencies

Prior to mixing, grain is ground to increase the surface area and subsequently improve the digestion rate, to decrease segregation and mixing problems, and to assist in processes such as extrusion or pelleting (Nir, 1996). And grinding to the proper size can improve a herd's feed efficiency and be more cost efficient (Norton, 1999). Reducing particle size from 1000 to 400 microns improved nutrient digestibility and lowered average daily feed intake which resulted in a 26% decrease in daily dry matter excretion and a 27% decrease in daily N excretion in the manure of finishing pigs (Wondra *et al.*, 1995c). While in another study, a particle size less than 600 microns was suitable for corn used for meal and pelleted diets. It has also been shown that uniform particle sizes provide improved nutrient (dry matter, N and gross energy) digestibilities (Wondra *et al.*, 1995a; 1995b). In poultry, particle size preference has been shown to vary with age, the preference for larger particles increases as the bird become older, and it may be related to beak dimensions (Bartov, 2000). In broilers, the positive effect of mesh coarseness on performance is seen even after the feed was subsequently pelleted and phytate P utilization of corn by broilers improved by increasing the particle size (Kasin and Edwards, 1998). The effect of corn or hard and soft grain sorghum particle size on growth performance and nutrient utilization in broiler chicks has been investigated (Cabrera *et al.* 1994). As particle size was reduced, energy required to grind increased, and production rate decreased. Corn required more energy to grind and had lower production rate than the sorghums. Growth rate, dailty feed consumption, and gain/fed were not affected by treatment.

The effects of grain particle size on nutrient digestibility have been studied (Owsley *et al.*, 1981). In ileal cannulated pigs, as the particle size was reduced, the upper gastrointestinal digestibility of N, DM, gross energy (GE), starch and most amino acids was increased. When the particle size of barley was reduced by 14% (789 microns vs. 676 microns) for starter pigs, their average daily gain (ADG) and gain to feed (G/F) improved by 5% (Goodband and Hines, 1988). Improved G/F and DM, GE and N digestibility were noted when the particle size of corn and grain sorghum was reduced (Ohh *et al.*, 1983). Extensive particle size reduction may not improve the performance of pigs fed wheat. In starter pigs fed diets with wheat ground to 860 microns or 1710 microns average particle size, the average daily gain and G/F were similar (Seerley *et al.*, 1988).

The development of esophageal ulcers, stomach lesions and keratinization in pigs has been correlated to fine grinding of feeds (Hedde *et al.*, 1985). Fine grinding (less than 600 microns) of corn and two grain sorghum genotypes negatively affected stomach morphology, but the improved performance in these animals may make fine grinding acceptable (Cabrera *et al.*, 1993). This study also showed that smaller grain particle size dramatically reduced DM and N excretion.

The influence of mill type (hammer mill vs. roller mill) on finishing pig performance and stomach morphology has been investigated by Wondra *et al.* (1993). Growth performance was not affected by mill type, but when corn was ground by a roller mill, pigs showed greater digestibilities of DM, N, and GE, while they also excreted 18% less DM and 13% less N than pigs fed hammer mill ground corn.

B. Feed (nutrient) uniformity and its effect on nutrient excretion and animal performance

Improper mixing of feeds results in reduced uniformity of the diet, leading to poor animal performance and increased nutrient excretion into the environment. Analytical results from 26 sow feed samples and 17 finishing feed samples were summarized by Spears (1996). Single samples were taken from each farm and analyzed by the North Carolina Feed Testing Laboratory. The mineral concentrations in the different feeds varied substantially. The mineral contents of the feeds were in excess of the requirements suggested by the National Research Council (NRC, 1998). Use of excess nutrients in order to avoid nutrient deficiencies when formulating diets accounts for variability in ingredient composition and accuracy of diet mixing, but it also increases nutrient excretion and diet cost. Nahm *et al.* (1998) noted that the livestock and poultry industries must be aware that if micro-ingredients of feed such as vitamins, amino acids, trace elements, enzymes, growth promotants and drugs are not properly distributed in the feed, there is a resultant adverse effect on animal performance. There is a greater importance for feed uniformity in very young animals and animals with a short digestive tract, as compared to older or larger animals that consume larger amounts of feed less often (Nahm and Carlson, 1998). In pig, Miner *et al.* (1997) found that the application of 1 to 4% (w/v) finely gound clinoptilotite to dairy slurry, immediately before spreading through a sprinkler system, reduced NH_3 emission rates by up to 60%. Even though the importance of diet uniformity is intuitive, there is very little credible research that relates diet uniformity to animal performance (Behnke, 1996).

In a survey of commercial feed mixers, over 50% did not meet the industry standard of a coefficient of variation (CV) of less than 10% when methionine or lysine was used as a tracer (Wicker and Poole, 1991). The results were similar when farm feed mixers were surveyed (Stark *et al.*, 1991). That survey indicated that 42% of participants had CV's of less than 10% (67% were between 10 and 20% and 11% had CV's greater than 20%). The tracer in this study was salt.

Although the accepted industry standard for mix uniformity of a complete diet is a CV of 10% or less, it has been shown that broiler chicks had maximum growth performance with a diet that had a CV of 12-23%, depending on the method of analysis (McCoy *et al.*, 1994). Nursery pigs have been reported to require feed mixed to a CV of at least 12% to maximize performance (Traylor, 1997). In both of these studies, P excretion was decreased when phytase was added to the chicken and pig diets.

Johnston and Southern (2000) determined the effect of varying mix uniformity of phytase on growth performance, mineral retention and bone mineralization. They found that P excretion increased linearly as phytase CV increased and P excretion tended to be higher for chicks fed the CV 103 (calcium - Ca 0.9% + aP 0.35% + 0 or 1200 FTU phytase units) treatment than those fed the CV0 (Ca 0.9% + aP 0.35% + 600 FTU phytase units). Ca and P excretion was numerically higher for the CV 69 (Ca 0.9% + aP 0.35% + 200 or 1000 FTU phytase units) treatment than for the CV 103 treatment.

The nutrient availability in animal feedstuffs may be increased through the use of enzymes. The actions of feed enzymes include any or all of the following: 1) supplement to the endogenous enzyme production of the host; 2) nutrient availability in the feed may be improved; 3) digestibility of the indigestible fiber materials may be improved; and 4) the anti-nutritional factors in feed ingredients may be decreased (Scott, 1991).

The CV's of the enzyme application improves with increased mixing of the liquid enzyme in the finished feed. Improvements in CV's have been seen during the transfer of the feed from the mixing screw, to the bin on the farm and to the feed hopper in the poultry house. It is recommended that finished feed be sampled immediately after blending/mixing to determine how well the feed mill is applying the enzyme. The quantity of enzyme is as important as the consistency of application. Although adequate field performance has been noted with CV's of 15-20% (Classen, 2000), the effectiveness of feed enzymes is significantly affected by the type of ingredients, cultivars, types of soils, diet ingredients, types of feed processing, age of animal, etc. (Duncan, 1973).

Every enzyme has a mode of action and a specific assay, although uniformity of these assays is as industry problem for a variety of reasons. Determination of the complete enzyme levels in feed is suspect because of the small quanity of enzyme in the feed, as well as presence of soluble inhibitors or the possibility of the enzyme binding to substrate (Classen, 2000). Therefore, the primary method used to determine the quality of an enzyme as a feed additive must be biological testing under commercial manufacturing and animal production conditions (Nahm, 1992; Classen, 2000).

C. Expanding / Pelleting processes

The process of expanding is a typical High-Intensive-Short Term (HIST) process involving an expander which is a simplified and low cost extruder having its own technical specification. The expander is used in industrial manufacturing of a compound as a pressure conditioner before the pellet mill in order to improve the pellet quality.

Multiple beneficial effects can be obtained through expanding. Nutrient digestibility is increased by expanders, including N digestibility resulting in reduced N excretion. They also are responsible for inactivation of anti-nutritional factors like protease inhibitors, denaturation of the tertiary protein structure, removal of resistance to proteolytic enzymes which decreases hydrolysis time in the gastrointestinal tract (Coelho, 1994). Expanders are also involved in improving the hydrolysis, gelatinization and melting of starch and polysaccharides, which includes the decrease in crystallinity and depolymerization of starch molecules, resulting in improved digestibility. Fat-splitting enzymes are inactivated by expanders and this reduces the potential for fat oxidation. Expanders inactivate several pathogenic organism such as *Salmonella* and *E. coli* (Delort-Laval, 1993).

Because of the correlation between starch modification and pellet quality, the nutritional importance of the starch modification by expanding can be used as benefit too in comparison to the conventional pelleting. Fancher *et al.* (1996) reported improved growth and feed conversion in male turkeys fed expanded diets compared to diets that were only pelleted. Beyer (2000) found that these parameters are improved by 5-10% when expanded diets are compared to conventionally pelleted rations in broiler trials. Edwards *et al.* (1999) demonstrated steam pelleting of corn, soybean meal or diets containing these ingredients, as well as extrusion of this diet did not increase phytate phosphorus utilization by broiler chicks. Moreover, extrusion of the diet decreased Ca, P and phytate P retention, and its ME value.

Pelleting of feeds has the potential to improve feed efficiency and reduce nutrient excretion. Wondra *et al.* (1995) reported that dry matter and N excretion in feces were decreased 23 and 22%, respectively, by pelleting. Feed efficiency was improved 6.6% in that study. Summarizing eight trials on pelleting diets for swine, Hancock *et al.* (1996) concluded that pelleting improved average daily gain (ADG) 6% and feed efficiency 6-7%. A 2% reduction in feed wastage can reduce the N and P in manure approximately 3% (based on a N and P retention of 35%) (Van Heugten and Van Kempen, 1999).

Broiler performance is affected more by addition of a beta-glucanase to a barley based diet when the feed is pelleted rather than a mash (Belyavin, 1994). Regardless of how phytase is added to the diet, inactivation of the enzyme is still a concern. Exogenous phytase addition can be done after expansion and/or pelleting (Aicher, 1998), which avoids heat inactivation of the enzyme. When properly stabilized enzymes are used, heat and pelleting trials show good enzyme recovery even at high temperatures (Classen *et al.*, 1991). A large number of commercial trials have shown that enzyme supplemented feeds pelleted at temperatures of 71-90 C (160-195 F) improved animal performance, indicating the survival and presence of added enzyme activities. Heat stable enzyme products are available, but methods to assay the enzyme stability remaining after the pelleting process has not been agreed upon (Bedford, 1993). Enzyme stabilization through improved production technology has allowed some dry enzyme products to be pelleted after conditioning at up to 88 C (190 F) and liquid enzymes to be stored in the feed mill up to four months prior to feeding (Lobo, 1999).

Some improvements seen with the extrusion process include improved digestibility of nutrients by rupturing cell walls, changing the chemical and physical properties of carbohydrates and proteins, and reductions in the protein and fat contents of corn, but there were no changes seen in the concentrations of various amino acids. Use of extruded corn in the diets of young pigs improved energy utilization but there was no effect on lysine or nitrogen utilization (Herkelman *et al.*, 1990). The trypsin inhibitor content of soybean meal is reduced by extrusion, but urease activity and utilization of lysine by young pigs were not affected (Rodhouse *et al.*, 1992). Steam pelleting or extrusion of corn, soybean meal or diets containing these ingredients did not increase phytate P utilization by broiler chicks (Edwards *et al.*, 1999).

Certain heat sensitive nutrients may be destroyed by expanders, but Coelho (1994) indicated that research showed this to be an insignificant concern. However, McEllhiney (1989) reported that feed formulations need to account for decreases in vitamin A potency of 29.3% due to regrinding, and another 12.9% decrease when reground mash is pelleted. A 17.9% loss of vitamin A was seen when feed was pelleted alone, without regrinding, but when it was reground, the loss increased to 38.4%. Pelleting of feed has been shown to increase the lysine requirement in growing turkeys compared to turkey fed similar diets in mash form, especially when lysine levels were marginal in the formulations (Jensen *et al.*, 1965). Because pelleting increased the productive energy of the diet, Beyer (2000) speculated that more lysine was required since the requirement of some nutrients is related to the level of other nutrients available to the bird. If pelleting increases the feed conversion by 10%, then the theoretical requirement for lysine in growing turkeys, for example, would be 1.43% compared to mash at 1.3% (NRC, 1994). Further research is still needed on the effect of feed form on the nutrient content of feed. Feed form may influence certain nutritional requirements and has been shown to interact with bird behavior, management and anatomical changes. Growth, feed conversion and product quality may all be improved by properly manufactured feed. Determination of the effect of feed conditioning and processing on nutrient availability is needed to increase the precision of feeding programs to reduce costs. Effeciency could be increased by refinements in crumble quality, pellet diameter and pellet length. Least cost feed formulation needs to evaluate the resulting impact on feed quality and bird performance.

IV. IMPROVING NUTRIENT EFFICIENCY BY TESTING THE COMPLETE FEED

Successful quality control programs must include sending finished rations for laboratory analysis. It is important to verify that the steps to improve efficiency have been accurate and whether or not the feed will do its job in the livestock herd. First, a representative fed sample is needed. A sample should be kept back, labeled with the date, and stored in an air tight container for the least one year.

A reliable laboratory should be chosen to send the sample to. Results should be reported within three days and should include contents of nutrients such as protein, fat, and fiber. Sometimes the limited number of amino acids, vitamins, trace minerals and others are included along with specialist's advice for farmers on how best to apply the analytical data (Nahm, 2000). There is an acceptable analytical variation for each nutrient.

There are two types of analytical methods used for quality control program in laboratories, which are the wet chemistry method and the dry chemistry method. Near Infrared Reflectance Analysis (NIRA) is a good example of dry chemistry method. NIRA may be the answer for proving rapid and accurate digestible energy and amino acid values for use in feed formulation.

V. CONCLUSION

Recently, the reduction of pollutants in animal manure has been approached through research into improving nutrient efficiency, mainly with pig and chicken test subjects. Nutrient efficiency has been improved through supplements (extended use of amino acids and related compounds, use of enzymes, and use of growth promotants) and modifying feeding programs (formulations closer to requirements, phase feeding, and increased use of highly digestible raw materials). These methods lead to a reduction of DM, N, P, and trace mineral contents as well as decreased odor of animal manure.

Feed manufacturing techniques including grinding methods to provide proper particle sizes and feed uniformity or expanding and pelleting techniques must be studied to improve feed efficiency and reduce manure pollutants as well as done cost effective way. Specialists also need to provide improved feed formulations based on analytical results of samples taken from the farms, which will result in reduced manure pollutants from poultry and swine.

ACKNOWLEDGMENTS

This research was supported by the Taegu University Research Grant, 2001. The author would like to thank them for their partial financial support.

REFERENCES

Aicher, E., 1998. Post pelleting liquid systems for enzymes - Use of Natophos phytase in broiler nutrition and waste management. In: BASF Technical Symposium. Jan. 19, BASF Corporation, Mount Olive, NJ, USA, pp. 35-46.

Bartov, I., 2000. Effect of storage and processing conditions on ingredients quality. In: Proceedings of the Worlds Poultry Science Conference (on CD), Montreal, Canada. Aug. 22-24.

Bedford, M.R., 1993. Matching enzymes to application. Feed Management 44 (3), 14, 16, 18.

Behnke, K.C., 1996. The impact of new processing technology of feed and animal performance. In: Proceedings of the California Animal Nutrition Conference, May 8-9, PG Ag Products, Fresno, CA, USA, pp. 116-129.

Belyavin, C.G., 1994. In-feed enzymes. Poul. Intern. November, pp. 54, 56.

Beyer, R.S., 2000. The impact of feed milling and manufacturing procedures on nutrient availability and microbial content of poultry feed. In: 2000 California Animal Nutrition Conference, May 10-11, PG Ag Products, Fresno, CA, USA, pp. 151-162.

Blair, R., Jacob, J.P., Ibrahim, S., Wang, P., 1999. A quantitative assessment of reduced protein diets and supplements to improve nitrogen utilization. J. Appl. Poultry Res. 8, 25-47.

Boisen, S., Fernander, J.A., Madsen, A., 1995. Studies on ideal protein requirements of pigs from 20 to 95 kg live weight. In: Proceedings of 6th International Symposium on Protein Metabolism and Nutrition. Hering, Denmark, p. 299.

Bridges, T.C., Turner, L.W., Cromwell, G.L., Pierce, J.L., 1995. Modeling the effects of diet formulation on nitrogen and phosphorus excretion swine waste. Appl. Eng. in Agric. 11(5), 731-740.

Cabrera, M.R., Hancock, J.D., Behnke, K.C., Bramel-Cox, P.J., Hines, R.H., 1993. Sorghum genotype and particle size affect growth performance, nutrient digestibility, and stomach morphology in finishing pigs. In: Swine Day Report-93, Kansas St. University, Manhattan, KS, USA, p. 129.

Cabrera, M.R., Hancock, J.D., Bramel-Cox, P.J., Hines, R.H., Behnke, K.C., 1994. Effects of corn, sorghum genotype, and particle size on milling characteristics and growth performance in broiler chicks. Poultry Sci. (Suppl.), 11.

Canh, T.T., Aarnink, A.J.A., Verstegen, M.W.A., Schrama, J.W., 1998a. Influences of dietary factors on the pH and ammonia emission of slurry from growing-finishing pigs. J. Anim. Sci. 76, 1123-1130.

Canh, T.T., Sutton, A.L., Aarnink, A.J.A., Verstegen, M.W.A., Schrama, J.W., Bakker, G.C.M., 1998b. Dietary carbohydrates alter the fecal composition and pH and the ammonia emission from slurry of growing pigs. J. Anim. Sci. 76, 1887-1897.

Carter, S.D., Cromwell, G.L., Lindemann, M.D., Cervantes, L.W., Ramirez, M., 1996. Amino acid supplementation of low protein, grain sorghum-soybean meat diets for pigs. J. Anim. Sci. 74 (Suppl. 1), 59 (Abstr.).

Classen, H.L., 2000. Exogenous enzymes use in animal feeding. In: 2000-01 Direct-Fed Microbial, Enzyme and Forage Additive Compendium. The Miller Publishing Company, Carol Stream, IL, USA, pp. 23-37.

Classen, H.L., Graham, H., Inborr, J., Bedford, M.R., 1991. Growing interest in feed enymes to lead to new products. Feedstuffs 63 (Jan. 28), 22-25.

Coelho, M.B., 1994. Ecological nutrition: A costly or smart move? Feedstuffs 66

(June 20), 13-15.

Coffey, M.T., 1992. An industry perspective on environmental and waste management issues: challenge for the feed industry. In: Proceedings of Georgia Nutrition Conference. University of Georgia, Athens, GA., USA, pp. 144-148.

Coffey, M.T., 1996. Environmental challenges as related to animal agriculture - swine. In: E.T. Kornegay (Ed.), Nutrient Management of Food Animals to Enhance and Protect the Environment. Lewis Publishers, New York, USA, pp. 29-39.

Cromwell, G.L., Coffey, R.D., 1995. Nutrient management from feed to field. In: Proceeding of the World Pork Expo., Des Moines, IA, USA, pp. 47-53.

Delort-Laval, J., 1993. The nutritional aspects of hydrothermal treatment of feed. In: Feed Production Tomorrow II Conference. Oct. 25-27. Bangkok, Thailand, pp. 24-42.

Duncan, M.S., 1973. Nutrient variation: Effect on quality control and animal performance. Ph.D. dissertation. Kansas St. University, Manhattan, KS, USA.

Edwards, H.M., Carlos, A.M., Kasim, A.B., Toledo, R.T., 1999. Effects of steam pelleting and extention of feed on phytate phosphorus utilization in broiler chickens. Poultry Sci. 78, 96-101.

Fancher, B., Rollins, D., Trimbee, B., 1996. Feed processing using the annular gap expander and its impact on poultry performance. J. Appl. Poultry Res. 5, 386-394.

Farrell, D.J., 2000. Maximum production of laying hens on diets without protein concentration. In: XX World's Poultry Congress (on CD), Montreal, Canada. August 20-24.

Farrell, D.J., Robinson, D., Priest, J., 1998. Low protein diets for layers: How low can we go? In: Annual Symposium Organized by the Poultry Research Foundation University of Sydney and the World's Poultry Science Association. ISSN No. 1034-6260. Sydney, Austrailia, p. 214.

Federation Europeenne des Fabricants d'Adjuvants pour la Nutrition Animale, 1992. Improvement of the environment: Possibilities for the reduction of nitrogen and phosphorus pollution caused by animal production. FEFANA, Belgium. Goodband, R.D., Hines, R.H., 1988. An evaluation of barley in starter diets for swine. J. Anim. Sci. 66, 3086-3091.

Hamilton, D.W. Arogo, J., 1999. Understanding farmstead odors: An annotated review. Prof. Anim. Sci. 15, 203-210.

Hancock, J.D., Wondra, K.J., Traylor, S.L., Mavromichalis, I., 1996. Feed processing and diet modifications affect growth performance and economics of swine production. In: Proceedings of Carolina Swine Nutrition Conference. November. NC, USA, pp. 90-109.

Hankins, S., Sutton, A., Patterson, J., Adeola, L., Richert, B., Heber, A., Kelly, D.,

Kephart, K., Mumma, R., Bogus, E., 2000. Diet modification may reduce odorous compounds in pig manure. In: Proceedings of Purdue Swine Day. August 31. West Lafayette, IN, USA, pp. 17-20.

Hedde, R.D., Lindsey, T.O., Parish, R.C., Daniels, H.D., Morgenthien, E.A., Lewis, H.B., 1985. Effect of diet particle size and feeding of H2-receptor antagonists on gastric ulcers in swine. J. Anim. Sci. 61, 179-184.

Henry, Y., and Dourmad, J.Y., 1993. Feeding strategy for minimizing N output in pigs. In: Verstegen, M.W.A., den Hartog, L.A., G.J.M. van Kempen, G.J.M., Metz, J.H.M. (Eds.), Nitrogen Flow in Pig production and Environmental Consequences. Pudoc Scientific Publishers, Wageningen, Netherlands, pp. 137-150.

Herkelman, K.L., Rodhouse, S.L., Veum, T.L., Ellersieck, M.R., 1990. Effect of extrusion on the ileal and fecal digestibilities of lysine in yellow corn in diets for young pigs. J. Anim. Sci. 68, 2414-2424.

Hobbs, P.J., Misselbrook, T.H. and Pain, B.F., 1995. Assessment of odours from livestock wastes by photpionization detector, an electronic nose, olfactometry and gas-chromatography-mass spectrometry. J. Agric. Eng. Res., 60:137-144.

Hobbs, P.J., Pain, B.F., Kay, R.M. Lee, P.A., 1996. Reduction of odorous compounds in fresh pig slurry by dietary control of crude protein. J. Sci. Food and Agric. 71, 508-514.

Jensen, L.S., Rant, G.O., Wagstaff, R.K., McGinnis, J., 1965. Protein and lysine requirements of developing turkeys as influencing by pelleting. Poultry Sci. 44, 1435-1441.

Jongbloed, A.W., Mroz, Z., Kemme, P.A., 1992. The effect of supplementary Aspergillus niger phytase in diets for pigs on concentration and apparent digestibility of dry matter, total phosphorus and phytic acid in different sections of the alimentary tract. J. Anim. Sci. 70, 1159-1163.

Johnston, S.L., and Southern, L.L., 2000. Effects of mix uniformity on performance of chicks explored. Feedstuffs 72 (May 26), 14-17, 41.

Kasin, A.B., Edwards, H.M., 1998. The effect of sources of corn and corn particle sizes on the utilization of phytate phosphorus in broiler chicks. Poultry Sci. 77 (Suppl. 1), 117 (Abstr.).

Kay, R.M., Lee, P.A., 1997. Ammonia emission from pig buildings and characteristics of slurry produced by pigs offered low crude protein diets. In: Proceedings of Symposium on Ammonia and Odour Control from Animal Production Facilities. Vinkeloord, The Netherlands, pp. 253-259.

Koch, F., 1990. Amino acid formulation to improve carcass quality and limit N load in waste. In: Proceedings of Carolina Swine Nutrition Conference. November. NC, USA, pp. 76-95.

Kornegay, E.T., Harper, A.F., 1997. Environmental nutrition: Nutrient management strategies to reduce nutrient excretion of swine. Prof. Anim. Sci. 13, 99-111.

Lobo, P., 1999. Factors to consider when adding enzymes to feed. Feed Management 50(10), 21-23.

Lyons, T.P., 1995. Biotechnology in the feed industry: A look forward and backward. In: Official Proceedings of Annual Pacific North America Animal Nutrition Conference. Oct. 10-12. Portland, OR., USA, pp. 134-147.

McCoy, R.A., Behnke, K.C., Hancock, J.D., McEllhiney, K.R., 1994. Effect of mixing uniformity on broiler chick performance. Poultry Sci. 73, 443-451.

McEllhiney, R.R., 1989. Feed pelleting in perspective. In: 1989 Proceedings of Maryland Nutrition Conference for Feed Manufacturers. May 16-17. University of Maryland, MD, USA. pp. 90-101.

Michal, J.J. and Frosoth, J.A., 1999. Decreasing supplemental phosphorus may reduce feed costs. Feedstuffs 71 (May 24), 11-13.

Miner, J.R., Raja, S.N., McGregor, W., 1997. Finely ground Zeolite as an odorous control additive immediately prior to sprinkle application of liquid dairy manure. In: Proceedings of the International Symposium on Ammonia and Odour Emissions from Animal Production. 6-7 Oct.. Vinkeloord, the Netherlands. pp. 717-720.

Morse, D. H., Head, H., Wilcox, C.J., Horn, H.H.V., Hissem, C.D., Harris, B. Jr., 1992. Effects of concentration of dietary phosphorus on amount and route of excretion. J. Dairy Sci. 75, 3039-3049.

Nahm, K.H., 1992. Practical Guide to Feed, Forage and Water Analysis (English Edition). Yuhan Pub. Co., Seoul, South Korea.

Nahm, K.H., 2000. A strategy to solve environmental concerns caused by poultry production. World's Poultry Science J. 54(4), 45-50.

Nahm, K.H., Carlson, C.W., 1998. The possible minimum chicken nutrient requirements for protecting the environment and improving cost efficiency. Asian-Australian J. Anim. Sci. 11(6), 755-768.

Nahm, K.H., Maeyong, W.J., Kim, D.J., Kang, C.W., 1998. A Textbook of Feed Resources (Korean Edition). Hyang Moon Pub. Co., Seoul, Korea, pp. 238-265.

National Research Council, 1994. Nutrient Requirement of Poultry (12th Ed.). National Academy Press, Washington, DC, USA.

National Research Council, 1998. Nutrient Requirements of Swine (10th Ed). National Academy Press, Washington, DC, USA.

Nir, I., 1996. The effect of food particle size and hardness on performance: Nutritional behavioral and metabolic aspects. In: Proceedings of the XX World's Poultry Conference, Vol. II. New Delhi, India, pp. 173-183.

Norton, H., 1999. Steps to controlling feed quality. Pork 99 (July), pp. 20-22.

Ohh, S.J., Allee, G.L., Behnke, K.C., Deyoe, C.W., 1983. Effects of particle size of corn and sorghum grain on performance and digestibility of nutrients for weaned pigs. J. Anim. Sci. 57 (Suppl. 1), 260 (Abstr.).

O'Neill, D.H., Phillips, V.R., 1992. A review of the control of odour nuisance from livestock buildings. Part III. Properties of the odorous substances which have been identified in livestock wastes or in the air around them. J. Agric. Eng. Res. 53, 23-50.

Owsley, W.F., Knabe, D.A., and Tanksley, Jr., T.D., 1981. Effect of sorghum particle size on digestibility of nutrients at the terminal ileum and over the total digestive tract of growing-finishing pigs. J. Anim. Sci. 52, 557-561.

Peisker, M., 1994. Influence of expansion on feed components. Feed Mix. 2, 26-31.

Pierce, J.L., Enright, K.L., Cromwell, G.L., Turner, L.W., Bridges, T.C., 1994. Dietary manipulation to reduce the N and P excretion by finishing pigs. J. Anim. Sci. 72 (Suppl.), 331 (Abstr.).

Rodhouse, S.L., Herkelman, K.L., Veum, T.L., 1992. Effect of extrusion on the ileal and fecal digestibilities of lysine, nitrogen, and energy in diets for young pigs. J. Anim. Sci. 70, 827-835.

Scott, T.A., 1991. Nutritional effects on waste production from monogastrics. In: Proceedings of Canadian Society of Animal Science Meetings. May. Chilliwack, B.C., Canada. pp. 35-41.

Seerley, R.W., Vandergrift, W.L.., Hale, O.M., 1988. Effect of particle size of wheat on performance of nursery, growing and finishing pigs. J. Anim. Sci. 66, 2484-2489.

Shurson, J., Whitney, M., Nicolai, R., 1999. Manipulating diets may reduce hydrogen sulfide emissions. Feedstuffs 71 (January 25), 12-17.

Spears, J.W., 1996. Optimizing mineral levels and sources for farm animals. In: Kornegay, E.T. (Ed.), Nutrient Management of Food Animals to Enhance and Protect the Environment. Lewis Publishers, New York, USA, pp. 259-275.

Spoelstra, S.F., 1980. Origin of objectionable odorous compounds in piggery wastes and the possibility of applying indicator components for studying odor development. Agric. Environ. 5, 241-260.

Stark, C.R., Behnke, K.C., Goodband, R.D., Hansen, J.A., 1991. On-Farm feed uniformity survey. In: Swine Day Report-1991. Kansas St. University, Manhattan, KS, USA, p. 144.

Summers, J.D., 1993. Reducing nitrogen excretion of the laying hen by feeding lower crude protein diets. Poultry Sci. 72, 1473-1478.

Sutton, A.L., Goodall, S.R., Patterson, J.A., Mathew, A.G., Kelley, D.T., and Meyerholtz, K.A., 1992. Effects of odor control compounds on urease activity in swine manure. J. Anim. Sci. 70 (Suppl. 1), 160 (Abstr.).

Sutton, A.L., Kephart, K.B., Patterson, J.A., Mumma, R., Kelly, D.T., Bogus, E., Jones, D.D., Heber, A., 1997. Dietary manipulation to reduce ammonia and odor compounds in excreta and an aerobic manure storages. In: Proceedings of International Symposium on Ammonia and Odour from Animal Production

Facilities. Vinkeloord, The Netherlands, pp. 245-252.

Sutton, A.L., Kephart, K.B., Verstegen, M.W.A., Canh, T.T. Hobbs, P.J., 1999. Potential for reduction of odors compounds in swine manure through diet modification. J. Anim. Sci. 77, 430-439.

Traylor, S.L., 1997. Effects of feed processing on diet characteristics and animal performance. MS Thesis, Kansas St. University, Manhattan, KS, USA.

Turner, L.W., Cromwell, G.L., Bridges, T.C., Carter, S., Gates, R.S., 1996. Ammonia emission from swine waste as influenced by diet manipulation. In: Proceedings of 1st International Conferance on Air Pollution from Agricultural Operations. Kansas City, MO. USA, pp. 453-458.

van der Peet-Schwering, C.M.C., Verdoes, N., Voermans, M.P., Beelen, G.M., 1996. Effect of feeding and housing on the ammonia emission of growing and finishing pig facilities. Research Institute of Pig Husbandry Rep. 5(3), 27-28.

Van Heugten, E., Van Kempen, T., 1999. Methods may exist to reduce nutrient excretion. Feedstuffs 71 (April 26), 12-13, 16-19.

Wicker, D.L., Poole, D.R., 1991. How is your mixer performing? Feed Management 42(9), 40.

Williams, P.E.V., 1995. Animal production and European pollution problems. Anim. Feed Sci. and Tech. 53, 135-144.

Williams, P.E.V., Pagliani, L., Innes, G.M., Pennie, K., Harris, C.I., Garthwaite, P., 1987. Effects of the beta agonist (Clenbuterol) on growth, carcass composition, protein and energy metabolism of veal calves. Br. J. Nutr. 57, 417-428.

Wilson, K.J., Beyer, R.S., 1997. Could the results of some nutrition feeding trial be confounded with feed form and bird behavior? Poultry Sci. 77 (Suppl. 1), 47.

Wondra, K.J., Hancock, J.D., Behnke, K.C., Hines, R.H., Stark, C.R., 1993. Effects of hammermills and roller mills on growth performance, nutrient digestibility and stomach morphology in finishing pigs. In: Swine Day Report-93. Kansas St. University, Manhattan, KS, USA, p. 135.

Wondra, K.J., Hancock, J.D., Behnk, K.C., Hines, R.H., Stark, C.R., 1995. Effects of particle size and pelleting on growth performance, nutrient digestibility, and stomach morphology in finishing pigs. J. Anim. Sci. 73, 757-761.

Wondra, K.J., Hancock, J.D., Behnke, K.C., and Stark, C.R., 1995c. Effects of mill type and particle size uniformity on growth performance, nutrient digestibility and stomach morphology in finishing pigs. J. Anim. Sci. 73, 2564-2573.

Wondra, K.J., Hancock, J.D., Kennedy, G.A., Behnke, K.C., Wondra, K.R., 1995b. Effects of reducing particle size of corn in lactation diets on energy and nitrogen metabolism in second-parity sows. J. Anim. Sci. 73, 427-432.

Wondra, K.J., Hancock, J.D., Kennedy, G.A., Hines, R.H., Behnke, K.C., 1995a. Reducing particles size of corn in lactation diets from 1200 to 400 micrometers improves sows and litter performance. J. Anim. Sci. 73, 421-426.

Wyatt, C.L. Harker, A., 1995. Application of feed enzymes to commercial wheat and barley based poultry feeds. In: Proceedings of California Nutrition Conference. University of California, Davis, Cal., USA, pp. 203-211.

...nces in Environmental Science and Technology. Vol. 20[14]. 343-XXX. 714

Woese, C.E.; Ranker, A., 1995. Application of feed enzymes to commercial wheat and barley based poultry feeds. In: Proceedings of California Nutrition Conference. University of California, Davis, Cal., USA. pp. 207-214.

World's Poultry Science Journal Vol. 59: 77-88 (2003)   243

Evaluation of the nitrogen content in poultry manure

K. H. Nahm*

Feed and Nutrition Laboratory, College of Natural Resources, Taegu University, Gyong San, 712-714, South Korea. E-mail: nahmkh@daegu.ac.kr

Proper estimation of the nitrogen (N) content of poultry manure and proper manure handling are necessary to ensure that application rates minimize emissions from the manure and nitrate leaching into the cropland. Uric acid and undigested proteins are the two main N components in poultry manure that cause ammonia emissions and nitrate leaching in the ground water. The ammonia that is applied to cropland may be 50 to 90% of total N, depending upon the way the manure has been stored or treated. Ammonia and hydrogen sulphide contents have been proven to be useful alternative measures of odour reduction. The order of importance in influencing ammonia formation is: litter pH > temperature > moisture content. Total fixation of ammonia was achieved below pH 4 and temperatures down 10 C are necessary to have a negative effect on degradation and volatilization. Adsorbants such as sawdust and straw enable the capture some of the readily available N and enable the microbial population to start immobilizing N. The organic fraction of poultry manure had a C/N ratio that varied from 1 to 27:1. Most of the N (approximately 60-70%) excreted in poultry manure is in the form of uric acid and urea. Total N, total Kjeldahl N (TKN), organic N, ammonium, nitrate and nitrite are significantly correlated with the amount of N mineralized as well as the fraction of organic N mineralized during incubation. Some useful equations are: Inorganic N (IN) = ammonium + nitrate + nitrite; Total N (TN) = TKN + nitrate + nitrite; Organic N = TKN - ammonium or TN - (ammonium + uric acid) or TN - IN; Available N (AN) = Inorganic N + 0.4 x organic N; Predicted available N (PAN) = 80% Inorganic N + 60% Organic N.

(Keywords: Ammonia emission; AN; inorganic N; nitrate; nitrite; nitrogen; organic N; PAN; TKN; TN)

* Corresponding author. Present address: 25001 Cashel Bay Rd., Manhattan, IL

60442, USA. E-mail: KHNahm1@cs.com

Introduction

Modern broiler and layer farm development has resulted in the production and accumulation of enormous amounts of poultry manure (litter and faeces). Disposal of this manure is of significant environmental concern.

Environmental pollution caused by nitrogen (N) occurs in two ways, as ammonia in the air or as nitrate in soil or ground water. Recently Jungbluth et al. (2001) reported that there is a third nitrogenous compound (N_2O) that is harmful to the environment although data about N_2O emissions from animal houses are lacking because of the difficulties in measuring very low N_2O concentrations. The concentrations of N (protein and non-protein nitrogen - NPN), calcium (Ca) and phosphorus (P) in poultry wastes are higher than in the wastes of other species, so the value of poultry wastes as a source of these nutrients provides more incentive for the utilization of this resource for plants and animals (Fontenot *et al.*, 1983). Uric acid is the majority of the NPN and is converted to ammonia, which is assimilated, by both plants and ruminants. Differences in feed, feed conversion by different species of animals, age of the animals, type of bedding material and water intake all affect the total nitrogen (TN) contents and N forms in animal manure (MAFF, 1994).

Manure types or manure from the same species of animals on different diets have not clearly been distinguished. And since excessive application of poultry manures into some cropping systems has resulted in ammonia emissions and nitrate contamination of ground water, better characterization of the forms and amounts of N in animal manure and a means of predicting organic N mineralization is needed. Mineralization from organic forms to mineral forms of N is a prerequisite for plant uptake. This paper reviews the scientific literature related to the poultry production research aimed at reducing N content of poultry manure and minimizing ammonia emissions and nitrate leaching into the ground water after application to the cropland.

Nitrogen sources

Uric acid and undigested proteins are the two main N components in poultry faeces, representing 70 and 30% of the TN, respectively (Groot Koerkamp, 1994). The proportion of uric acid and faecal undigested feed N can be highly influenced by animal diet. Factors increasing faecal N output include usage of low-digestible feedstuffs; presence of antinutritive factors such as various fibre sources, trypsin and chymotrysin inhibitors; lectins; phenolic compounds; and tannins (Baidoo, 2000; Nahm, 2002).

Absorbed amino acids that cannot be used for protein deposition are broken down, and the N, in the form of uric acid in poultry, is excreted in the faeces. Amino acids are the building blocks of protein. The various proteins in muscle, vital organs, bone, blood and other tissues and fluids of the body consist of 20 primary amino acids. Chickens must receive sufficient levels of essential amino acids in their diet for protein synthesis to occur at an optimal rate.

The use of crystalline lysine and methionine in poultry diets has been a common practice for many years. While many of the other essential amino acids have been available, their cost has restricted their use in practical diets. This, however, is changing as a result of biotechnology, new fermentation technologies and other new technological advances. The price of these amino acids has decreased in recent years and they are now being used to a limited extent in poultry diets. In one study, when dietary crude protein was lowered from 17 to 13% for 24-week-old laying hens, faecal N excretion was reduced as much as 34% without affecting egg production (Summers, 1993). Several researchers (Moran, Jr. and Bushong, 1992; Moran, Jr., 1994) have shown that reducing the dietary protein content 10 and 15%, while maintaining the required essential amino acid levels within each age period for broilers, will reduce litter N content (percent dry matter) approximately 24% without impairing weight gain. However, for various reasons (e.g., costs, time for research and development) implementation is limited or impossible in a short time. Moreover, N-excretion cannot be totally prevented by those methods.

The process of N loss

In animal manure, N is found as both ammonia and organic N. With manure storage pits or anaerobic lagoons, the organic N conversion to ammonia results in volatilization and loss of N ammonia into the air. This ammonia release contributes to odour, area wide acid rain and N enrichment of the ground water. Depending on how the manure has been stored or treated, up to 50 to 90% of the total N found in the manure applied to cropland may be in the form of ammonia (Miner et al., 2000).

Application of manure to cropland or to the soil results in a change from an anaerobic to an aerobic environment. Ammonia, present partially in the form of ammonium, is temporarily immobilized in the soil by the attraction to the negatively charged soil particles. Aerobic bacteria then initiate the process of conversion of ammonia to nitrite and then nitrate. When water moves downward through the soil, nitrate is carried with the water and concentrates in groundwater.

Ammonia emission in the air and nitrate contamination of groundwater are generated from decomposition of nitrogenous compounds in poultry manure, principally uric acid and undigested protein. The decomposition of uric acid is described in Figure 1, which was simplified by Vogels and Van der Drift (1976) and undigested proteins change to ammonia as well as other chemicals. As seen in Figure 1, this decomposition process requires the presence of water and oxygen, while ammonia and carbon dioxide are products of the degradation process. Microorganisms commonly found in manure produce the enzymes uricase and urease, which are specific to this reaction. Uric acid may also be degraded by anaerobic microorganisms along other pathways, but these anaerobic pathways are much slower than aerobic pathways. Temperature, pH and moisture content influences the degradation of uric acid and proteins. The last steps of the degradation of uric acid depend on urease activity, pH and temperature. Dry and liquid poultry manures have been shown to have degradation rates of 8 and 40% per day, respectively (Burnett and Dondero, 1969), while a rate of 20% per day has been reported for litter under optimal conditions (35℃, pH 9) (Elliot and Collins, 1982).

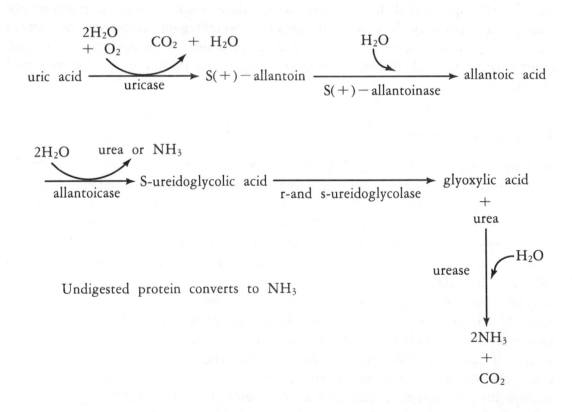

Figure 1. Aerobic decomposition of uric acid (Vogels and Van der Drift, 1976)

Decomposition of organic nitrogenous materials, or degradation, is kinetically very slow by non-biological means and therefore microorganisms are required to mediate this reaction. At temperatures above 30℃, this process is known as composting and it requires aerobic conditions (de Bertolde *et al.*, 1983; Miller, 1989). When sufficient water and oxygen are available in dry poultry manure, composting will take place. Relatively large amounts of organic material can be lost due to the degradation process and volatilization of water vapour and carbon dioxide. When oxygen is absent, degradation is called rotting or fermentation (Groot Koerkamp *et al.*, 1990). When anaerobic conditions are present such as in wet slurry, many gaseous compounds may be released. Some examples of these gases include ammonia, methane, carbon dioxide, hydrogen sulphide and volatile fatty acids. N was mainly bound in organic forms in aerobic manure while about two-thirds of the N in anaerobic manure was in the ammonium form (Kirchmann and Witter, 1989).

Painter (1977) gave a review of microbial transformations of inorganic N. Three main processes were indicated in this review. 1) The fixation of dinitrogen resulting in ammonia production (aerobic or anaerobic), 2) Ammonia can be converted to nitrite and subsequently nitrate through nitrification (autotrophic or heterotrophic). Autotrophic nitrification is thought to be more important, but oxygen must be available. This lowers the ammonia concentration. 3) Microorganisms can utilize nitrate for their N source (assimilation-synthesis of N), or for their oxygen (dissimilation). Ammonia is generally preferred to nitrate for assimilation, since nitrate must first be reduced to ammonia for this process. In dissimilation, the end products can be nitrite, nitric acid, nitrous oxide or dinitrogen. When the last three products are formed, the process is called denitrification. The conditions must be anaerobic or nearly so, for dissimilation. There still needs to be more research into this mechanism of N loss and the potential environmental impact of N from poultry manure.

Manure odours are never pure samples of one odorant, but certain a mixture of many different odorants. Even though individual odorants may be below the detection level, they may be smelled. Odorant volatility may be used to divide compounds in the same chemical family into three odour notes (Hamilton and Arogo, 1999). The odour chord may be divided into the highly volatile compounds of the top notes (e.g., hydrogen sulphide and ammonia), the persistent compounds of the base notes [e.g., organic acids, phenolic compounds, indole and skatole, organic sulphides (5 carbons) and dust-borne odorants] and the compound with medium volatility of the middle notes [e.g. aldehydes, alcohol, ketones, amines, mercaptans and organic sulfides (2 to 4 carbons)]. Ammonia and hydrogen sulphide have been the two constituents most commonly measured odours, and volatile fatty acid concentrations also have been used as a surrogate (Miner *et al.*, 2000).

Most researchers seem to agree that none of the volatile fatty acids is a major constituent of odour from poultry facilities, but the removal or reduction in ammonia and hydrogen sulphide concentrations has frequently been proven as a useful measure of odour reduction.

Factors that affect the content of N in poultry manure

For plant uptake, mineralization of N from organic forms to mineral forms is necessary. The N fertilizer value of a manure is calculated by adding its inorganic N contents and the mineralizable organic N fraction. Factors that influence this total N content of manure include differences in feed, feed conversion by different animal species, age of animal, bedding material and water intake (MAFF, 1994). pH, temperature and moisture contents are important for better management of poultry manure. Elliott and Collins (1982) reported that the order of importance in influencing NH_3 formation of poultry manure was: litter pH > temperature > moisture content.

pH
Hydrolysis of uric acid and undigested protein in the poultry manure plays a major role in determining the rate of ammonia formation (Giddens and Rao, 1975). Since the behaviour of most volatile compounds depends upon pH, the loss of ammonia and volatile fatty acids from cattle and poultry manure was studied as a function of pH (Derikx et al., 1994). Their results indicated that above pH 8 all ammonia was volatilized and below pH 5 all volatile fatty acids evaporated. They said that total fixation of ammonia was achieved below pH 4 and the amount of acid or alkali needed to obtain the desired pH varied strongly between the various kinds of manure. It was shown that by reducing slurry pH, ammonia volatilization can be prevented and ammonia loss can be reduced by the addition of aluminum chloride, ferric chloride, aluminum sulphate, calcium chloride and other chemicals to the slurry. However, due to the common duct for urine and faeces elimination in poultry, N contents of poultry manure are generally higher than those for other livestock manure. And the N content in poultry manure decreases with time after the manure is excreted, which influences the manure application rate recommended.

The pH of the litter and uric acid degradation are important properties that will affect the NH_3 production and volatilization processes, litter pH rises with litter use. The pH of the litter depends strongly on the age and number of birds grown on it. Typically, new sawdust and wood shavings have pH values in the 5 to 6.5 range (Turnbull and Snoeyenbos, 1973). The hydrolysis reactions result in elevated pH levels that facilitate NH_3 volatilization (Reynolds and Wolf, 1987). The N in poultry manure can be conserved by either inhibiting the hydrolysis of uric acid to

NH₃ or by reducing NH₃ volatilization.

TEMPERATURE

The uric acid and urea are rapidly hydrolyzed to NH_3 and CO_2 by the enzymes urease and uricase if temperature, pH and moisture are adequate for microbial activity (Ronf and Lomprey, Jr., 1968; Siegel *et al.*, 1975). Temperatures down to 10 ℃ are necessary to have a substantial effect on degradation and volatilization. Using temperatures below a range of 20 to 25 ℃ as a control parameter inside the poultry houses may interfere with the climatization of the birds' environment; higher temperatures should be prevented (Groenestein and van Ouwerkerk, 1990). Hadas *et al.* (1983) reported that temperature in the range of 14 to 35 ℃ had little effect on the rate of mineralization but affected N loss from poultry manure pellets by delaying nitrification at 14 and 35 ℃ compared with 25 ℃. Elevated temperatures accelerated bacterial ammonification, gaseous NH_3 production, and mass transfer of NH_3 from the litter to the house atmosphere (Elliott and Collins, 1982). When temperature is fixed, the ammonium content and pH of slurry were the main factors influencing the ammonium emission (Canh *et al.*, 1998; Nahm, 2001a).

MOISTURE

Adding water to manure such as slurry lowers the N concentration, but the increase in the amount of slurry is a big disadvantage. Water also serves an important and complex role in the process of NH_3 volatilization from uric acid and urea. Moisture is required for both dissolution of solid urea forms and subsequent urea hydrolysis, which must occur prior to NH_3 volatilization. This is the reason why the most common remedy for elevated NH_3 levels is to increase ventilation rates above values needed for proper letter moisture control (Elliott and Collins, 1982). This is principally a dilution effect.

Microbial activity is also a moisture-dependent factor that influences the NH_3 volatilization. The bacteria responsible for uric acid decomposition are primarily aerobic, so excessively wet litter should suppress NH_3 production due to the prevailing anaerobic conditions (Schefferle, 1965). Another study (Valentine, 1964) showed that as the house relative humidity approached 100%, the wet and soggy litter stopped "working" and NH_3 formation decreased. Also when very dry conditions are present, the amount of moisture is insufficient for microbial activity (Turnbull and Snoeyenbos, 1973), or inadequate for hydrolysis of urea (Ernst and Massey, 1960).

Dry matter determination by drying at 105 ℃ is one of the most widespread methods used in the characterization of manure at labs. Loss of volatile compounds during dry-matter determination may lead to considerable errors in mass balances (Nahm, 2001b).

The ratio of C and N in manure

It appears that some adsorbents have been successful in minimizing ammonia emission, particularly during the first few days of composting (Kithome *et al.*, 1999). Composting of poultry manure has a high potential for NH_3 volatilization since poultry wastes are generally high in N concentrations and C/N ratios are very low. Addition of carbon (C) and adsorbents to poultry manure may be beneficial since they would capture some of the readily available N and allow the microbial population to develop and begin N immobilization (Alexander, 1977; Serna and Fomares, 1991).

It is likely that high C bedding materials (cellulosic wastes), such as sawdust, wood shavings, rice hulls and straw would have a strong immobilizing effect when present in manures. Highly lignified, mature materials have been previously shown to immobilize N during the decomposition process (Mueller *et al.*, 1998). Thomsen and Kjellerup (1997) demonstrated that field application of straw-containing manure resulted in an increased immobilization of N compared with manure that did not contain straw. Organic matter decomposition is influenced by the chemical composition of the material decomposing and the soil characteristics (Douglas and Magdoff, 1991). Hemicellulose to N (Lupway and Haque, 1998), concentration of N (Gordilla and Cabrera, 1997), carbon (Reinertsen *et al.*, 1999), and ratios of chemical components such as C and N and lignin to N (Mueller *et al.*, 1998) have all been shown to be correlated with rates of organic C or N mineralization.

Between species, the manure composition varies (Levi-Minzi *et al.*, 1990; Serna and Fomares, 1991), and *in vitro* incubation experiments have shown that organic C and N are less mineralizable in cattle manure than swine and poultry (Levi-Minzi *et al.*, 1990; Saviozzi *et al.*, 1993). It has also been reported (Douglas and Magdoff, 1991) that horse and beef cattle manure had significantly lesser amounts of mineral N than the control, resulting in net N immobilization. Composted sheep manure, vegetable matter mixtures and dehydrated poultry manure/cocoa shell blend resulted in net N immobilization that was not significantly different from the control. The C/N ratios of these residues were between 11 and 25, which are ratios thought to result in mineralization. The organic fraction of poultry manure had a C/N ratio that varied from 1 to 27:1 (Bitzer and Sims, 1988). In general, as the organic N content of residues increases, C/N decreases and N mineralization is more rapid. The percentage of organic N mineralized during the experiment was negatively correlated with amount of C, the initial C/N ratio of the manure, and the loss of C during the experiment (Subair *et al.*, 1999). They found that total NH_3 volatilization was negatively correlated with C added, initial C/N ratio, and the loss of C, but was positively correlated with the manure pH, and manure pH was negatively correlated with C added, initial C/N ration, and the loss of C. Lignin content and lignin/N ratio of organic amendments were not significantly correlated with NH_3 volatilization, the loss of C or manure pH (Subair et al., 1999).

Gordilla and Cabrera (1997) found that total mineralizable N could be predicted from uric acid-N and TN concentration (R_2 = 0.91), or from uric acid-N concentration and C/N of the litter (R_2 = 0.95). These scientists showed through the chemical analysis of the litter that total carbon (TC) was relatively homogeneous among samples whereas TN ranged from 26.8 to 59.6g N kg^{-1}. They suggested that C/N ranged from 6:1 to 16:1, mainly due to differences in TN. Other scientists (Gale et al., 1991; Sims and Wolf, 1994) showed similar results. Compared to two broiler litter composts with C:N ratios of 10:1, composted hen manure with a C:N ratio of 20:1 showed immobilization of N at 25d (Tyson and Cabrera, 1993). Immobilization of N is favoured by higher C:N ratios (Alexander, 1977). One report (Van Kessel et al., 2000) showed a declining exponential relationship between the initial potential rate of C mineralization and the C to N ratio of the manure components. When the C to N ratio increased from approximately 3 to 15, the initial potential rate of C mineralization dropped dramatically. When the C to N ratio was above 15, the initial potential rate of C mineralization was low and insensitive to changes in the C to N ratio. However, they observed relationships between the C to N ratio and the decomposition of organic soil amendments that have been inconsistent. Barbarika et al. (1985) demonstrated that sewage sludges with C to N ratios ranging from 2.4 to 16 and increasing C to N ratios had a negative affect on N mineralization. However, Serna and Fomares (1991) demonstrated a strong relationship between the C:N ratio and N mineralization, r = -0.69, while Floate (1970) showed the same relationship in sheep faeces to be weak, r = -0.56. Another study (Castellanos and Pratt, 1981) found no relationship between C:N ratios and N mineralization for a variety of fresh and stored animal manure. With low C/N wastes, it may be beneficial to add both C and adsorbents. The adsorbents would capture some of the readily available N and would give the microbial population ample time to develop and begin immobilizing N.

Presence of oxygen can affect the ability of fibrous materials to immobilize N. Kirchmann and Witter (1989) and Jeong et al. (1997) studied the addition of straw for C/N in aerobic and anaerobic situation, and they reported that increased straw addition reduced ammonia volatilization during aerobic decomposition. Straw caused no immobilization of N under anaerobic conditions. In aerobic manure, N was mainly bound in organic forms whereas in anaerobic manure about two-thirds of the N was in ammonium form. C/N ratios in the organic matter of anaerobic manure were higher (33.1-87.5) than in the aerobic manure (9.5-18.0). When oxidants are not present, ammonia fixation takes place with oxidized groups like the quinones that are present or are activated by an alkaline pH. In the presence of O_2 or other oxidants, greater fixation of NH_3 by organic material may result since simultaneous reactions of oxidants and NH_3 occur when sites on the organic complex reach an appropriate stage of oxidation (Nyborg, 1969; Nommik, 1970).

The coarse fraction of manure had a higher C/N ratio than the fine fraction, which suggests that the conditions allowed more N immobilization. The increased immobilization of N by the straw or shavings would result in the coarse fraction having a smaller slope than the fine fraction. In one report (Gale and Gilmour, 1986), the coarse, fine and mixed fractions in a comparison among fractions had slopes of 0.52, 0.64 and 0.25 respectively at 25℃. This difference in slopes may have been minimized by the physical separation of the sites for mineralization (manure) and immobilization (straw or shavings) (Gilmour et al., 1985). A smaller observed slope would occur when the fraction were mixed and the physical separation was smaller, resulting in more immobilization.

Organic materials with C:organic nitrogen (ON) ratios of 15 or more will immobilize N, while C:ON ratios of less than 15 result in mineralization with lower C:ON ratios having greater mineralization rates (Kirchmann, 1985; Mary and Recous, 1994). When the C:N ratio increased from 14 to 25, the ammonia emissions of manure decreased (Beck et al., 1997; Maeda and Matsuda, 1997). No ammonia emissions were reported when the C:N ratio was above 40 (Maeda and Matsuda, 1997). Chadwick et al. (2000) suggested that the manure C:ON ratio was the best accounting for 40% of the variation in mineralization measured. A better assessment is needed under field conditions for the interaction between manure ON pools and N mineralization.

Total N contents and N changes in poultry manure

The manure source of N in feed is protein which is made from units of amino acids. This N is one of the main factors for air and water pollution in the human environment. Analysis of TN content in poultry feed would give the reliable information to predict the TN and other types of N content in poultry manure. Net N mineralization of manure is related to the crude protein content of the biosolids (Hattori and Mukai, 1986). However, nutrient content of hen manure varies due to such factors as climate, feed composition, production phase and management (Wallingford et al., 1975) and the value of poultry manure as a fertilizer is usually based on its macronutrient, especially N.

Scientists have used different methods to determine the TN content of poultry manure. Reported levels include: 68% of TN in the ammoniacal form at 7.3% dry matter (MacMillan *et al.*, 1972); uric acid-N averaging 55 and 63% of TN in chick excreta of birds fed control and high-protein diets, respectively (Featherson and Scholz, 1968). Fifty% of TN in the ammoniacal (Reddy *et al.*, 1980), and TN levels of 4.59 and 1.70% (dry matter basis) for fresh and composted chicken manures, respectively (Castellanos and Pratt, 1981). One study (Giddens and Rao, 1975) determined that poultry litter lost 47.6% of the TN in the form of volatilized ammonia when manure samples were air-dried for 10 days. They suggested that the rate of ammonia volatilization was determined by hydrolysis of uric acid in the manure. Uric acid and undigested protein represent 70 and 30% of TN, respectively (Groot Koerkamp, 1994).

TN, total Kjeldahl N (TKN), ON, NH_4-N, NO_3-N and NO_2-N are significantly correlated with the amount of N mineralized as well as the fraction of ON mineralized during the incubation. The efficiency of N utilization by livestock animals is low. Domestic animals can excrete about 70% of the N contained in their feed (Husted *et al.*, 1991) although this percentage is highly dependent on protein intake and animal species. And most of the N (approximately 60-70%) excreted in poultry manure is in the form of uric acid and urea (Shuler *et al.*, 1979). These mean that a substantial amount of the N losses are associated with inefficiencies in digestion and absorption. Applying poultry manure to croplands at rates greater than 13.5 Mg ha^{-1} (wet weight basis) consistently resulted in NO_3-N levels in groundwater in excess of the 10 Mg L^{-1} limit established by the United States Environmental Protection Agency (USEPA, 1976; Liebhardt *et al.*, 1979).

Mineralization from organic forms to mineral forms of N is a prerequisite for plant uptake. The primary importance is the timing of N mineralization from the organic fraction of the manure (Sims, 1986). Mineral forms (inorganic forms) of N are the sum of the NH_4-N, NO_3-N and NO_2-N (Sims, 1986) although NH_4-N is the dominant form of inorganic N in poultry manure (Biter and Sims, 1988).

Equations for estimating N content of poultry manure

Manures are usually evaluated as to their ability to supply N to crops, either in terms of the equivalent amount of fertilizer N required to produce an equal yield (Herron and Erhart, 1965) or as the amount of available N released from the manure (Pratt *et al.*, 1973; Mathers and Goss, 1979). Mathers and Goss (1979) calculated the required amount, but on the basis of TN content of the manure. However, in order to use manures efficiently in irrigated crops together with fertilizers, more detailed information, on a shorter time interval basis, is required.

After measuring the contents of ammonium nitrate N and nitrite N (Bremner, 1965), scientists have been using the following equations. The amount of inorganic N (IN) is taken as the sum of NH_4-N and NO_3-N (De Silva and Breitenbeck,

1997; Sims, 1986). TN content and ON content are calculated with the amount of TKN, nitrate and nitrite with the equation for TKN + NO_3-N + NO_2-N and TKN-NH_4-N, respectively (Douglas and Magdoff, 1991). ON was also calculated as TN -IN (Bitzer and Sims, 1988) or TN - (ammonium + uric acid) (Chadwick et al., 2000). Total C can be determined on dried ground material following digestion with dichromate (MAFF, 1986). A modification of the approach to Knezek and Miller (1976) can be used to estimate available N (AN) (AN = IN + 0.4 x ON). Bitzer and Sims (1988) assumed that 20% of the IN in the poultry manure will be lost between time of sampling and actual incorporation into soil and that 2 days would be required to transfer, apply, and incorporate the manure. They also assumed that 60% of manure ON would be mineralized during the 4 to 5 months of the normal growing season for corn. On this basis, predicted available N (PAN) = 80% IN + 60% ON could be calculated.

Conclusion

Potential environmental problems, such as nitrate contamination of ground water and ammonia emissions, must be considered in the agricultural utilization of poultry manure. Knowledge of several aspects of poultry manure transformations in the soil is necessary to manage poultry manure as an N source efficiently.

As the greatest percentage of the N in poultry manure is in the organic fraction, information on the rate and extent of N mineralization is necessary to predict N availability. Additionally, given the fact that from 20 to 40% of the TN in poultry manure has been reported to be in the inorganic form (Sims, 1986, 1987). Poultry manure must be analyzed for total and IN, and application rates must be based on realistic crop yield goals. Based on this study, it would seem that the approach used to estimate available N was reasonable. Another study evaluated a method to estimate the amount of available N in poultry manure to maximize crop response and minimize N losses to the environment. Manure application rates were based on PAN. It is necessary to provide a better assessment of the availability and interaction between manure ON pools and N mineralization under field conditions. And N mineralization was generally greatest from the poultry manures > pig manures > cattle manures (Chadwick et al., 2000).

During aerobic decomposition, increasing straw additions reduced ammonia volatilization. Straw did not immobilize N under anaerobic conditions. Based on this concept, C/N ratios in the organic matter of anaerobic manure were higher than aerobic manure. Total carbon and lignin contents give further information on manure quality.

Poultry manure generally has a higher N content than other livestock manures and the N content of poultry manure can decrease from the time the N is excreted into the manure (as uric acid). This influences the recommended manure application rate and the rate at which the N decomposes to the ammoniacal N forms. However, TN content and form of N in manure vary in relation to animal type, age, diet (especially protein content of feed) and the manure management system.

Although no single chemical parameter still could quantitatively predict N mineralization, knowledge of total mineralization N and N mineralization rates is needed to prevent over application, which may result in NO_3-N leaching into ground water and ammonia emission in the air.

Acknowledgement

This research has been sponsored partially by the research fund of 2002 Taegu University. The author appreciates their financial support.

References

Alexander, M. (1977) Nitrification. In: *Introduction to Soil Microbiology* (2nd Edition). John Wiley and Sons, Inc., New York, NY, USA. pp. 225-250.

Baidoo, S.K. (2000) Environmental impacts of swine, poultry nutrition discussed. *Feedstuffs* (June 26):12-15.

Barbarika, A., Jr., Sikora, L.J. and Colacicco, D. (1985) Factors affecting the mineralization Of nitrogen in sewage sludge applied to soils. *Soil Science Society of America Journal* **49**:1403-1406.

Beck, J., Kack, M., Hentschel, A., Csehi, K., and Jungbluth, T. (1997) Ammonia emissions from composting animal wastes in reactors and windows. In: Voermans, J.A.M., Monteny, G.J. (Eds.), Ammonia and Odour Emission from Animal Production Facilities, *International Conference Proceedings*. Vinkeloord, The Netherlands: Dutch Society of Agricultural Engineering. pp. 381-388.

Bitzer, C.C. and Sims, J.T. (1988) Estimating the availability of nitrogen in poultry manure through laboratory and field studies. *Journal of Environmental Quality* **17**:47-54.

Bremmer, J.M. (1965) Inorganic forms of nitrogen. In: Methods of Soil Analysis. (C.A. Black et al. Eds.), Agronomy No. 9, Part 2. Madison, Wisconsin, USA. pp. 1179-1237.

Burnett, W.E. and Dondero, N.C. (1969) Microbiological and chemical changes in poultry manure associated with decomposition and odour generation. In: *Proceedings of Cornell University Conference of Agriculture Waste Management*, Rochester, NY, USA. pp. 271-274.

Canh, T.T., Aarnink, A.J.A., Verstegen, M.W.A. and Schrama, J.W. (1998) Influence of dietary factors on the pH and ammonia emission of slurry from growing-finishing pigs. *Journal of Animal Science* **76**:1123-1130.

Castellanos, J.Z. and Pratt, P.F. (1981) Mineralization of manure nitrogen-correlation with laboratory indexes. *Soil Science Society of America Journal* **45**:354-357.

Chadwick, D.R., John, F., Pain, B.F., Chambers, B.J. and Williams, J. (2000) Plant uptake of nitrogen from the organic nitrogen fraction of animal manures: a laboratory experiment. *Journal of Agricultural Science* **134**:159-168.

de Bertolde, M., Vallini, G. and Pera, A. (1983) The biology of composting: a review. *Waste Management & Research* **1**:157-176.

Derikx, P.J.L., Willers, H.C. and ten Have, P.J.W. (1994) Effects of pH on the behaviour of volatile compounds in organic manures during dry-matter determination. *Bioresource Technology* **49**:41-45.

De Silva, A.P. and Breitenbeck. G.A. (1997) Nitrogen enrichment of organic wastes by ammoniation. *Journal of Environmental Quality* **26**:688-694.

Douglas, B.F. and Magdoff, F.R. (1991) An evaluation of nitrogen mineralization indices for organic residues. *Journal of Environmental Quality* **20**:368-372.

Elliot, H.A. and Collins, N.E. (1982) Factors affecting ammonia release in broiler houses. *Transaction of the ASAE* **25**:413-424.

Ernst, J.W. and Massey, H.F. (1960) The effect of several factors on volatilization of ammonia formed from urea in the soil. *Soil Science Society of America Proceedings* **24**:87-90.

Featherson, W.R. and Scholz, R.W. (1968) Changes in liver xanthine dehydrogenate and uric acid excretion in chicks during adaptation to a high protein diet *Journal of Nutrition* **95**:393-398.

Floate, M.S. (1970) Decomposition of organic materials from hill soils and pastures. II. Comparative studies on carbon, nitrogen and phosphorus from plant materials and sheep feces. *Soil Biology and Biochemistry* **2**:173-185.

Fontenot, J.P., Smith, L.W. and Sutton, A.L. (1983) Alternative utilization of animal wastes. *Journal of Animal Science* **57** (**Suppl. 2**):221-223.

Gale, P.M. and Gilmour, J.T. (1986) Carbon and nitrogen mineralization kinetics for poultry litter. *Journal of Environmental Quality* **15**(4):423-426.

Gale, P.M., Phillips, J.M., May, M.L. and Wolf, D.C. (1991) Effect of drying on the plant nutrient content of hen manure. *Journal of Productive Agriculture* **4**: 246-250.

Giddens, J. and Rao, A.M. (1975) Effect of incubation and contact with soil on microbial and nitrogen changes in poultry manure. *Journal of Environmental Quality* **4**:295-278.

Gilmour, J.T., Clark, M.D. and Sigua, G.C. (1985) Estimating net N mineralization from CO2 evolution for sewage sludge and plant tissues. *Soil Science Society of American Journal* **49**:1398-1402.

Groot Koerkamp, P.W.G. (1994) Review on emissions of ammonia from housing systems for laying hens in relation to sources, processes, building design and manure handling. *Journal of Agricultural Engineering Research* **59**:73-87.

Groot Koerkamp, P.W.G., Verdoes, N., Monteny, G.J. and De Haan, T. (1990) *Towards Housing System with Low Ammonia Emission: Sources and Processes.* Stuurgroep Emissiearme Huisvestingssystemen, DLO, Wageningen, The Netherlands. p 83.

Gordilla, R.M. and Cabrera, M.L. (1997) Mineralizable nitrogen in broiler litter: I. Effect of selected litter chemical characteristics. *Journal of Environmental Quality* **26**:1672-1679.

Groenestein, C.M. and van Ouwerkerk, E.N.J. (1990) Model for calculating the energy balance in laying hens (KIP). *Report 227.* IMAG, Wageningen, The Netherlands. p 36.

Hadas, A., Bar-Yosef, B., Davidov, S. and Sofer, M. (1983) Effect of pelleting, temperature, and soil types on mineral nitrogen release from poultry and dairy manures. *Soil Science of American Journal* **47**:1129-1133.

Hamilton, D.W. and Arogo, J. (1999) Understanding farmstead odors: An annotated review. *The Professional Animal Scientist* **15**:203-210.

Hattori, H. and Mukai, S. (1986) Decomposition of sewage sludges in soil as affected by their organic matter composition. *Soil Science and Plant Nutrition* **32**:421-432.

Herron, G.M. and Erhart, A.B. (1965) Value of manure on an irrigated calcareous soil. *Soil Science Society of American Proceeding* **29**:278-281.

Husted, S., Jensen, L.S. and Jorgensen, S.S. (1991) Reducing ammonia loss from cattle slurry by the use of acidifying additives: the role of the buffer system. *Journal of Science and Food Agriculture* **57**:335-349.

Jeong, K.H., Kim, T.I., Choi, K.C., Han, J.D. and Kim, W.H. (1997) Changes of compost properties during aerobic composting of poultry manure. *Korean Journal of Animal Science* **39**(6):731-738.

Jungbluth, T., Hartung, E. and Brose, G. (2001) Greenhouse gas emissions from animal houses and manure stores. *Nutrient Cycling in Agroecosystems* **60**:133-145.

Kirchmann, H. (1985) Losses, plant uptake and utilization of manure nitrogen during a production cycle. *Acta Agriculture Scandinavia* **24**(**Suppl.**):75.

Kirchmann, H. and Witter, E. (1989) Ammonia volatilization during aerobic and anaerobic manure decomposition. *Plant and Soil* **115**:35-41.

Kithome, M., Paul, J.W. and Bomke, A.A. (1999) Reducing nitrogen losses during simulated composting of poultry manure using adsorbents or chemical amendments. *Journal of Environmental Quality* **28**:194-201.

Knezek, B.D. and Miller, R.H. (1976) Application of sludges and wastewater on agricultural land. Research Bulletin 1090. Ohio Agricultural Research and Development Center, Wooster, OH, USA. pp. 1.1-1.2.

Levi-Minzi, R., Riffaldi, R. and Saviozzi, A. (1990) Carbon mineralization soil amended with different organic materials. *Agriculture, Ecosystem and Environment* **31**:325-335.

Liebhardt, W.C., Golt, C. and Tupin, J. (1979) Nitrate and ammonium concentrations of ground water resulting from poultry manure applications. *Journal of Environmental Quality* **8**:211-215.

Lupway, N.Z. and Haque, I. (1998) Mineralization of N, P, K, Ca and Mg from sesbania and leucaena leaves varying in chemical compositions. *Soil and Biological Biochemistry* **30**:337-343.

Maeda, T., and Matsuda, J. (1997) Ammonia emissions from composting livestock manure. In: Voermans, J.A.M. and Montency, G.J. (Eds.), Ammonia and Odour Emmission from Animal Production Facilities, *International Conference Proceedings*. Vinkeloord, The Netherlands: Dutch Society of Agricultural Engineering. pp. 145-153.

MacMillan, K., Scott, T.W. and Bateman, T.W. (1972) A study of corn response and soil nitrogen transformations upon application of different rates and sources of chicken manure. In: *Proceedings Cornell Agricultural Waste Management Conference*, Rochester, N.Y., USA. pp. 481-494.

Mary, B., and Recous, S. (1994) Measurement of nitrogen mineralization and immobilization fluxes in soil as a means of predicting net mineralization. *European Journal of Agriculture* **3**:1-10.

Mathers, A.C. and Goss, D.W. (1979) Estimating animal waste applications to supply crop nitrogen requirements. *Soil Science of Society of American Proceedings* **43**:364-366.

Miller, F.C. (1989) Matrix water potential as an ecological determinant in compost, a substrate dense system. *Microbial Ecology* **18**:59-71.

Miner, J.R., Humenik, F.J. and Overcash, M.R. (2000) *Managing Livestock Wastes to Preserve Environmental Quality*. 2000 Iowa State University Press, Ames, Iowa 50014, U.S.A.

Ministry of Agriculture, Fisheries and Food (1986) *The Analysis of Agricultural Materials*, MAFF Reference Book 427. 3rd Edition. London:HM60, UK.

Ministry of Agriculture, Fisheries and Food (1994) *Fertilizer Recommendations*. MAFF Reference Book 209. 6th Edition, MHSA, London, UK.

Moran, Jr. E.T. (1994) Significance of dietary crude protein to broiler carcass quality. In: *Proceedings Maryland Nutrition Conference for Feed Manufacturers*. University of Maryland, College Park, MD, USA. pp. 1-11.

Moran, Jr. E.T. and Bushong, R.D. (1992) Effects of reducing dietary crude protein to relieve litter nitrogen on broiler performance and processing yields. *19th*

World Poultry Science Meetings. Amsterdam, The Netherlands. III:466-470.

Mueller, T., Jensen, L.S., Nielsen, N.E. and Magid, J. (1998) Turnover of carbon and nitrogen in a sandy loan soil following incorporation of chopped maize plants, barley straw and blue grass in the field. *Soil and Biological Biochemistry* **30**:561-571.

Nahm, K.H. (2001a) Causes of nitrogen loss during animal manure analysis. *Korean Journal of Poultry Science* **27**:319-336.

Nahm, K.H. (2001b) Evaluation the nitrogen content in animal manure with conventional Kjeldahl methods. *Institute of Science and Technology* **8(1)**:41-52. Taegu University.

Nahm, K.H. (2002) Efficient feed nutrient utilization to reduce pollutants in poultry and swine manure. *Critical Review in Environmental Science and Technology* **32(1)**:1-16.

Nommik, H. (1970) Non-exchangeable binding of ammonium and amino nitrogen by Norway spruce raw humus. *Plant Soil* **33**:581-595.

Nyborg, M. (1969) Fixation of gaseous ammonia by soils. *Soil Science* **107**:131-136.

Painter, H.A. (1977) Microbial transformation of inorganic nitrogen. *Progress in Water Technology* **8**:3-29.

Pratt, R.F., Broadbent, F.E. and Martin, J.P. (1973) Using organic wastes as nitrogen fertilizers. *California Agriculture* **27(6)**:10-13.

Reddy, K.R., Khaleel, R. and Overcash, M.R. (1980) Nitrogen, phosphorus and carbon transformations in a coastal plain soil treated with animal manures. *Agricultural Wastes* **2**:225-238.

Reinertsen, S.A., Elliott, L.F., Cochran, V.L. and Campbell, G.S. (1999) Role of available carbon and nitrogen in determining the rate of wheat straw decomposition. *Soil and Biological Biochemistry* **16**:459-464.

Reynolds, C.M. and Wolf, D.C. (1987) Effect of soil moisture and air relative humidity on ammonia volatilization from surface-applied urea. *Soil Science* **143**: 144-152.

Ronf, M.A. and Lomprey, Jr. R.F. (1968) Degradation of uric acid by certain aerobic bacteria. *Journal of Bacteriology* **96**:617-622.

Saviozzi, A., Levi-Minzi, R. and Riffaldi, R. (1993) Mineralization parameters from organic materials added to soil as a function of their chemical composition. *Bioresource Technology* **45**:131-135.

Schefferle, H.E. (1965) The decomposition of uric acid in buildup poultry litter. *Journal of Applied Bacteriology* **28**:412-420.

Serna, M.D. and Fomares, F. (1991) Comparison of biological and chemical methods to predict nitrogen mineralization in animal wastes. *Biological and Fertilized Soils* **12**:89-94.

Shuler, M.L., Roberts, E.D., Mitchell, D.W. and Kargi, F. (1979) Process for the aerobic conversion of poultry manure into high-protein feedstuffs. *Biotechnology and Bioengineering* **21**:19-38.

Siegel, R.S., Hafez, A.A.R. and Stout, P.R. (1975) Management procedures for effective Fertilization with poultry manure. *Compost Science* **16**:5-9.

Sims, J.T. (1986) Nitrogen transformations in a poultry manure amendable soil: Temperature and moisture effects. *Journal of Environmental Quality* **15**:59-63.

Sims, J.T. (1987) Agronomic evaluation of poultry manure as a nitrogen source for conventional and no-tillage corn. *Agronomy Journal* **79**:563-570.

Sims, J.T. and Wolf, D.C. (1994) Broiler waste management: agricultural and environmental issues. *Advanced Agronomy* **52**:1-83.

Subair, S., Fyles, J.W. and O'Halloran, I.R. (1999) Ammonia volatilization from liquid hog manure amended with paper products in the laboratory. *Journal of Environmental Quality* **28**:202-207.

Summers, J.D. (1993) Reducing nitrogen excretion of the laying hen by feeding lower crude protein diets. *Poultry Science* **72**:1473-1478.

Thomsen, I.K. and Kjellerup, V. (1997) Yields and N uptake of barley and ryegrass from soils with added animal manure differing in straw and urine content. *European Journal of Agronomy* **7**:285-292.

Turnbull, P.C.B. and Snoeyenbos, G.H. (1973) The role of ammonia, water activity and pH in the salmonellacidal effects of long-used poultry litter. *Avian Digest* **17**:72-86.

Tyson, S.C. and Cabrera, M.L. (1993) Nitrogen mineralization in soils amended with composted and uncomposted poultry litters. *Communication Soil Science and Plant Analysis* **24** (**17&18**):2361-2374.

U.S. Environmental Protection Agency (1976) Quality criteria for water. U.S. Government Printing Office, Washington, DC, USA.

Valentine, H. (1964) A study of the effect of different ventilation rates on the ammonia concentrations in the atmosphere of broiler houses. *British Poultry Science* **5**:149-159.

Van Kessel, J.S., Reeves, III, J.B. and Meisinger, J.J. (2000) Nitrogen and carbon mineralization of potential manure components. *Journal of Environmental Quality* **29**:1669-1677.

Vogels, G.D. and Van der Drift, C. (1976) Degradation of purines and pyrimidines by microorganisms. *Bacteriological Reviews* **40**:403-468.

Wallingford, G.W., Powers, W.L. and Murphy, L.S. (1975) Present knowledge on the effects of land application of animal waste. In: *Managing Livestock Wastes. Proceeding 3rd International Symposium Livestock Wastes*, Urbana-Champaign, IL, USA. April 21-24. pp. 580-582, 586.

Bioavailability of Phosphorus in Poultry Manure

K. H. Nahm*

Feed and Nutrition Laboratory, College of Natural Resources, Taegu University, Gyong San, 712-714, South Korea. E-mail: nahmkh@daegu.ac.kr

ABSTRACT

Phosphorus (P) is a critical nutrient for both animals and plants. P is provided in the diet to poultry as a natural constituent of ingredients and by inorganic salts as supplemental materials. It has been suggested that the P in poultry manure may be a potential source of soil and water hypermineralization. Almost all strategies to control P inputs are based on total P (TP) although most of the P (80 to 90%) in the runoff is in the soluble form, which is the form of most available for algae uptake. Bioavailable P may be changed from TP to bioavailable P (BAP) and grouped into soluble P (SP) or dissolved P (DP) or dissolved reactive P (DRP), total particulate P (PP) and sediment P (SEP). Particulate P is transported into bioavailable PP (BPP). Poultry manures contain significant amount of P composed of inorganic and organic P, which are changed from inorganic P to dissolved inorganic P and from organic P to dissolved organic P when they are in the soluble forms of the runoff. Most of the P in all manures and composts is inorganic (60-90% of TP) with smaller amounts of organic and residual forms. Water extractable P in poultry manure may be used to estimate the potential for land-applied poultry manures or composts to enrich leachate and surface runoff. The Redfield ratio can be used for obtaining reasonable standards for total P concentration. The proper Redfield ratio for N to P is about 15 to 16:1 when receiving water to the water lab is acceptable. The Redfield ratio of poultry manure is generally two or less. Manure analysis is needed to control the positive and negative long-term effects of manure use in order to minimize P loss into receiving waters.

(Keywords: BPP, DP, DRP, P, Redfield ratio, SEP, SP, TP, water contamination)

* Corresponding author. Present address: 25001 Cashel Bay Rd., Manhattan, IL 60442, USA. Tel. & Fax: + 815-478-5069. E-mail: KHNahm1@cs.com

INTRODUCTION

Poultry manure (including litter that consists of manure plus bedding materials) is one of the best organic fertilizer sources available and is an alternative to mineral fertilizers. Excessive application of poultry manure has a negative environmental impact. Currently the environmental problem of most concern associated with animal manure is Phosphorus (P), since it is the limiting nutrient for eutrophication in fresh water systems (Schindler, 1977). Eutrophication of fresh water reduces esthetic appeal as well as causing fish kills through oxygen deprivation. It is most important that management practices reduce eutrophication by P from agricultural watersheds (Daniel *et al.*, 1994; Sharpley *et al.*, 1994a).

Most strategies developed to reduce P inputs, as well as the mathematical models used to develop these strategies, have been based on total P (TP). It has recently become important with advances in identifying sources of P and the desire to define management strategies that the TP load capable of being utilized for biological growth be identified (Sonzogni *et al.*, 1980). A substantial portion of the TP load may be in the unavailable form that has little impact on water quality, so P bioavailability is critical when comparing control alternative for cost effectiveness.

High P concentrations (14-76 mg P L^{-1}) in runoff from pastures receiving poultry litter, have been found to be mostly dissolved inorganic P (IP) (about 85%) with only small quantities of particulate P (PP) (Edwards and Daniel, 1993). Dissolved IP is directly available to algae and the best management practices used to decrease P runoff should consider the bioavailable-P (BAP) load rather than the TP load (Sonzogni *et al.*, 1982).

Significant degradation of surface water quality is sometimes associated with P from animal manure. One of the factors determining the mechanism of P transport and potential availability is the chemical composition of P in animal manure. Therefore, effective manure P management may be significantly enhanced by identification and quantification of the various forms of P in animal manure. Currently, little research has addressed P forms in animal manure, including poultry manure. Studies on this matter have often adopted methods used for soil analysis (Leinweber *et al.*, 1997; Dao, 1999).

Despite these complexities, there are some generalizations that can be made regarding eutrophication, based on the large body of scientific literature on this topic. The purpose of this paper is to summarize current information on the bioavailability and extraction methods of the various forms of P delivered to surface water bodies from different sources, especially emphasizing poultry manure, and provide a perspective on the management implications of this information in the lab and field.

PHOSPHORUS AS AN ESSENTIAL NUTRIENT FOR POULTRY

Phosphorus requirements are found in the ARC (1989) and NRC (1994) and other references summarizing the nutrient requirements for poultry. Phosphorus is an essential nutrient for the development and maintenance of the skeletal system, as well as fat and carbohydrate metabolism P. Phosphorus serves a structural role as an element of the phospholipids in cell membranes, and is essential for cell multiplication, differentiation and growth as a component of nucleic acids. Phosphorus takes part in energy metabolism as a constituent of ATP (adenosine triphosphate) and creatinine phosphate.

It is well known that P deficiency results in reduced growth, abnormal bone mineralization, which results rickets, bone weakness, inappetance and a high mortality rate (Nelson, 1967; Hulan et al., 1985; Nelson et al., 1990; O'Rourke et al., 1990; Mohammed et al., 1991; NRC, 1994; Angel et al., 2000). Cage fatigue of layers also is related to P deficiency (Gillis et al., 1953; Temperton et al., 1965a, b; Van der Klis et al., 1997). Even though the exact P requirement is not well-established in poultry, decreased feed consumption, growth rate, laying rate, skeletal development, eggshell quality are seen when chickens are fed excess P (Anderson, 1991; Van der Klis and Versteegh, 1996).

One aspect of nutrient management plans calls for a reduction in P intake of animals to minimize the amount of P excreted in the manure. Precision feeding, the formulation of dietary nutrients to meet the animal's exact needs at each stage of life, has been estimated to reduce P excretion 10-25% (Wicker, 1999).

BIOAVAILABLE FORMS OF PHOSPHRUS

Best management practices implemented to decrease P runoff should consider the BAP load, rather than focusing on the TP load (Sonzogni et al., 1982). Bioavailable P in agricultural runoff represents P potentially available for algal uptake and consists of soluble P (SP) and a variable portion of PP (Sharpley et al., 1992). Most SP is immediately available for algal uptake (i.e., bioavailable) (Walton and Lee, 1972; Peters, 1981). Particulate P is associated with sediment and organic material in runoff, however, it may be a variable but long-term source of BAP in surface water (Fig. 1). In a later report Sharpley et al. (1994b, 1996) indicated that BAP includes dissolved P (DP) instead of SP and a portion of PP. Dissolved P is immediately available for aquatic biota uptake, but PP is a secondary and long-term source of BAP in surface water (Sharpley, 1993).

The bioavailability of particulate P (BPP) can vary from 10 to 90% depending on the nature of the eroding soil and nature of the receiving water (Daniel et al., 1998). There is an appreciable variation in both TP (14-88% as BAP) and PP

(9-69% as BPP) bioavailability depending on agricultural practice (Sharpley *et al.*, 1992). Bioavailable P varies dynamically due to physical and chemical processes that control SP and BPP transport. Soluble P transport relies on desorption- dissolution reactions that control the release of P from soil, fertilizer reaction products, vegetative cover and decaying plant residues. BPP depends on physical process that control soil loss and particle-size enrichment and the chemical properties of the eroded soil material that control P sorption and availability.

In surface runoff, the transport of P can occur as DP and sediment P (SEP) (Liu *et al.*, 1997). Using algal assay procedures and a variety of waters, Walton and Lee (1972) reported that DP was essentially 100% available, but other investigators (Dick and Tabatabai, 1977) have found that DP is not completely available to support algal growth. Sediment P, which includes P absorbed by soil particles and other organic matter, may be a long-term source of P to aquatic biota (Liu *et al.*, 1997).

Water movement over soil that received broadcast manure or fertilizer application, or that tests high in P, can further increase BAP loading (Sharpley *et al.*, 1993), particularly as dissolved reactive P (DRP), which is immediately available for algal uptake (Peters, 1981). Dissolved reactive P in runoff occurs by desorption, dissolution and extraction of P from crop residues, manure or recently applied P fertilizer (Daniel *et al.*, 1998; Sauer *et al.*, 1999). Both DRP and BAP contributed to BAP losses in runoff from established forages. The loss of DRP from these forages was affected more by DRP concentration than runoff volume, since DRP concentration is positively correlated to soil P concentration (Zemenchik *et al.*, 2002).

Animal manures and slurry contain significant amounts of P, which is composed of inorganic and organic P. The inorganic and organic forms of P were found to vary according to manure type and animal diet, especially the organic P (OP) varies from 10 to 80% of total and decreases as the manure ages (Gerritse and Zugec, 1977). Some of these OP compounds in manure are relatively stable and mobile in soils (Gerritse, 1981). A substantial part of the TP in soil solution and leachates which were manured can be present as dissolved organic phosphorus (Fig. 1). The dissolved organic P may be more mobile than inorganic orthophosphate in soil and thus it can be an important P source for surface water eutrophication (Chardon *et al.*, 1997). These scientists said that the dissolved organic P fraction constitutes the largest part of TP (more than 70%) in soil solutions below a depth of 50 cm that received animal slurry. Zhang *et al.* (1994) reported that the application of inorganic P fertilizer combined with organic manure may be an effective way of protecting inorganic P against intensive sorption in soils.

P Fraction	Chemical Characteristics	References
Soluble P (SP) (Dissolved P: DP) (Dissolved reactive P: DRP)	SP(DP or DRP) : Immediately available DRP in runoff occurs by desorption, dissolution and extraction of P from crop residue and manure.	9, 14
Particulate P → Bioavailable PP (PP) (BPP)	BAP : A larger portion of TP losses PP : A secondary and long-term source of BAP BPP : Potentially available and 0−95% of PP	5, 8, 9, 10, 12, 13, 14
Sediment P (SEP)	SEP : Long term source of P. Associated with PP and organic material in runoff.	4
Inorganic P → Dissolved (IP) Inorganic P	IP : ≅ 85% of TP in poultry litter > 85% of TP in poultry manure Most of the P in all manures and composts was inorganic(60−90%) with smaller amounts in organic and residual forms.	1, 2, 5, 6, 7, 13, 15
Organic P → Dissolved (OP) Organic P	OP : > 70% of TP is in soil	3

Total → Bioavailable P
Phosphorus (BAP)

Figure 1. Bioavailable P forms

1. Barnett (1994a); 2. Barnett (1994b); 3. Chardon et al. (1997); 4. Daniel et al. (1998); 5. Edwards and Daniel (1993); 6. He and Honeycutt (2001); 7. Leinweber (1996); 8. Liu et al. (1997); 9. Pote et al. (1996); 10. Sharpley (1997); 11. Sharpley et al. (1991); 12. Sharpley et al. (1992); 13. Sharpley and Moyer (2000); 14. Zemenchik et al. (2002); 15. Zhang et al. (1994).

BIOAVAILABILITY OF PHOSPHORUS

In several areas of the world where the production of P in manure from confined animal operations exceeds local crop requirements for P, the loss of P in agricultural runoff is of increasing concern. The P levels in soil become concerns of agronomy to extend to impact environment.

Less information is available on the relationship between soil P and BAP transport in runoff (Sharpley et al., 1996). Soil test P accounted for 58 and 98% of the variation in DP concentration of runoff (Sharpley et al., 1996). Rather than soil test P, P loss is determined more by variability in runoff volume and erosion due to climatic, topographic and agronomic factors. There is a need for a more comprehensive approach for reliable yet flexible recommendations for fertilizer and manure P management along with their sampling in the field and lab.

Bioavailable P losses in runoff from established forage were both DRP and BPP (Zemenchik et al., 2002). In grasslands, most of the BAP in runoff is DRP since sediment concentrations are quite low. It has been shown that as sediment concentrations decrease in runoff, the percentage of BAP that is DRP increases and the percentage that is BPP decreases.

Bioavailable P loading may be increased by water movement over soil that has been treated with broadcast manure or fertilizer P applications, or that tests high in P (Sharpley et al., 1993). Sharpley et al. (1994a, b) showed based on the results of several studies that DRP in runoff to be positively correlated to plant-available P in shallow (0 to 1 cm) soil samples. Dissolved reactive P in surface runoff was found to be strongly correlated to P fertilizer surface applied to bahiagrass (*Paspalum Notatum Flugge*) pastures and significantly contributed to the formation of a 310 km^2 algae bloom in Lake Okeechobee, FL in 1986 (Rechcigl et al., 1992). Dissolved reactive P losses in runoff from established forage were more affected by DRP concentrations than by runoff volume, and DRP concentrations are positively correlated to soil P which is influenced by the practice of broadcast manure (Zemenchik et al., 2002). In this study, a 170% increase in soil P concentration from 1993 to 1994 lead to a 400% increase in DRP losses, even with the runoff volume decreasing by 44% over the same period. On the other hand, BPP losses were affected more by runoff volume and less by BPP concentrations (Zemenchik et al., 2002).

Increasing the bioavailability of P transported in runoff from conservation tillage practices may not result in as great a reduction in the topics status of a water body as expected from analysis of TP loads only. It is necessary to examine the BAP transport in runoff, as both SP and BPP, to reliably evaluate biological responses of a body of water (Sharpley et al., 1992) and to manage agricultural P inputs.

Amounts of P exported from watersheds are tied to watershed hydrology in terms of when and where surface runoff occurs, soil P contents and amount of P added as fertilizer or manure. As soil P content increases, the potential for PP and DP transport in runoff increases (Daniel *et al.*, 1998). Sharpley (1997) reported that PP concentration increased slightly although DP and BAP concentration decreased with increases in incubation time between litter application and rainfall. This scientist said the slight increase in PP may result from the sorption of P following litter addition. And the bioavailability of PP can vary from 10 to 90% depending on the nature of the eroding soil and nature of the receiving surface water (Daniel *et al.*, 1998).

Because animal wastes are returned to the soil and serve to fertilize crops, it is important to know the proportion of P that will be available to plants, a short-term crop response being dependent mainly on the inorganic forms (Bromfield, 1960). High concentrations of P (14-76 mg P L^{-1}) have been found in runoff from pastures treated with poultry litter, most of which is dissolved inorganic P (about 85%) with only small amounts of PP (Fig. 1) (Edwards and Daniel, 1993). One study (Sonzogni *et al*, 1982) concluded that dissolved inorganic P is directly available to algae and that the best management practices used to decrease P runoff should focus on BAP load rather than TP load. There is consistently more inorganic (63 to 92%) than organic (5 to 25%) P in manure and composts, but the relative distribution of P within inorganic and organic fractions was highly variable when measured by a modified Hedley fraction (Sharpley and Moyer, 2000).

EXRACTION METHODS FOR P ESTIMATION

Different forms of P are found in manure with varying degrees of dissolution capacity. Some forms may be more extractable than others when in contact with precipitation. In order to better understand manure P dynamics and to further enhance our capacity in managing manure P to reduce water pollution, it is important to characterize manure P. Manure P has been characterized into lipid P, inorganic P and acid soluble organic P and residual P by extracting manure samples with an alcohol/ether (3:1) mixture, followed by 5% trichloro acetic acid (TCA), and then ashing the residue (McAuliffe and Peech, 1949). A modification of this procedure was used to characterize P in the feces of several animal species (dairy cows, feeder and finishing cattle, hogs, broilers and layer poultry) and a wide variation in P content was found (Barnett, 1994a, b). The inorganic and acid soluble organic P extracted by TCA, which is considered available for plants may be a mixture of readily soluble plus some that is less soluble when in contact with rainwater under natural conditions (McAuliffe *et al.*, 1949; Barnett, 1994b).

There has been put forth a great deal of effort to study the connection between

P runoff loss and certain forms of P in soils. A significant correlation has been noted between dissolved P in runoff and the amount of soil P extracted with Mehlich-3 (Sharpley *et al.*, 1994b), Bray-1 (Romkens and Nelson, 1974), 0.1 M NaCl (Sharpley *et at.*, 1978), or water (Schreiber, 1988; Yli-Halla *et al.*, 1995; Pote *et al.*, 1999). Estimating the amount of P that is available for plants has been tested by dozens of laboratory methods, among which use of 0.5 M $NaHCO_3$ (Olsen *et al.*, 1954) as a single chemical solution has been successfully used on a wide range of acid to alkaline soils (Tiessen and Moir, 1993). Use of 0.1 M NaOH to extract P from soils or sediments is well correlated with algal P uptake (Sonzogni *et al.*, 1982; Wolf *et al.*, 1985). Many researchers (Hedley *et al.*, 1982) have adapted a sequential extraction procedure to separate the P in soil into several fractions associated with plant availability and various physico-chemical associations (Ca-bound P, Fe- and Al- associated P, etc.).

The extraction methods such as algal culture tests (USEPA, 1996), NaOH (Logan *et al.*, 1979; Butkus *et al.*, 1988), NH_4F (Dorich *et al.*, 1985), ion exchange resins (Huettl *et al.*, 1979; Hanna, 1989) and citrate-dithionite-bicarbonate (Logan *et al.*, 1979) require long-term incubation (100 days), and collection of a large volume of runoff to provide an adequate amount of sediment for analysis. Therefore, it is necessary to provide a rapid method to estimate BPP concentration of runoff in order to better estimate the response of a body of water to agricultural P inputs for managing eutrophication. Sharpley *et al.* (1991) suggested that a rapid and interference free method to routinely determine the total bioavailable P (TBP) and BPP (TBP minus SP) concentration of runoff could be estimated from the amount of P extracted from 20 ml of unfiltered runoff sample by 180 ml of 0.11 M NaOH on an end-over-end shaker for 17 hours. These extraction methods will improve estimation of the bioavailability of runoff P and impact on the biological productivity of surface waters and chicken manure. The proposed extraction method is applicable to quantify the bioavailability of P transported in agricultural runoff (Sharply *et al.*, 1991).

Several studies have evaluated the forms of inorganic and organic P in manures by sequential extraction with dilute bases (NaOH, $NaHCO_3$) and acids (H_2SO_4, HCl) and alcohol mixtures (Zhang *et al.*, 1994; Leinweber, 1996). Phosphorus fractionation in poultry manures (Dou *et al.*, 2000) determined through sequential extractions resulted in removal of 49% of the total inorganic P by deionized water, 19% by 0.5 M $NaCO_3$, 5% by 1M NaOH, 25% by 1.0 M HCl in the poultry manure (Table 1). In the independent extraction procedure, H_2O, $NaHCO_3$, NaOH, HCl and trichloroacetic acid (TCA) extracted 84 to 96% of the TP in manure. P release was not greatly affected by extraction time (shaking time), but generally exhibited a pattern of rapid decline with increasing number of repeated extraction (Dou *et al.*, 2000). A major portion of P in the manure samples being soluble in

Table 1. Extractable P concentrations in poultry manure litter

Extractants	Of the total P (%)	Of the total inorganic P (%)	Of the total P (%)		Of the total inorganic P (%)	
	Independent Extraction	Sequential Extraction				
	Poultry Manure				Poultry Composite	Poultry Litter
	Dou *et al.* (2000)			Leinweber (1996)	Sharpley and Moyer (2000)	
H$_2$O	63—64	49	50—67	27	25	28
NaHCO$_3$ (0.5 M)	64—72	19	13—20	31	35	34
NaOH (0.1 M)	33—54	5	5	13	—	—
HCl (1.0 M)	90—97	25	5—20	15	31	33
TCA (5%)[1]	84—96	—	—	—	—	—

[1] TCA: Trichloroacetic acid

weak extractions such as water or bicabonate indicates a high potential of P runoff loss from manure if surface applied. Extracting manure with water for 1 hour appears to provide a quick measure of the relative magnitude of P that is most available for dissolution and potential runoff loss (Dou *et al.*, 2000; Sharpley and Moyer, 2000). Sharpley and Moyer (2000) reported that the potential for P to be leached from manure and compost was most closely related to water extractable inorganic P concentration of the respective materials. This suggests that the water extractable P concentraction of land-applied manure or compost may be used to estimate the release of P and its potential to enrich leache and surface runoff.

Pote *et al.* (1996) investigated which soil test P extraction method would be best for predicting DRP and BAP concentration and load in runoff. According to these scientists, the highest correlations to DRP and BAP levels in runoff were obtained when soil test P was extracted by distilled water, acidified ammonium oxalate, or Fe oxide paper strip. However, correlation of STP with DRP load (range: 43.4 to 472.8 g ha^{-1}) and BAP load (54.2 to 542.0 g ha^{-1}) were not useful ($r^2 < 0.18$), possibly because runoff volumes were highly variable (Pote *et al.*, 1996).

P CONCENTRATIONS IN POULTRY MANURE

High concentrations of DRP in surface runoff occurs with surface application of poultry manure to pastures (Vervoort *et al.*, 1998; Sauer *et al.*, 1999), and intense animal manure production results in accelerated eutrophication due to the elevated DRP (Duda and Finan, 1983), resulting in environmental concerns. In a runoff event simulated 1 day after application of 6.7 mg ha^{-1} of poultry litter to tall fescue, the concentration of DRP in the runoff was 13.5 mg P L^{-1} (Sauer *et al.*, 1999). Since P is added to chicken diets to ensure rapid growth, poultry litter typically contains 8 to 25.8 g P kg^{-1} dry weight, with about 4.9 g P kg^{-1} as water-soluble reactive P (Edwards and Daniel, 1992).

Barnett (1994a) reported that the TP concentration averaged 25 g kg^{-1} for poultry manure and 20 g kg^{-1} for poultry litter. These concentrations vary greatly, however, as a function of animal diet and manure collection, treatment and storage with the coefficient of variations ranging from 30 to 100% (Barnett, 1994a; Eck and Stewart, 1995).

To determine the availability of the forms and relative solubilities of inorganic and organic P in manures, modifications of the Hedley sequential extraction procedure have been used (Sharpley and Moyer, 2000). The TP of manures ranged from 2.6 to 40 g kg^{-1}, with 60 to 90% existing an inorganic P and 0.8 to 3.9 g kg^{-1} as organic forms in the available P forms. These solubilities also showed that the inorganic and organic P varied among animal species and manure types. For poultry manure, 25 to 49% of the inorganic P was water-extractable P, 20 to 35% was bicarbonate extractable, and 25 to 30% was acid extractable (Leinweber, 1996; Sharpley and Moyer, 2000).

REDFIELD RATIO AND P CONCENTRATION

Impact assessments of long-term surface application of poultry litter on soil indicate P levels eventually increase. P concentrations in runoff decrease with time after application because manure litter constituents are moved into water through soil by rainfall and incorporated by fauna. However, there are no standards available that clearly indicate reasonable TP concentrations in receiving waters. Certainly, for most lakes, streams, reservoirs and estuaries concentrations of 100 μg TP/L are unacceptably high and concentrations of 20 μg/L are often a problem (Correll, 1998).

Atomic ratios which have become known as the Redfield ratios (Redfield, 1958) may be used to establish reasonable standards for TP concentrations in various receiving waters for research. The N to P ratio is approximately 15 to 16:1. When there are limiting amounts of P in receiving waters, the phytoplankton biomass has an N/P atomic ratio significantly higher than the Redfield ratio of 15 to 16 (Correll, 1998). The ratio of dissolved inorganic N to total P has been found to be the best predictor of chlorophyll responses in the mesocosms, followed by particulate N to particulate P ratios (Morris and Lewis, 1988).

The relationship of overall chlorophyll in 133 lakes with the total N and total P in the surface water has been analyzed (Prairie *et al.*, 1989). The 133 lakes were selected to ensure an even distribution of lakes with ratios of total N to total P of 5 to 75. When natural systems have atomic ratios of other elements to P greater than the Redfield ratio, they are assumed to be systems that have algal growth or biomass limited by P or algal growth ratios that are greatly reduced.

The ratio of N to P in algae can vary approximately four-fold depending on which stage of the algal cell division cycle is present (Correll and Tolbert, 1962), twofold due only to variation in either light intensity or light quality (Wynne and Rhee, 1986), fourfold due to changing temperature to light (Jahnke *et al.*, 1986), and threefold between algal species when all other variables were held constant (Wynne and Rhee, 1986). Redfield ratios were reported to be 5 to 20 under N or P limitations (Terry *et al.*, 1985) or 7 to 30 in other reports (Rhee and Gotham, 1980). These studies indicate that the Redfield ratios are approximate and do not universally apply. Correll (1998) proposed that a good rule is not to use the Redfield ratio concept when dealing with algal populations exposed to significant changes in available N or P concentration in the last few days or when the population has growth rates limited by light. When the P status of a receiving water is assessed only by P concentrations in the water column, it is best to measure the sum of dissolved and particulate total P than to rely on dissolved orthophosphate concentrations.

In normal poultry litter, the N to P ratio is generally two or less. Plants use roughly eight times more N than P. Therefore, when annual application of manures are applied on a N basis, the level of P builds up in the soil (Huneycutt *et al.*, 1988; Soil Conservation Service, 1992). Nitrogen and P are contained in duck feces in the ratio of 3.3:1 by atoms (Ryther and Dunstan, 1971). These scientists reported that total N and P analyses of dissolved and suspended matter in the tributaries and in Moriches Bay itself gave N/ P ratios of 2.3:1 to 4.4:1, consistent with the presumed origin of this material.

An increase in the N/P ratio of manure is the most important benefit of manure amendments. Increasing the N/P ratio of manure would more closely approach the crop N and P requirements of 3:1 rather than the ratios of 1:1 for some manure types. Minimizing potential soil P accumulations would be possible by the addition of manure based on crop N requirements (Daniel *et al.*, 1998).

MINIMUM P LOSS OF POULTRY MANURE

Information tool for farmers to use is poultry manure analysis with soil testing, showing that poultry manure is a valuable source of P. The positive and negative long-term effects of manure use and the time required to build-up or deplete soil nutrients can be demonstrated with manure analysis in combination with soil testing. Soil analysis can identify soils that need P fertilization, those that contain excess P that should not have manure applied, and soils where moderate manure application may be of value.

Data available from routine soil tests and supplemental information on site vulnerability to P loss could help to identify fields requiring more intensive sampling and testing. An indexing procedure to rank site vulnerability to P loss based on source (soil P and fertilizer or manure inputs) and transport factors (runoff and erosion potentials) has been developed (Lemunyon and Gilbert, 1993). Similar P applications should not be used in adjacent fields having similar soil test P but different susceptibilities to runoff and erosion due to contrasting topography and management.

Chemical analyses of the poultry manure may be obtained or average values of similar manures may be used if available. Chemical analyses values reported by laboratories on a dry weight basis should be converted to an "as is" basis for calculating application rates.

CONCLUSIONS AND FUTURE STUDIES

P is generally considered the limiting nutrient responsible for eutrophication in lakes and reservoirs. One of the major sources of P runoff from agricultural lands is animal wastes such as poultry manure. Environmentally sound use of the animal manure produced by the poultry industry is the greatest nutrient management challenge now faced by many countries.

Treatment and sampling methods and management guidelines should be available in lab and field to minimize gross environmental problems. Although not much research has been reported that address is P forms in animal manure, studies on this topic have often adopted methods used for soil analysis (Leinweber et al., 1997; Dao, 1999). There must be different forms of P in poultry manure with varying degrees of dissolution capacity. Thus, characterizing manure P is an important step to better understand manure P dynamics and further enhance our capability in managing manure P for reduced environmental pollution.

There is still no clear, widely accepted dogma about the concentration of P in receiving waters which can cause environmental pollution (Parry, 1998). It is often desirable to predict if a receiving water will have excessive P, especially an area with a high concentration of chicken operations. Research and data analysis are needed to establish reasonable standards for total P and dissolved P concentrations in various types of receiving waters and other P sources.

ACKNOWLEDGMENT

This research was supported by Taegu University Research Grant, 2002. The author would like to thank them for their partial financial support.

REFERENCES

Anderson, J.J.B. 1991. Nutritional biochemistry of calcium and phosphorus. *J. Nutr. Biochem.* **2**, 300.

Angel, R., Applegate, T.J. and Christman, M. 2000. Effect of dietary non-phytate phosphorus (nPP) level on broiler performance and bone measurements in the starter and grower phase. *Poultry Sci.* **79**(**Suppl**.), 22.

ARC 1989. The Nutrient Requirements of Poultry. Commonwealth Agricultural Burean, Slough, UK.

Barnett, G.M. 1994a. Phosphorus forms in animal manure. *Bioresour. Technol.* **49**, 139.

Barnett, G.M. 1994b. Manure P fractionation. *Bioresour. Technol.* **19**, 149.

Bromfield, S.M. 1960. Sheep feces in relation to the phosphorus cycle under pastures. *Aust. J. Agric. Res.* **12**, 111.

Butkus, S.R., Welch, E.B., Horner, R.R. and Spyridakis, D.E. 1988. Lake response modeling using biologically available phosphorus. *J. Water Pollut. Control Fed.* **60**, 1663.

Chardon, W.J., Oenema, O., del Castilho, P., Vriesema, R., Japenga, J. and Blaauw. D. 1997. Organic phosphorus in solutions and leachates from soils treated with animal slurries. *J. Environ. Qual.* **26**, 372.

Correll, D.L. 1998. The role of phosphorus in the eutrophication of receiving waters: A review. *J. Environ.Qual.* **27**, 261.

Correll, D.L. and Tolbert, N.E. 1962. Ribonucleic acid - polyphosphate from algae. I. Isolation and physiology. *Plant Physiol.* **37**, 627.

Daniel, T.C., Scharpley, A.N., Edwards, D., Wedepohl, R. and Lemunyon, J.L. 1994. Minimizing surface water eutrophication from agriculture by phosphorus management. *J. Soil. Water Conserv.* **49**, 30.

Daniel, T.C., Sharpley, A.N. and Lemunyon, J.L. 1998. Agricultural phosphorus and eutrophication: A symposium overview. *J. Environ. Qual.* **27**, 251.

Dao, T.H. 1999. Coamendments to modify phosphorus extractability and nitrogen/ phosphorus ratio in feedlot manure and composted manure. *J. Environ. Qual.* **28**, 1114.

Dick, W.A. and Tabatabai, M.A. 1977. Determination of orthophosphate in aqueous solutions containing labile organic and inorganic phosphorus compounds. *J. Environ. Qual.* **6**, 82.

Dorich, R.A., Nelson, D.W. and Sommers, L.E. 1985. Estimating algal available phosphorus in suspended sediments by chemical extractions. *J. Environ. Qual.* **14**, 400.

Dou, Z., Toth, J.D., Galligan, D.T., Ramberg, C.F., Jr. and Ferguson, J.D. 2000. Laboratory procedures for characterizing manure phosphorus. *J. Environ. Qual.* **29**, 508.

Duda, A.M. and Finan, D.S. 1983. Influence of livestock on nonpoint source nutrient levels of streams. *Trans. ASAE* **26**, 1710.

Eck, H.V. and Stewart, B.A. 1995. Manure. In: J.E. Rechcigl (Ed.), *Environmental aspects of soil amendments*. Lewis Publ., Boca Raton, FL, USA. pp. 169.

Edwards, D.R. and Daniel, T.C. 1992. Environmental impact of on-farm poultry waste disposal - A review. *Bioresour. Tech.* **41**, 9.

Edwards, D.R. and Daniel, T.C. 1993. Effects of poultry litter application rate and rainfall intensity on quality of runoff from fescuegrass plots. *J. Environ. Qual.* **22**, 361.

Gerritse, R.G. 1981. Mobility of phosphorus from pig slurry in soils. In: T.W.G. Hucker and G. Catroux (Ed.), *Phosphorus in sewage sludge and animal waste slurries*. Reidel, Dordrecht, The Netherlands. pp. 347.

Gerritse, R.G. and Zugec, I. 1977. The phosphorus cycle in the pig slurry measured from 32PO4 distribution rates. *J. Agr. Sci. Camb.* **88**, 101.

Gillis, M.B., Norris, L.C. and Heuser, G.F. 1953. Phosphorus metabolism and requirements of hens. *Poultry Sci.* **32**, 977.

Hanna, M. 1989. Biologically available phosphorus: Estimation and prediction using an anion-exchange resin. *Can. J. Fish. Aquat. Sci.* **46**, 638.

Hedley, M.J., Stewart, J.W.B. and Chauhan, B.S. 1982. Changes in inorganic and organic soil phosphorus fractions induced by cultivation practices and by laboratory incubations. *Soil Sci. Soc. Am. J.* **46**, 970.

Huettl, P.J., Wendt, R.C. and Corey, R.B. 1979. Prediction of algal available phosphorus in runoff suspensions. *J. Environ. Qual.* **8**, 130.

Hulan, H.W., Groote, G., Fontaine, G., De Munter, G., McRae, K.B. and Proudfoot, F.G. 1985. The effect of different totals and ratios of dietary calcium and phosphorus on the performance and incidence of leg abnormalities of male and female broiler chicken. *Poultry Sci.* **64**, 1157.

Huneycutt, H.G., West, C.P. and Phillips, J.M. 1988. Response of bermuda grass, tall fescue, and toll fescue-clover to broiler litter and commercial fertilizer. Bull. 913. Arkansas Agric. Exp. Stn., Univ. of Arkansas, Fayetteville, Ar., USA.

Jahnke, J., Kick, H.J. and Aletsee, L. 1986. On the light and temperature dependence of the minimum and maximum phosphorus contents in cells of the marine plankton diatom *Thalassiosira rotula* Meunier. *J. Plankton Res.* **8**, 549.

Leinweber, P. 1996. Phosphorus fraction in soils from an area with high density of livestock population. *Z. Pflanzeneraehr. Bodenkd.* **159**, 251.

Leinweber, P., Haumaier, L. and Zech. W. 1997. Sequential extractions and 31P-NMR spectroscopy of phosphorus forms in animal manures, whole soils and particle-size separates from a densely populated livestock area in northwest Germany. *Biol. Fertil. Soils* **25**, 89.

Lemunyon, J.L. and Gilbert, R.G. 1993. Concept and need for a phosphorus assessment tool. *J. Prod. Agric.* **6**, 483.

Liu, F., Mitchell, C.C., Hill, D.T., Odom, J.W. and Rochester, E.W. 1997. Phosphorus recovery in surface runoff from swine lagoon effluent by overland flow. *J. Environ. Qual.* **26**, 955.

Logan, T.J., Oloya, T.O. and Yaksich, S.M. 1979. Phosphate characteristics and bioavailability of suspended sediments from stream draining into Lake Erie. *J. Great Lakes Res.* **5**, 112.

McAuliffe, C. and Peech, M. 1949. Utilization by plants of phosphorus in farm manure: I. Labeling of phosphorus in sheep manure with P12. *Soil Sci.* **68**, 179.

McAuliffe, C., Peech, M. and Bradfield, R. 1949. Utilization by plants of phosphorus in farm manure: II. Availability to plants of organic and inorganic forms of phosphorus in sheep manure. *Soil Sci.* **68**, 179.

Mohammed, A., Gibney, M.J. and Taylor, T.G. 1991. The levels of inorganic phosphorus, calcium and cholecalciferol on the digestibility of phytate-P by the chicken. *Br. J. Nutr.* **66**, 251.

Morris, D.P. and Lewis, W.M. 1988. Phytoplankton nutrient limitation in Colorado mountain lakes. *Freshwater Biol.* **20**, 315.

Nelson, T.S. 1967. The utilization of phytate phosphorus by poultry - A review. *Poultry Sci.* **46**, 862.

Nelson, T.S., Harris, G.C., Kirby, L.K. and Johnson, Z.B. 1990. Effect of calcium and phosphorus on the incidence of leg abnormalities in growing broilers. *Poultry Sci.* **69**, 1496.

NRC 1994. Nutrient Requirements of Poultry. 9th Ed.. National Research Council, National Academy Press, Washington, DC, USA.

O'Rourke, W.F., Phillips, P.H. and Cravens, W.W. 1952. The phosphorus requirements of growing chickens as related to age. *Poultry Sci.* **31**, 962.

Olsen, S.R., Cole, C.V., Watanabe, F.S. and Dean, L.A. 1954. Estimation of available phosphorus in soils by extraction with sodium bicarbonate. USDA Circ. 939. US Gov. Printing Office, Washington, DC, USA.

Parry, R. 1998. Agricultural phosphorus and water quality: A US environmental protection agency perspective. *J. Environ. Qual.* **27**, 258.

Peters, R.H. 1981. Phosphorus availability in Lake Memphremagog and its tributaries. Limnol. *Oceanogr.* **26**, 1150.

Pote, D.H., Daniel, T.C., Nichols, D.J., Sharpley, A.N., Moore, P.A., Jr., Miller,

D.M. and Edwards, D.R. 1999. Relationship between phosphorus levels in three Ultisols and phosphorus concentrations in runoff. *J. Environ. Qual.* **28**, 170.

Pote, D.H.. Daniel, T.C., Sharpley, A.N., Moore, P.A., Jr., Edwards, D.R. and Nichols, D.J. 1996. Relating extractable phosphorus in a silt loam to phosphorus losses in runoff. *Soil Sci. Am. J.* (**in press**).

Prairie, Y.T., Duarte, C.M. and Kalff, J. 1989. Unifying nutrient-chlorophyll relationships in lakes. *Can. J. Fish. Aquat. Sci.* **46**, 1176.

Rechcigl, J.E., Payne, G.G., Bottcher, A.B. and Porter, P.S. 1992. Reduced phosphorus application on bahiagrass and water quality. *Agro. J.* **84**, 463.

Redfield, A.G. 1958. The biological control of chemical factors in the environment. *Am. Sci.* **46**, 1.

Rhee, G-Y. and Gotham, I.J. 1980. Optimum N:P ratios and coexistence of planktonic algae. *J. Phycol.* **16**, 486.

Romkens, M.J.M. and Nelson, D.W. 1974. Phosphorus relationships in runoff from fertilizer soil. *J. Environ. Qual.* **3**, 10.

Ryther, J.H. and Dunstan, W.M. 1971. Nitrogen, phosphorus and eutrophication in the coastal marine environment. *Science* **171**, 1008.

Sauer, T.J., Daniel, T.C., Moore, P.A., Jr., Coffey, K.P., Nickols, D.J. and West, C.P. 1999. Poultry litter and grazing animal waste effects on runoff water quality. *J. Environ. Qual.* **28**, 860.

Schindler, D.W. 1977. The evolution of phosphorus limitation in lakes. *Science* **195**, 260.

Schreiber, J.D. 1988. Estimating soluble phosphorus (PO4-P) in agricultural runoff. *J. Miss. Acad. Sci.* **33**, 1.

Sharpley, A.N. 1997. Rainfall frequency and nitrogen and phosphorus runoff from soil amended with poultry litter. *J. Environ. Qual.* **26**, 1127.

Sharpley, A.N., Chapra, S.C., Wedepohl, R., Sims, J.T., Daniel, T.C. and Reddy, K.R. 1994a. Managing agricultural phosphorus for protection of surface waters: Issues and options. *J. Environ. Qual.* **23**, 437.

Sharpley, A.N., Daniel, T.C. and Edwards, D.R. 1993. Phosphorus movement in the landscape. *J. Prod. Agric.* **6**, 492.

Sharlpey, A., Daniel, T.C., Sims, J.T. and Pote, D.H. 1996. Determining environmentally sound soil phosphorus levels. *J. Soil and Water Cons.* **51**(2), 160.

Sharpley, A.N. and Moyer, B. 2000. Phosphorus forms in manure and compost their release during simulated rainfall. *J. Environ. Qual.* **29**, 1462.

Sharpley, A., Sims, J.T. and Pierzynski, G.M. 1994b. Innovative soil P availability indices: Assessing inorganic phosphorus. In: J. Havlin, J. Jacobsen, P. Fixen and G. Hergert (Eds.), *New direction in soil testing for nitrogen, phosphorus and potassium.* Am. Soc. Agron., Madison, WI, USA. pp. 113-140.

Sharpley, A.N., Smith, S.J., Jones, O.R., Berg, W.A. and Coleman, G.A. 1992. The transport of bioavailable phosphorus in agricultural runoff. *J. Environ. Qual.* **21**, 30.

Sharpley, A.N., Syers, J.K. and Tillman, R.W. 1978. An improved soil-sampling procedure for the prediction of dissolved inorganic phosphate concentration in surface runoff from pasture. *J. Environ. Qual.* **7**, 455.

Sharpley, A.N., Troeger, W.W. and Smith, S.J. 1991. The measurement of bioavailable phosphorus in agricultural runoff. *J. Environ. Qual.* **20**, 235.

Soil Conservation Service. 1992. Agricultural waste management handbook. US Gov. print. Office, Washington, DC, USA.

Sonzogni, W.C., Chapra, S.C., Armstrong, D.E. and Logan, T.J. 1982. Bioavailability of phosphorus inputs to lakes. *J. Environ. Qual.* **11**, 555.

Sonzogni, W.C., Jeffs, D.N., Konrad, J.C., Robinson, J.B., Chesters, G., Coote, D.R. and Ostry, R.C. 1980. Pollution from land runoff. *Environ. Sci. Technol.* **14**, 148.

Sonzogni, W.C., Chapra, S.C., Armstrong, D.E. and Logan, T.J. 1982. Bioavailability of phosphorus inputs to lakes. *J. Environ. Qual.* **11**, 555.

Temperton, H., Dudley, F.J. and Pickering, G.J. 1965a. Phosphorus requirements of poultry. V. The effects during the subsequent laying year of feeding growing diets containing no animal protein or supplementary phosphorus. *Br. Poultry Sci.* **6**, 135.

Temperton, H., Dudley, F.J. and Pickering, G.J. 1965b. Phosphorus requirements of poultry. VI. The phosphorus requirements of growing pullets between 8 and 18 weeks of age. *Br. Poultry Sci.* **6**, 143.

Terry, K.L., Hirata, J. and Laws, E.A. 1985. Light-, nitrogen-, and phosphorus-limited growth of *phaeodactylum tricornutum* Bohlin strain TFX-1: Chemical composition, carbon partitioning, and the dial periodicity of physiological process. *J. Exp. Mar. Biol. Ecol.* **86**, 85.

Tiessen, H. and Moir, J.O. 1993. Characterization of available P by sequential extraction. In: M.R. Carter (Ed.), *Soil sampling and methods of analysis*. Lewis Publ., Boca Raton, FL, USA. pp. 75.

US Environmental Protection Agency. 1996. Environmental indicators of water quality in the United States. USEPA Rep. 841/R-96-002. USEPA, Office of Water (450F), U.S. Gov. Print Office, Washington, DC., USA.

Van der Klis, J.D. and Versteegh, H.A.J. 1996. Phosphorus nutrition of poultry. In: *Proceedings of the Nottingham Feed Manufacturers Conference*. Nottingham, UK. pp. 71-83.

Van der Klis, J.D., Versteegh, H.A.J., Simons, P.C.M. and Kies, A.K. 1997. The efficacy of phase in corn-soybean meal-based diets for laying hens. *Poultry Sci.* **76**, 1535.

Vervoort, R.W., Radcliffe, D.E. and Cabrera, M.L. 1998. Field scale nitrogen and phosphorus losses from hayfields receiving fresh and composted broiler litter. *J. Environ. Qual.* **27**, 1246.

Walton, C.P. and Lee, G.F. 1972. A biological evaluation of the molybdenum blue method for orthophosphate analyses. *Tech. Int. Ver. Limnol.* **18**, 676.

Wicker, D.L. 1999. Phosphorus reduction techniques examined. *Feedstuff* **71(24)**, 12. August 2.

Wolf, A.M., Baker, D.E., Pionke, H.B. and Kunishe, H.M. 1985. Soil tests for estimating labile, soluble, and algae-available phosphorus in agricultural soils. *J. Environ. Qual.* **14**, 341.

Wynne, D. and Rhee, G.Y. 1986. Effects of light intensity and quality on the relative N and P requirements (the optimum N/P ratio) of marine planktonic algae. *J. Plankton Res.* **8**, 91.

Yli-Hallan, M., Hartikainen, H., Elcholm, P., Turtola, E., Puustinen, M. and Kallio, K. 1995. Assessment of soluble phosphorus load in surface runoff by soil analysis. *Agric. Ecosyst. Environ.* **56**, 53.

Zemenchik, R.A., Wollenhaupt, N.C. and Albrecht, K.A. 2002. Bioavailable phosphorus in runoff from Alfalfa, Smooth Bromegrass, and Alfalfa-Smoth Bromegrass. *J. Environ. Qual.* **31**, 280.

Zhang, Y.S., Werner, W., Scherer, H.W. and Sun, X. 1994. Effect of organic manure on organic phosphorus fraction in two paddy soils. *Biol. Fertil. Soils* **17**, 64.

Influences of Fermentable Carbohydrates on Shifting Nitrogen Excretion and Reducing Ammonia Emission of Pigs

K. H. Nahm*

Feed and Nutrition Laboratory, College of Natural Resources, Taegu University, Gyong San, 712-714, South Korea. E-mail: NahmKH@Daegu.ac.kr

ABSTRACT: There is increasing evidence that nitrogen (N) excretion is shifted from urea in urine to bacterial protein in feces when fibrous feedstuffs are included in the diet. Carbohydrates also beneficially affect the host by selectively stimulating the growth and activity of one or a limited number of bacterial species which are already resident in the cecum and colon of pigs, and are known to extend health-promoting properties. Ammonia emissions were reduced significantly in monogastric animal manure by adding a variety of carbohydrate sources to the basal diet although certain fractions of carbohydrates are not involved or are less involved in reducing these emissions. When sucrose thermal oligosacchride caramel (STOP) was added to the basal diet of pigs at 2%, both stored manure and fresh manure had reductions of 62 and 37%, respectively, in NH_3-N, while total Kjeldahl nitrogen (TKN) in the stored manure and fresh manure declined by 55 and 35%, respectively. Addition of cellulose at 5% to the pigs basal diet resulted in NH_3-N reductions of 73 and 68% in stored and fresh manure, respectively. TKN levels were reduced by 35 and 61%, respectively, in stored manure and fresh manure. Addition of paper products at 2.5-5.0% reduced ammonia emission by 29-47%. Soybean hulls added at 10% reduced emissions 21-41%. When sugar beets were added at 6.1% of the diet, ammonia reduction was 45%. A 0.15% addition of lactosucrose resulted in a 50% reduction in ammonia emissions from the cecal contents of chicks. Lactosucrose when supplemented at 1.5 g/day to the dog and 0.175 g/day to the cat resulted in ammonia reductions of 53% and 47%, respectively, in their feces. The inclusion of fermentable carbohydrates in pig diets can be a practical method for ammonia emission control and reducing nitrogen excretion. However, these effects on ammonia emission and nitrogen excretion need to be verified in practical situations. Primary odor-causing compounds evolve from excess degradable proteins and lack of specific fermentable carbohydrates during microbial fermentation. Continued research to incorporate protein degradation with fermentable carbohydrates in the lower gastrointestinal tracts of pigs will further control odors and N excretion from swine manure.

(Key words: carbohydrate, fresh manure, nitrogen, odor, STOP, stored manure, TKN)

* Corresponding author. Present address: 25001 Cashel Bay Rd., Manhattan, IL 60442, USA. E-mail address: KHNahm1@cs.com

I. INTRODUCTION

In monogastric animals (pigs, rats, mice, cats and dogs), the odor components of feces are products of hindgut (colon and cecum) fermentation. The degradation of endogenous and undigested food proteins by bacterial enzymes during biochemical processes results in production of these components. Several putrefactive compounds are produced during colonic fermentation of endogenous and undigested amino acids (Bakke, 1969; Tabor and Tabor, 1985), and these compounds cause the malodor of feces. Research reports (Hartung and Phillips, 1994; Hobbs *et al.*, 1995) have identified numerous compounds of odors (ranging from 30 to more than 200) from the anaerobic degradation of livestock manures.

The major groups of fecal odor components include ammonia, aliphatic amines (e.g., agmatine, cadaverine, histamine, phenylethylamine, putrescine and tyramine), branched-chain fatty acids (e.g., isobutyrate and isovalerate), indoles (e.g., indole, 3-methylindole, 2-methylindole, 2,3-methylindole, 2,5-methyindole, and 5-chloroindole), phenols (e.g., phenol, p-cresol, and 4-ethylphenol), and volatile sulfur-containing compounds (e.g., dimethyldisulfide, diethy disulfide, di-n-propyl sulfur-containing compounds (e.g., dimethyl disulfide, diethyl disulfide, di-n-propyldisulfide, and di-n-butyldisulfide) (Kreuzer and Machmuller, 1993).

Ammonia emissions from pig husbandry are one of the substantial contributors to odor and environmental pollution (Aspimon and Kruse-Plass, 1990). Oxidative deamination of various amino acids results in ammonia production. The catabolism of amino acids and production of ammonia also involve nonoxidative ammonia lyase reactions and the Strickland reaction (Gottschalk, 1986). The bacteria genera involved in the deamination reactions include *Bacteroides*, *Eubacterium* and *Clostridium* (Gottschalk, 1986).

The majority of the ammonia emissions from pig operations originates from the urea in urine (Muck and Steenhuis, 1981). The urease present in feces converts urea into ammonia and carbon dioxide (Stevens *et al.*, 1989). Ammonia volatilization is influenced by the ammonia concentration and pH of the slurry (Freney *et al.*, 1983). Lowering dietary nitrogen (N) intake can reduce urea excretion (Gatel and Grosjean, 1992).

Most researchers seem to agree that none of fatty acids is the major constituent of odor from livestock or poultry facilities. Miner *et al.* (2000) said that ammonia and hydrogen sulfide have been the two constituents most commonly measured in manure odors. Their removal or reduction in concentration has frequently proven to be a useful alternative measure of odor reduction.

There has been a growing interest recently in manipulating gut microbial composition towards a potentially more remedial community. The host is beneficially affected by nondigestible food ingredients because they selectively stimulate the growth or activity of one or a limited number of bacterial species (e.g., *Bifidobacterium* and *Lactobacillus*) which already reside in the colon and have some health-promoting properties (Gibson and Roberfroid, 1995). Modulating the colonic microbiota by increasing the numbers of desirable bacterial species and therefore changing the composition of colonic microbiota in humans and other species including pigs may be possible through the intake of such indigestible food (feed) ingredients. Examples of these food (feed) ingredients include indigestible fiber, nonstarch polysaccharides (NSP), oligosaccharides and resistant starches.

Including fibrous feedstuffs in the diets of pigs increasingly has been shown to shift N excretion from urea in urine to bacterial protein in feces (Kirchgessner *et al.*, 1993; Canh *et al.*, 1997). Researchers have proposed possible benefits of the end products (volatile fatty acid - VFA) of fiber fermentation when NSP was incorporated into pig and other monogastric animal diets. These VFA may also influence the pH of feces and slurry (Farnworth *et al.*, 1995).

The following discussion is a summary of research on the potential impacts of various carbohydrate sources in the diets to control odors and the excretion of nutrients in the manure with emphasis placed on N excretion from pig manure (urine and feces).

II. TYPES OF CARBOHYDRATES

The term, carbohydrates, generally means plant carbohydrate fractions. Carbohydrates are formed from two components, namely the cell wall and cell contents. Hall (2001) has provided detailed information about carbohydrate fractions (Fig. 1).

Research reports have mentioned that cell wall fractions are fiber. However, analytical methods in the laboratory have encountered various types of problems for deciding the correct content of fiber in plant samples. And fiber is not a nutritionally,

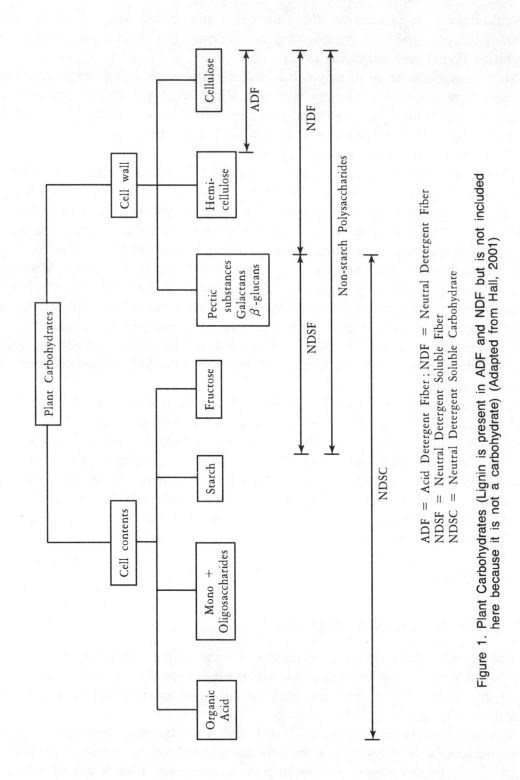

Figure 1. Plant Carbohydrates (Lignin is present in ADF and NDF but is not included here because it is not a carbohydrate) (Adapted from Hall, 2001)

ADF = Acid Detergent Fiber ; NDF = Neutral Detergent Fiber
NDSF = Neutral Detergent Soluble Fiber
NDSC = Neutral Detergent Soluble Carbohydrate

chemically, or physiologically uniform material. Trowell *et al.* (1976) defined dietary fiber (DF) as NSP + lignin, which recognizes the principle component of DF to be NSP and lignin which are resistant to hydrolysis by the digestive enzymes (Choi *et al.*, 1999).

The NSP complex could be defined as the water insoluble cell wall (WICW) including water-insoluble NSP and lignin and water-soluble NSP (Carre, 1990). This report indicated that digestion of water-insoluble NSP is nearly zero in poultry, while birds are able to digest a major part of water-soluble NSP. Swine could digest part of the hemicellulose and water-insoluble NSP (Keyo *et al.* 1970). Hall (2001) separated neutral detergent-soluble fiber from NSP.

Neutral detergent-soluble fiber is composed of pectin substances, $(1 \rightarrow 3)$ $(1 \rightarrow 4)$ beta-glucans, fructans and other NSP not included in neutral detergent fiber (NDF). These carbohydrates must be fermented by microbes to be digested as they cannot be digested by mammalian enzymes. Soluble fiber ferments very quickly (20-40% per hour) except for soybean hulls (about 4% per hour) (Hull, 2001). Pectins predominate in soluble fiber and tend to yield more acetate than other non-fiber carbohydrates (Strobel and Russell, 1986). Except for fructans, fermentation of soluble fiber yields little or no lactate, and at more acidic pH, its fermentation is reduced, similar to the fermentation of NDF. Common soluble fiber sources include legume forages, citrus pulp, beet pulp, soybean hulls and soybean meal (Hull, 2001). Non-fiber carbohydrates have been found to have similar yields of microbial protein when the pH is relatively neutral and fermentation rates are similar, even though the types of organic acids produced from their fermentation differ.

Organic acids are included in non-fiber carbohydrates for convenience, even though they are not true carbohydrates. Examples of these include the fermentation acids found in silage of ruminants and plant organic acids found in fresh forage and dry feed (Hall, 2001). Organic acids from fermented feeds are utilized by the animal but do not support appreciable microbial growth in the gastrointestinal tract (GIT).

Monosaccharides (simple sugars) and oligosaccharides are considered "sugars". Oligosaccharides are short chains of two to about 20 sugars units long. In plants, the predominant sugars are glucose, fructose and the disaccharide sucrose. Sugars have a tendency to ferment rapidly and may ferment to lactic acid. Most of the oligosaccharides may be digested by mammalian enzymes and the resulting monosaccharides are absorbed by the animals. Some common sources of sugars include molasses, citrus pulp, almond hulls, some bakery waste, soybean meal and fresh forages or dry feed.

Starch is a molecule made up of alpha-linked chains of glucose that are stored by plants in crystalline granules. The alpha-linkages in the starch allow it to be digested by microbes in the GIT, but there is a great variation in the rates of fermentation and digestion, depending on the processing, storage method and plant source of the starch. When starch ferments, lactic acid may form. Small grains, corn and sorghum grains and their by-products, potatos and bakery wastes are all common sources of starch.

III. CARBOHYRATES WHICH SHIFT N EXCRETION AND ODOR PRODUCTION

A. Fiber

Fiber in the form of cellulose and hemicellulose is one of the major substrates fermented in the large intestine, and is shown in Figure 1 as the NDF fraction. By definition, dietary fiber includes a wide spectrum of components (Southgate and Englyst, 1985). A combination of various purified dietary fibers, estimated separately, may not have the same effect on ileal nitrogen flow as a natural dietary fiber of similar composition. Some scientists have been doing research with the purified fiberous fraction, while most scientists have been doing research with natural dietary fiber fractions for the practical usage.

Dietary fiber can increase the excretion of N at the terminal ileum of nonruminant animals (Potkins et al., 1991; Sauer et al., 1991) (Table 1 and 2). Schulze et al. (1995) found out that increases in ileal N with dietary NDF depended on the level and type of NDF. Cellular proliferation in the cecum and distal colon could be influenced by the source or quantity of dietary fiber and dietary fiber likely influences intestinal cell proliferation through many mechanisms, some of which are interactive (Fleming et al., 1992).

As the level of fiber addition increases, the excretion of N in the feces, expressed as a proportion of N intake, tends to increase, with the effect being significant for the straw diet (Morgan and Whittemore, 1988). These scientists reported that urinary N excretion, expressed in a similar manner, fell as more fiber was consumed, with a significant drop seen for the oatfeed and sugar-beet pulp diets.

The effect of fiber on N digestibility varies. Supplementation with wood cellulose reduced N digestibility (Partridge et al., 1982), but oatfeed has been shown to have no effect in some experiments (Potkins et al., 1984), but it caused a reduction in others (Morgan et al., 1984). In pigs, diets containing straw meal not only reduced the urinary N excretion (Malmlof and Hakansson, 1984), but this decrease exceeded the increase in fecal N excretion and thus increased N retention (Low, 1985). In the hindgut of the pig, the fermentation of fiber is affected by a proliferation of bacteria that retain N during their growth and are passed out in the feces, resulting in the decreased digestibility (Malmlof and Hakansson, 1984).

Table 1. Effect of Diet on pH and Nitrogen Components in Pig Manure (Sutton *et al.*, 1996a, 1996b, 1997, 1998)

Diet	Fresh Manure				Stored Manure			
	pH	DM (%)	NH_3-N (% DM)	TKN^2 (% DM)	pH	DM (%)	NH_3-N (mg/L)	TKN (mg/L)
Standard	7.67^{a1}	12.6^b	5.33^a	10.91^a	8.32^a	9.12^a	7432^a	10322^a
A.A. Suppl.	6.93^b	14.7^b	3.54^b	7.02^b	7.30^b	6.56^b	3454^b	5488^b
STOC (10% CP & A.A)	7.08^b	15.3^b	3.36^b	7.14^b	7.32^b	6.02^b	2813^b	4640^b
Cellulose (10% CP & A.A.)	6.40^b	18.9^a	1.73^c	4.33^c	6.92^b	6.42^b	2010^b	6751^b

Standard: 13% crude protein diet from commercial diet
A.A. Suppl.: 10% crude protein diet with four synthetic essential amino acids to meet the NRC requirement (lysine, threonine, tryptophan and methionine)
STOC: the amino acid supplemented diet with 2% sucrose thermal oligosaccharide caramel (STOC)
Cellulose: The amino acid supplemented diet with 5% cellulose
[1]a,b,c: Different letter superscripts within a column indicate means are significantly different (p < 0.05).
[2]TKN: Total Kjeldahl Nitrogen

Table 2. Effects of Carbohydrate Sources in Diets on Ammonia Emission Reduction in Monogastric Animal Manure

Carbohydrate	Amount Added to Basal Diet	Reduction Quantity of Ammonia Emission from Manure	Reduction Rate of Ammonia Emission (%)	Sources	References
	-------%-------	-----------ppm-----------			
Lactosucrose	0.15	150 (control) to 75	50	Chick Cecal Contents	1
Paper Products	2.5-5.0	Expressed as a Percentage	29-47	Liquid Manure of Swine	2
Soybean Hull	10	21.3 (control) to 12.5	41	Pit of Swine Manure	3
Soybean Hull	10	13.1 (control) to 10.4	21	Pit of Swine Manure	4
		--------mmol/day--------			
Sugar Beet	6.1	31.3 (control) to 17.2	45	Slurry of Swine Manure	5
	-----g/day-----	-----------ppm-----------			
Lactosucrose	1.5	1663 (control) to 777	53	Feces (Dog-Fed for 14 Days)	6
Lactosucrose	0.175	1418 (control) to 748	47	Feces (Cat-Fed for 14 Days)	7

1. Terada *et al.* (1994); 2. Subair *et al.* (1999); 3. Kendall *et al.* (1999); 4. De Cemp *et al.* (2001); 5. Canh *et al.* (1998a); 6. Terada *et al.* (1992); 7. Terada *et al.* (1993)

Ammonia volatilization is reduced by reducing the N excretion in urine as urea, the primary precursor of ammonia volatilization, and by shifting the N excretion into feces, primarily in the form of bacterial protein. A significant reduction of N excretion in the urine could be attained by changing the carbohydrate structure in the diet to increase bacterial utilization of N in the cecum and colon. Bacterial carbohydrate fermentation in pigs mainly takes place in the cecum and colon but also, at a certain proportion, before the end of the ileum (Kass *et al.*, 1980; Rowan *et al.*, 1992). Providing the presence of a fermentable carbohydrate by inclusion of dietary fiber in the diet, the microorganisms in the hind gut retain more N for their own growth, which leads to an increase in fecal N output (Cummings *et al.*, 1976; Sauer *et al.*, 1980). This effect of dietary fiber on the ability of microorganisms to retain N within the gut has also been demonstrated to depress daily urinary N output (Mosenthin and Henkel, 1978). Varel (1987) elaborated in more detail about fibrolytic bacteria and the pig large intestine. He said that the total number of microorganisms in the pig large intestine do not change when a high fiber diet such as 50 or 80 % alfalfa meal is fed. However, the fiber-degrading organisms increase and obviously replace others. According to his study, the increase in fibrolytic bacteria normally coincides with an increase in enzyme activity (cellulase and xylanase), indicating that diet can be used to enhance fibrolytic activity. The cellulolytic organisms in the pig, *Bacteroides succinogenes* and *Ruminococcus flavefaciens*, are similar to those in the rumen and are present in comparable numbers, which indicates that there is a significant potential for fiber degradation in the pig large intestine (Varel, 1987). However, there exists a clear difference between rumen and hindgut fermentation efficiency even on the basis of true fermentation (Kreuzer *et al.*, 1991; Roth-Maier *et al.*, 1993).

Kirchgessner *et al.* (1994) investigated the degree of fermentation of the non-starch polysaccharides and the respective efficiency of bacterial protein synthesis with the use of wheat bran and alfalfa meal in a natural complex. They provided at levels of 0 g, 225 g and 675 g wheat bran per day to adult sows and 0 g, 575 g and 1150 g alfalfa meal per day to adult sows, both in addition to a basal diet covering maintenance requirements. They found that 40-60% of the NSP from wheat bran and alfalfa meal was degraded and fecal N composition was not significantly affected by the supplements, whereas the excretion of all nitrogenous fractions increased. These results suggest that it is largely the sugar composition of fiber which controls the fermentation process. When they are arranged in complex structures in the plant cell wall, the sugars are broken down through mechanisms which are still unknown. Sutton *et al.* (1997, 1998) show that reducing crude protein (CP) in typical corn-soybean meal diets from 13% to 10% and supplementing with limiting amino acids and the addition of 5% cellulose reduced ammonia excretion levels in fresh (68% reduction for NH_3-N and 61% reduction for TKN, wet basis) and stored (73% reduction for NH_3 and 35% reduction for TKN) pig manure compared with the standard commercial diet which was fed 13% crude protein (CP) diet (Table 1).

Malmlof and Hakansson (1984) reported that inclusion of 17% straw meal (high fiber) in the standard diet significantly decreased apparent fecal digestibility of crude protein and daily urinary excretion, but a low fiber diet caused the highest level of urinary nitrogen excretion throughout the 24-hours. However, paper lignin content was not correlated with ammonia volatilization, suggesting that the effectiveness of paper products in reducing ammonia volatilization is not controlled by lignin content but rather by other more labile components (Subair et al., 1999). Paper products have potential as amendments to reduce ammonia loss because their high carbon (C) and low N contents would be expected to cause N immobilization. Research has been conducted about reducing ammonia volatilization from liquid hog manure addition of paper bag, filter paper, newsprint, and pulp sludge at 2.5 and 5% (fresh liquid hog manure weight) and then evaluated in a 56 day incubation study. When the rate increased from 2.5 to 5%, ammonia volatilization was reduced by 47, 40, 37 and 29%, respectively, compared to the control (Subair et al., 1999).

Similar observations have been reported in response to the addition of Solka-floc to the basal diet for growing pigs. Solka-floc is an typical example of the fiber that is normally encountered in pig diets. Additional cellulose (Solka-floc) modified the route of N excretion, since the apparent digestibility of N was reduced, with little effect on N retention (Partridge et al., 1982).

Research on fiber utilization in swine has become of interest for several reasons. The pig can utilize fiber for growth and up to 30% of its maintenance energy may be derived from VFA produced in the large intestine (Varel, 1987). This report said that the total number of microogranisms in the pig large intestine do not change when a high fiber diet such as 50 or 80% alfalfa meal is fed. Sows can maintain normal reproductive performance when fed diets conditioning 96 to 100% alfalfa meal (Calvert et al., 1985; Pond et al., 1985). The nature and chiefly the association between the fiber sugar were key variables in the fermentability, and the amount of short-chain fatty acids produced were closely related to the in vitro fermentation of the main sugars available such as uronic acid, acetic acid, propionic acid, xylose and butyric acid (Salvador et al., 1993). And supplements of different fiber fractions and higher levels impared the digestibility of other nutrients showing no benefit to the host animals. Diets without fiber reduced mucosal barrier functions and increase the risk of bacterial translocation and septicema (Spaeth, 1990).

B. Soluble Fiber Sources and NSP

Nonstarch polysaccharide includes not only hemicellulose and cellulose, but pectic substances, galactans, β-glucans and fructans. However, part of hemicellulose and water-insoluble NSP can be digested by swine (Keyo et al., 1970). Recently many scientists have been doing research with natural dietary fractions for practical usage. Common sources of soluble fiber (fermentable fiber) include legume forages, citrus pulp, beet pulp, soybean hulls and soybean meal (Table 2). Cellulose (non-fermentable fiber) may be purposely added for bulk and glucose from cellulose in the fibers is poorly used by bacteria (Goodlad and Mathers, 1991).

A high concentration of fermentable carbohydrates (soybean hull, sugar beet pulp and coconut expeller) increases the VFA concentration of feces and slurry and reduces the pH and ammonia emission from the slurry of growing pigs (Canh et al., 1998b) (Table 1 and 2). They said that the ammonia emission from slurry will decrease by approximately 38%, if the daily intake of NSP reaches 700 g as the highest level of soybean hulls or sugar beet pulp diets fed to the pigs. The soybean hulls diet had the greatest effect on the reduction of pH and the ammonia emission in their research. This study suggested that the feces from pigs fed the soybean hulls diets contained more fermentable fractions than those obtained from pigs fed the other diets. High concentrations of the easily fermentable carbohydrates, cellulose and hemicellulose, in combination with a low concentration of ligin, seem to promote the highest rate of fermentation (Canh et al., 1997; 1998a, 1998b). Mroz et al. (1993) showed that manure from pigs fed cellulose had significantly reduced ammonia emission compared to manure from pigs fed corn starch, hemicellulose and pectin.

Soybean hulls are an inexpensive byproduct of soybean processing that are high in fiber and low in energy and protein contents. De Camp et al. (2001) reported that the addition of 10% soybean hulls with 3.4% supplemental fat to a commercial diet can have a positive effect an odor reduction (a 32% reduction in hydrogen sulfide gas and 21% reduction in ammonia emission) in the room air, a 20% decrease in four-hour aerial ammonia concentration and 11% numerical decrease in the odor detection threshold and manure characteristics without hindering pig performance. Bakker (1996) further supported this concept by showing a reduced urinary N excretion with cellulose and other NSP sources (sugar beet pulp, soybean hulls, coconut meal and potato starch) in pig diets. According to the Canh et al. (1998b), when the levels of NSP (coconut expeller, soybean hulls and dried sugar beet pulp) were increased from 15 to 49% in the pig diet, greater levels of ammonia emission were reduced from 35.8 to 6.4%.

The differences in fecal bacteria N excretion per unit of fermented matter might be provided by the nutrient directly associated with fiber in feedstuffs but not in purified substrates (Kirchgessner *et al.*, 1993). In spite of the availability of nutrients from the basal diets, bacteria from the hindgut may grow better on a substrate containing both degradable matter and essential elements because they are firmly attached to the fibers during degradation and only these have an opportunity to have a permanent supply of nutrients. There may also be a lower excretion of bacterial protein per unit of fermented matter with feedstuffs that mainly contain concentrated easily fermentable carbohydrates. The fermentability of fiber sugars is based mainly on the chemical structure of the fibers.

Many studies have used sugar-beet pulp as the fiber source since it is a NSP that has been shown to be extensively degraded in the hindgut of pigs. Sugar-beet fiber is a slowly fermentable fiber and partially soluble fiber compared with soluble and rapidly fermentable fiber like inulin. Inulin is a polysaccharide degradable in the first half of large intestine (fermentability 100%) whereas the sugar-beet fiber is degraded throughout the large intestine (less and slow fermentability 70%) (Coudray *et al.*, 1997).

Canh *et al.* (1997) reported that there is no effect of the diet on total N excretion. However, the N excretion pattern differed between diets. Pigs fed the by-product- and the sugar-beet pulp-based diets excreted less N via urine and more N via feces that pigs the grain- and topioca-based diets. The excretion pattern appears to be more related to the crude fiber content than the NSP content. Therefore, as shown in Table 2, cellulose appears to be the most important NSP component influencing the pattern of N excretion. Mroz *et al.* (1993) found the highest fecal N excretion in pigs fed cellulose, and the lowest value was noted in pigs fed pectins, while feeding hemicellulose gave intermediate results. And the amount of urea secreted from blood into the large intestine increases when dietary fiber increases (Low, 1985), resulting in a reduced urea and ammonia content in the portal plasma (Malmlof, 1985).

For average daily gain there are sex differences throughout trial periods and treatment differences during some phases. Kendall *et al.* (1999) reported that the barrows gain faster and consumed more feed through the trial and the pig fed corn-soybean diet (12.4% CP, 0.65% lysine + 0.15% lysine) had 0.9 kg/day higher average daily gain than the pigs fed the diet with 10 % soybean meal supplement (9.7% CP, 0.65% lysine + 0.372% lysine adding 0.05 % tryptophane and 0.42% threonine) for weeks 3-9. DeCamp *et al.* (2001) an industry-type control diet for barrows and gilts or the control diet with the addition of 10% soybean hulls and 3.4% supplement fat for a six week period. They said that the diets were formulated to meet or exceed the nutrient requirements for sex and phase of growth based on NRC (1998). Their research results showed that pigs fed the soybean hulls diet had a 13.8% increase in average daily gain (0.9 kg versus 0.79 kg) during week 1-3 and barrows had a greater average daily gain at all time

(0.93 kg versus 0.84 kg per day). Diets containing fermentable NSP or specific organic compounds increase small intestinal dimensions and the capacity for nutrient absorption in dogs (Buddington et al., 1999), change enteric bacterial population and the microbial ecology in different segments to show the differences in VFA in the intestinal system in swine (Sutton et al., 1991) and improve Ca balance without adverse effects or other mineral retention. These findings demonstrate that although fermentable fiber does not directly provide nutrition, it can be considered an "essential" component of swine diets.

C. Oligosaccharides

Recently, fiber sources which are readily fermented by intestinal bacteria, such as beet pulp, oligofructose, sucrose thermal oligosaccharide caramel (STOC) and gum arabic have been added to human, dog and pig food (Willard et al., 1994; Gibson and Roberfroid, 1995; Orban et al., 1997). The term oligosaccharide refers to glycosides composed of 3 to 10 monosaccharide unit. Many oligosaccharides are indigestible in the small intestine of most animals because of their unique glycosidic linkages. In the colon, however, they are fermentable by various bacterial species. Crittenden and Playne (1996) categorized foodgrade oligosaccharide with prebiotic properties into 8 major classes in descending ordor based on their commercial production volume worldwide. These are lactulose, galactooligosaccharides, fructooligosaccharides (FOS), isomaltooligosaccharides, soybean oligosaccharides, lactosucrose, mannon oligosaccharide (MOS), genitooligosaccharides, and xylooligosaccharides. Among these eight, FOS and lactosucrose have been focused on in human, dog and pig research for reducing N excretion and ammonia emission (Table 1 and 2).

Fructooligosaccharides are natural compounds found in various plants (e.g., onion, wheat and others) (Fishbein et al., 1988). In general, these compounds are not digested by mammals, but may be metabolized by bacterial species. There are demonstrable differences among bacteria regarding their ability to grow when FOS are a carbohydrate source (Willard et al., 1994) and intestinal bacterial populations apparently can be affected by such dietary constituents. From FOS, STOC were produced. The STOC are produced by thermal treatment of amorphous anhydrous acidified sucrose, yielding a complex mixture containing fructose-rich oligosaccharides and di-fructose di-anhydrous (Manley-Harris and Richards, 1994).

Table 1 shows that a significant added benefit with 2% STOP in the diet was the reduction of pH of fresh (8% reduction) and stored (12%) pig manure compared with the 13% commercial diet, which resulted in better control of ammonia volatilization (Sutton et al., 1996a, 1996b, 1997, 1998). This table showed that addition of 2% STOP reduced ammonia excretion levels in fresh (37 % reduction for NH_3-N and 35% for TKN, wet basis) and stored (62% reduction for NH_3-N and 55% for TKN) pig manure compared with the standard commercial diet which contained 13% crude protein diet. Additionally, Orban *et al.* (1997) showed that microbial populations in their study were not significantly altered by STOC in pigs. This was surprising because STOC has been shown to increase the populations of *Bifidobacteria* in poultry studies (Orban *et al.*, 1993, 1995). They have shown that broilers fed STOC diets supplemented with NRC-recommended levels of trace minerals and vitamins perform as well as birds fed control diets supplemented with twice the level of trace mineral and vitamins. However, Fukuyasu *et al.* (1987) found that the effect of STOC on growth performance of pigs was remarkable. There is evidence that FOS alter VFA patterns in the lower GIT, (reduce the proportion of acetate and increase the proportion of propinate), decrease the total number of aerobes (predominantly coliform), increase *Bifidobacteria* (Hidaka *et al.*, 1986; Howard *et al.*, 1995), and reduce the amount of odorous compounds from swine manure (Hidaka *et al.*, 1986).

A similar trend was noted when chickens were supplemented with a carbohydrate complex, lactosucrose (0.15% of the diet) for 62 days (Terada *et al.*, 1994). This study found that not only were the cecal numbers of *Bifidobacteria* (per gram of wet feces) increased, but the lactosucrose supplementation reduced the numbers (per gram of wet feces) of the lecithinase-positive clostridia including *C. perfringens*, *Bacteriodaceae* and *Staphylococci*. Depending on the type of manure handling system used and the duration of storage, immediately after the feces are excreted from the pig odorous volatile organic compounds, short-chain VFA and other volatile carbon-, nitrogen- and sulfur-containing compounds from microbial fermentation in the GIT can be emitted. Intestinal bacterial populations also apparently can be affected by carbohydrate sources.

Feeding oligosaccharides has positive changes on the microbial ecology of the colon including increasing the number of desirable bacteria (e.g., *Bifidobacteria* and *Lactobacilli*) and decreasing the number of pathogenic or less desirable bacteria. The production of fecal odor components is mainly the responsibility of these pathogenic or less desirable bacterial populations (Morris and Boeker, 1983; Tabor and Tabor, 1985). In a human study (Hara *et al.*, 1994), lactosucrose supplementation (3 g/day) decreased the fecal concentrations (μg/g dry feces) of key odor components including ammonia (from 975 to 428), disulfides (from 20 to 15), phenol (from 124 to 58), ethylphenol (from 38 to 9), skatole (from 87 to 29) and indole (from 214 to 67). Another study with chickens (Tarada *et al.*, 1994) showed that lactosucrose supplementation (0.15% of diet) decreased cecal concentrations (μg/g wet cecal contents) of ammonia (from 150 to 75), phenol (from 33 to 20) and p-cresol (from 91 to 60). These studies did not measure the fecal concentrations of amines, but the results showed that lactosucrose decreases numbers of *C. perfringens* in human and chicken feces and due to these decreased numbers the lactosucrose is thought to be effective in decreasing amine production in the colon.

Studies have indicated that inclusion of FOS in the diet at the highest level (0.5%) reduced fecal concentrations of putrescine, cadaverine, tyramine and total amines by 42, 45, 64 and 20%, respectively, in the dog, while in the cat, fecal concentrations of cadaverine, tyramine and total amines were reduced by 22, 45 and 18%, respectively (Hussein and Sunvold, 2000a,b).

The research (Pettigrew, 2000) available to date suggests strongly that adding MOS (0.2-0.3% for starting pigs, 0.2-0.4% for 7-14 days age and 0.05-0.3% for finishing pigs, depending on the study) to the diet of starting pigs improves their performance. The improvement is especially large and consistent where growth rates are at levels often found in commercial production. He reported that the best approach seems to be feeding a high dietary level of MOS in the first post-weaning diet and then gradually reducing the level as the pigs grow. The data on finishing pigs allow the possibility that MOS may improve growth performance, but they do not show it clearly (Kavanagh, 1999; LeMieux and Southern, 1999; Maxwell et al., 1999).

Unfortunately, published research examining the potential role of carbohydrate complexes such as FOS, STOC or lactosucrose in improving the microbial ecology of the pigs GIT are limited. However, it is possible that carbohydrate complexes could improve fermentation in the pigs GIT in a manner similar to that reported for dogs, cats, humans and chickens.

D. Resistant Starches

The rate of starch digestion *in vivo* has been found to be highly dependent on crystallinity and the food ingredient form. Consequently, starches from many sources are not completely digested in the small intestine (Englyst and Cummings, 1990). Physical entrapment, the presence of resistant starch granules or retrogradation may contribute to incomplete digestion of starches in the small intestine. It is possible that starch may be physically entrapped in a cellular or multicellular structure that inhibits contact with amylase (e.g., starch within a whole cereal grain or in pasta). Gelatinization occurs when starch is heated in a excess or water and further heating causes the amylopectin and amylose molecules of starch to associate and a gel forms (Miles et al., 1985). Starch that is resistant to amylolytic degradation is also produced by this process.

Regardless of the reason for starch resistance, the starch that is not digested in the small intestine enters the colon where it is fermented by colonic bacteria. In one study (Kleessen et al., 1997) using rats, the effects of feeding different forms (native or retrograded) of resistant potato starch (10% of the diet) were studied over five months. Feeding of resistant starch encouraged the growth of desirable bacteria (e.g., *Bifidobacterium* and *Lactobacillus*) and suppressed growth of pathogenic bacteria such as Clostridia.

Research with humans (Phillips *et al.*, 1995) also indicated that feeding 34 g of resistant starch decreased fecal pH from 6.9 to 6.3 and increased fecal concentrations of total short-chain fatty acids by 20%. The positive effects of resistant starch on reducing fecal odor in rats (Mallett *et al*, 1988; Levart *et al.*, 1991) or humans (Birkett *et al.*, 1996) may extend to pigs. In another study humans were fed diets containing high (39 g/day) or low (5 g/day) levels of resistant starch for 3 weeks (Birkett *et al.*, 1996). The high levels of resistant starch increased daily fecal N excretion by 55% and decreased daily fecal excretions of ammonia and phenols by 18 to 42%, respectively. Birkett *et al.* (1969) suggested that resistent starch can significantly reduce the accumulation of the putreactive compounds in the human colon.

One report (Mosenthin *et al.*, 1992) indicated that addition of starch to the pig to stimulate bacterial growth resulted in increased fecal N excretion in the form of bacterial N, reduced ammonia absorption in the colon and consequently reduced urinary N excretion. The addition of casein and starch infusion in the large intestine of pigs increased N retention and decreased N output in the urine, but increased protein excretion in the feces (Gargallo and Zimmerman, 1981). Further research examining the potential of resistant starches in decreasing fecal odor components in pigs should be done. The positive effects of resistant starch on reducing fecal odor in rats and human may be expected in pigs.

There are benefits for the host animal when fermentation of cereal fiber, from bran and some resistant starch occurs in the large bowel. Fermentation has possible implications for protection against large bowl cancer (Burkitt, 1969), increasing fecal weight (Stephen and Cummings, 1980), contributing to fecal bulking (McBurney *et al.*, 1985), reducing transit time (McBurney *et al.*, 1985) and supplying nutrients (70% of the energy used by the coloncyte is derived from short chain fatty acid) (Roediger, 1980). However, the amount of resistant starch consumed by different individuals and populations is unknown at present and hence its role in proections against colon cancer is uncertain.

IV. CARBOHYDRATES THAT INFLUENCE pH LEVELS IN SLURRY

Gaseous emission from slurries are affected by environmental conditions such as temperature, oxygen content, humidity, and air exchange rate and by pH, buffering capacity and dry matter content of the slurry. The ammonia concentration and pH of the slurry are important factors influencing the ammonia emission (Freney *et al.*, 1983) (Table 1). pH is affected by the type of diet (Canh *et al.*, 1998a) and the dietary electrolyte balance (Patience *et al.*, 1987). Since the behavior of most volatile compounds depends upon pH, the loss of ammonia and VFA from animal manure was studied as a function of pH (Derikx *et al.*, 1994).

According to the research of Subair *et al.* (1999), liquid hog manure pH was negatively correlated with C loss, indicating that microbial decomposition of paper amendments (paper products) lowered manure pH but this effect did not appear to be important in controlling ammonia volatilization. Addition of 5% cellulose reduced ammonia excretion levels and pH in fresh and stored pig manures (Sutton *et al.*, 1997).

Composting of the diet significantly affected the pH of urine and feces of pigs. When pigs were fed the sugar-beet pulp based diet, the pH of the slurry was 0.44 to 1.13 units lower than when pigs were fed grain or by-products or grains plus tapioca (Canh *et al.*, 1997). This effect was similar for the feces, but to a lesser extent.

An important factor affecting the acid-base status in animals is the dietary electrolyte balance (dEB). Normal body function relies on a constant blood pH and therefore dietary changes will alter renal excretion of H^+ and other electrolytes (Patience *et al.*, 1987; Tucker *et al.*, 1988; Haydon and West, 1990). Urinary pH was found to be lowest in a sugar-beet pulp based diet, which had a lower dEB level, and highest in by-product based diets having the highest dEB level (Canh *et al.*, 1997).

In a study with humans (Hara *et al.*, 1994), daily supplementation of lactosucrose (3 g) decreased fecal pH from 6.3 to 5.9 (due to the increase in concentrations of acetate and lactate). And feeding resistant starch to rats decreased fecal pH from 7.4 to 5.4 which was evident by the increase in bacterial protein synthesis in the colon and by the reduction in renal N excretion (Younes *et al.*, 1995). Weanling pig fed 1% galactan (DM basis) had decreased ileal pH and *E. coli* in the small intestine, and *E. coli* is often associated with postweaning secretory diarrhea (Hampson *et al.*, 1985). Addition of 2% STOC (Sutton *et al.*, 1997) also reduced pH in fresh and stored manures of pigs. They reported that the pH of fresh manure was reduced 0.69 units, and the pH of stored manure was reduced 1.00 units.

The source and the level of fermentable carbohydrates in the diet are always an important factor affecting the pH and the ammonia emission in slurry. The addition of soybean hulls to the diet had the greatest effect on reducing the pH and ammonia emission, and the effects of sugar-beet pulp and coconut expeller were approximately the same (Canh *et al.*, 1998a). In other papers, Canh *et al.* (1997, 1998b) demonstrated that the inclusion of 30 % sugar-beet pulp in a pig diet lowered the slurry pH by 0.97 unit. These scientists concluded that the slurry pH was related to slurry VFA concentration. A reduced CP (9.7%) diet with the addition of 10% soybean hulls (9.7% CP, 0.65% lysine for growing-finishing pigs) with supplemental lysine (0.372%), tryptophan (0.005%), and threonine (0.042%)

for the remaining 6 weeks had a greater decrease in pit pH by up to 0.3 unit (Kendall *et al.*, 1999) (Table 2). These researchers showed that the number one factor of importance in influencing ammonia formation is slurry pH.

V. FUTURE RESEARCH

Many studies have reported that dietary manipulation by the addition of fiber, NSP, oligosaccarides and resistant starches can affect cecal and colonic fermentation. Research continues to determine the level and type of fiber that allows for optimal cecal and colonic bacterial populations.

In recent reports, these carbohydrates have been found to affect fecal nitrogen content and odor production. Future research concentrating on the fecal nitrogen reduction and odor reduction will focus on the following topics.

1. Increasing nutrient utilization to reduce nutrient excretion.
2. Carbohydrate component manipulation to regulate bacterial fermentation in the gastointestinal tract.
3. Determining the populations of bacteria in the lower GIT and their relationships.
4. Ecological factors that affect microbial populations in the lower GIT.
5. Development of carbohydrate sources that improve growth rates, reduce odor production and promote proper microbial populations in the lower GIT.
6. Development of carbohydrate sources that reduce odor while maintaining proper acid-base balances, which maintain a buffering function in the diet.

ACKNOWLEDGMENTS

This research was supported by the Taegu University Research Grant, 2002. The author would like to thank them for their partial financial support.

REFERENCES

Aspimon, H.M. and Kruse-Plass, M., 1990. The role of ammonia as an atmospheric pollutant. In: V.C. Nielsen, J.H. Voorburg and P. L'Hermite (Ed.), *Odor and Ammonia Emissions from Livestock Farming*. Elsevier Applied Science, London and New York. P 17.

Bakke, O.M., 1969. Urinary simple phenols in rats fed diets containing different amounts of casein and 10% tyrosine. *J. Nutr.* **98**, 217-221.

Bakker, G.C.M., 1996. Interaction between carbohydrates and fat in pigs: Impact on energy evaluation of feeds. Ph.D. thesis. Wageningen Institute of Animal Sciences, The Netherlands.

Birkett, A., Muir, J., Phillips, J., Jones, G. and O'Dea, K., 1996. Resistant starch lowers fecal concentrations of ammonia and phenols in humans. *Am. J. Clin. Nutr.* **63**, 766-772.

Buddington, R.K., Buddington, K.K., Sunvold, G.D., 1999. Influence of fermentable fiber on small intestinal dimensions and transport of glucose and proline in dogs. *AJVR* **60(3)**, 354-358.

Burkitt, D.P., 1969. Related disease-Related cause. *Lancet* **2**, 1229-1231.

Calvert, C.C., Steele, N.C., Rosebrough, R.W., 1985. Digestibility of fiber components and reproductive performance of sows fed high levels of alfalfa meal. *J. Anim. Sci.* **61**, 595-599.

Canh, T.T., Aarnink, A.J.A., Verstegen, M.W.A. and Schrama, J.W., 1998a. Influence of dietary factors on the pH and ammonia emission of slurry from growing-finishing pigs. *J. Anim. Sci.* **76**, 1123-1130.

Canh, T.T., Sutton, A.L., Aarnink, A.J.A., Verstegen, M.W.A., Schrama, J.W. and Bakker, G.C.M., 1998b. Dietary carbohydrates alter the fecal composition and pH and the ammonia emission from slurry of growing pigs. *J. Anim. Sci.* **76**, 1887-1895.

Canh, T.T., Verstegen, M.W.A., Aarnink, A.J.A. and Schrama, J.W., 1997. Influence of dietary factors on nitrogen partitioning and composition of urine and feces of fattening pigs. *J. Anim. Sci.* **75**, 700-706.

Carre, B., Derouet, L. and Leclereg, B., 1990. Digestibility of cell wall polysaccharides from wheat (bran or whole grain), soybean and white lupin meal in cockerels, muscovy ducks and rats. *Poultry Sci.* **69**, 623-633.

Choi, I.H., Son, J.H. and Nahm, K.H., 1999. Dietary fiber fraction for grains containing high levels of water-soluble non-starch polysaccharides. *Jpn Poult. Sci.* **36**, 269-274.

Coudray, C., Bellanger, C.C., Castiglia-Delavaud, C., Remesy, C., Vermorel, M. and Rayssignuier, Y., 1997. Effect of soluble or partly soluble dietary fibers supplementation on absorption and balance of calcium, magnesium, iron and zinc in healthy young men. *Erop. J. Clinical Nut.*, **51**, 375-380.

Crittenden, R. and Playne, M., 1996. Production, properties and applications of food-grade oligosaccharides. *Trends. Food Sci. Technol.*, **7**, 353-361.

Cummings, J.H., Hill, M.J., Jenkins, D.J.A., Pearson, J.R. and Wiggins, H.S., 1976. Changes in fecal composition and colonic function due to cereal fiber. *American J. Clin. Nutr.* **29**, 1468-1473.

De Camp, S.A., Hill, B., Hamkins, S.L., Herr, C.T., Richert, B.T., Sutton, A.L., Kelly, D.T., Cobb, M.L., Bundy, D.W. and Powers, W.J., 2001. T. Lundeen (Ed.), With added fat, soybean hulls may reduce odor without impairment. *Feedstuff* **74** (**44**), 10, 22,. October 22.

Derikx, P.J.L., Willers, H.C. and ten Have, P.J.W., 1994. Effects of pH on the behaviour of volatile compounds in organic manures during dry matter determination. *Bioresource Technology* **49**, 41-45.

Englyst, H.N. and Cummings, J.H., 1990. Non-starch polysaccharides (dietary fiber) and resistant starch. In: I. Furda and C.J. Brine (Eds.), *New Developments in Dietary Fiber: Physiological, Physiochemical, and Analytical Aspects.* New York: Plenum Press, NY, USA. pp 205-226.

Farnworth, E.R., Modler, H.W. and Mackie, D.A., 1995. Adding Jerusalem artichoke (*Helianthus tuberosus L.*) to weanling pig diets and the effect on manure composition and characteristics. *Anim. Feed Sci. Technol.* **55**, 153-160.

Fishbein, L., Kaplan, M. and Gough, M., 1988. Fructooligosaccharide: a review. *Vet. Hum. Toxicol.* **30**, 104-107.

Fleming, S.E., Fitch, M.D. and De Vries, S., 1992. The influence of dietary fiber on proliferation of intestinal mucosal cells in miniature swine may not be mediated primarily by fermentation. *J. Nutr.* **122**, 906-916.

Freney, J.R., Simson, J.R. and Denmead, O.T., 1983. Volatilization of ammonia. *Dev. Plant Soil Sci.* **9**, 1-11.

Fukuyasu, T., Oshida, T. and Ashida, K., 1987. Effect of oligosaccharides on growth of piglets and on bacterial flora, putrefactive substances and volatile fatty acids in their feces. *Bull. Anim. Hyg.* **26**, 15-19.

Gargallo, J. and Zimmerman, D., 1981. Effect of casein and starch infusion in the large intestine on nitrogen and metabolism of growing swine. *J. Nutr.* **111**, 1390-1396.

Gatel, F. and Grosjean, F., 1992. Effect of protein content of the diet on nitrogen excretion by pigs. *Livest. Prod. Sci.* **31**, 109-118.

Gibson, G.R. and Roberfroid, M.B., 1995. Dietary modulation of the human colonic microbiota: Introducing the concept of probiotics. *J. Nutr.* **125**, 1401-1412.

Goodlad, J.S. and Mathers, J.C., 1991. Digestion by pigs of non-starch polysaccarides in wheat and raw peas fed in mixed diets. *Br. J. Nut.* **65**, 259-270.

Gottschalk, G., 1986. Bacterial Metabolism (2nd Ed.), Spinger-Verlag, New York, NY, USA.

Hall, M.B., 2001. Formulate for non-NDF carbohydrates in dairy rations. *Feedstuffs* **73** (**38**), 13-14, 23. September 10.

Hampson, D.J., Hinton, M. and Kidder, D.E., 1985. Coliform numbers in the stomach and small intestine of healthy pigs following weaning at three weeks of age. *J. Comp. Pathol.* **95**, 353-359.

Hara, H., Li, S., Sasaki, M., Maruyama, T., Terada, A., Ogata, Y., Fujita, K., Ishigami, H., Hara, K., Fujimori, I. And Mitsuoka, T., 1994. Effective dose of lactosucrose on fecal flora and fecal metabolites of humans. *Bifidobact. Microflora* **13**, 51-63.

Hartung, J. and Phillips, V.R., 1994. Control of gaseous emissions from livestock buildings and manure stores. *J. Agric. Eng. Res.* **57**, 173-189.

Haydon, K.D. and West, J.W., 1990. Effect of dietary electrolyte balance on nutrient digestibility determined at the end of the small intestine and over the total digestive tract in growing pigs. *J. Anim. Sci.* **68**, 3687-3692.

Hidaka, H., Eida, T., Takizawa, T., Tokanagen, T. and Tashiro, Y., 1986. Effect of fructooligosacchrides on intestinal flora and human health. *Bifidobact. Microflora* **5**, 37-50.

Hobbs, P.J., Misselbrook, T.H. and Pain, B.F., 1995. Assessment of odours from livestock wastes by photoionization detector an electronic nose, olfactometry and gas-chromatography-mass spectrometry. *J. Agric. Eng. Res.* **60**, 137-144.

Howard, M.D., Gordon, D.T., Pace, L.W., Garleb, K.A. and Kerley, M.S., 1995. Effects of dietary supplementation with fructooligosaccharides on colonic microbiota population and epithelial cell proliferation in neonatal pigs. *J. Pediatr. Gastroenterol. Nutr.* **21**, 297-303.

Hussein, H.S. and Sunvold, G.D., 2000a. The efficacy of fructooligosaccharides in decreasing cat fecal odor. Res. Vet. Sci. 2000 (to be submitted). In: G.A. Reinhart, and D.P. Carey, 2000 (Ed), *Dietary strategies to decrease dog and cat fecal odor components of recent advances in canine and feline nutrition.* Orange Frazer Press, Wilmington, Ohio, USA. pp 176-190.

Hussein, H.S. and Sunvold, G.D., 2000b. The efficacy of fructooligosaccharides in decreasing dog fecal odor. Am. J. Vet. Res. 2000 (to be submitted). In: G.A. Reinhart and D.P. Carey, 2000, (Ed), *Dietary strategies to decrease dog and cat fecal odor components of recent advances in canine and feline nutrition.* Orange Frazer Press, Wilmington, Ohio, USA. pp 153-168.

Kass, M.L., van Soest, P.J., Pond, W.G., Lewis, B. and McDowell, R.E., 1980. Utilization of dietary fiber from alfalfa by growing swine. I. Apparent digestibility of diet components in specific segments of the gastrointestinal tract. *J. Anim. Sci.* **50**, 175-191.

Kavanagh, N.T., 1999. Performance response to Bio-Mos: Grower/Finisher pigs. Oldcastle Laboratories, Oldcastle, Ireland. *Report to Alltech Ireland.*

Kendall, D.C., Richert, B.T., Sutton, A.L., Frank, J.W., DeCamp, S.A., Bowers, K.A., Kelly, D., Cobb, M. and Bundy, D., 1999. Effects of fiber addition (10% soybean hulls) to a reduced crude protein diet supplemented with synthetic amino acids versus a standard commercial diet on pig performance, pit composition, odor and ammonia levels in swine buildings. *Purdue 1999 Swine Day Report*, pp 1-6.

Keyo, J.E., van Soest, P.J. and Young, E.P., 1970. Effect of increasing dietary cell wall content on the digestibility of hemicellulose and cellulose in swine and rats. *J. Anim. Sci.* **31**, 1177-1183.

Kirchgessner, M., Kreuzer, M., Machmuller, A. and Roth-Maier, D.A., 1994. Evidence for a high efficiency of bacterial protein synthesis in the digestive tract of adult sows fed supplements of fiberous feedstuffs. *Anim. Feed Sci. Technol.* **46**, 293-299.

Kleessen, B., Stoof, G., Proll, J., Schmiedl, D., Noack, J., and Blaut, M., 1997. Feeding resistant starch affects fecal and cecal microflora and short-chain fatty acids in rats. *J. Anim. Sci.* **75**, 2453-2462.

Kreuzer, M., Heindl, U., Roth-Maier, D.A. and Kirchgessner, M., 1991. Cellulose fermentation capacity of the hindgut and nitrogen turnover in the hindgut of sows as evaluated by oral and intracecal supply of purified cellulose. *Arch. Anim. Nutr.* **41**, 359-372.

Kreuzer, M. and Machmuller, A., 1993. Reduction of gaseous nitrogen emission from pig manure by increasing the level of bacterially fermentable substrates in the ration. In: M.W.A. Verstegen, L.A. den Hartog, G.J.M. van Kempen and J.H.M. Metz (Ed.), *Nitrogen Fflow in Pig Production and Environmental Consequences.* EAAP Publ. No. 69. Pudoc., Wageningen, The Netherlands. pp 151-156.

LeMieux, F.M., Southern, L.L., 1999. Effect of Bio-Mos in finishing pigs. Louisiana State University, Boton Rouge, *Report to Alltech, Inc..*

Levart, M.A., Remesy, C. and Demigne, C., 1991. Very acidic fermentation in the rat caecum during adaptation to a diet rich in amylase-resistant starch (crude potato starch). *J. Nutr. Biochem.* **2**, 31-36.

Low, A.G., 1985. Role of dietary fiber in pig diets. In: W. Haresign and D.J.A. Cole (Ed.) *Recent Advances in Animal Nutrition.* Butterworths, London, UK. p 87.

Mallett, A.K., Bearne, C.A., Young, P.J., Rowland, I.R., and Berry, C., 1988. Influence of starches of low digestibility on the rat cecal microflora. *Br. J. Nut.* **60**, 597-604.

Malmlof, K., 1985. Effects of wheat straw meal on some blood plasma variables in the growing pig. In: Pig Research at the Department of Animal Nutrition and Management 1974-1984. *Swedish University of Agricultural Science* **152**, 16.

Malmlof, K. and Hakansson, J., 1984. The effect of dietary fiber level on the diurnal pattern of urinary nitrogen excretion in swine. *Swed. J. Agric. Res.* **14**, 53-57.

Manley-Harris, M. and Richards, G.N., 1994. Thermalysis of sucrose for food products: a sucrose caramel designed to maximize fructose oligosaccharides for beneficial moderation of intestinal bacteria. *Zuckerindustrie* **119**, 924-930.

Maxwell, C., da Rodas, B., Johnson, Z., 1999. Effeciency of Bio-Mos in improving gain and efficiency in grow/finish pigs. Univ. of Arkansas, Fayettesville, USA. *Report to Alltech Inc..*

McBurney, M.I., Horvath, P.J., Jeraci, J.L., van Soest, P.J., 1985. Effect of *in vivo* fermentation using human fecal inoculum on the water holding capacity in dietary fiber. *Br. J. Nut.* **53**, 17-24.

Miles, M.J., Morris, V.J., Orford, P.D. and Ring, S.G., 1985. The roles of amylose and amylopection in the gelation and retrogradation of starch. *Carbohyd. Res.* **135**, 271-281.

Miner, R.J., Humenik, F.J. and Overcash, M.R., 2000. *Managing Livestock Wastes to Preserve Environmental Quality* (1st Ed.), Iowa State University Press, Ames, Iowa, USA.

Morgan, C.A. and Whittemore, C.T., 1988. Dietary fiber and nitrogen excretion and retention by pigs. *Anim. Feed Sci. Technol.* **19**, 185-189.

Morgan, C.A., Whittemore, C.T. and Cockburn, J.H.S., 1984. The effect of level and source of protein, fiber and fat in the diet on the energy value of compounded pig feeds. *Anim. Feed Sci. Technol.* **11**, 11-34.

Morris, D.R. and Boeker, E.A., 1983. Biosynthetic and biodegradative ornithine and arginine decarboxylase from *Echerichia coli.. Methods Enzymol.* **94**, 125-134.

Mosenthin, R. and Henkel, H., 1978. Der Einfluss Planzlicher Gerustsubstanzen in Futter auf die N-Ausscheidung im Kot beim Schwein. Z. Tierphysiol. *Tierernahr. U. Futtermittelkde.* **40**, 122-123.

Mosenthin, R., Sauer, W.C., Henkel, H., Ahrens, F. and deLange, C.F.M., 1992. Tracer studies of urea kinetics in growing pigs. II. The effect of starch infusion at the distal ileum on urea recycling and bacterial nitrogen excretion. *J. Anim. Sci.* **70**, 3467-3472.

Mroz, Z., Jongbloed, A.W., Beers, S., Kemme, P.A., DeJong, L., van Berkum, A.K. and van der Lee, R.A., 1993. Preliminary studies on excretory patterns of nitrogen and anaerobic deterioration of fecal protein from pig fed various carbohydrates. In: M.W.A. Verstegen, L.A. den Hartog, G.J.M. van Kempen and J.H.M. Metz (Ed.), *Nitrogen Flow in Pig Production and Environmental Consequences*. EAAP Publ. No. 69. Pudoc., Wageningen, The Netherlands. pp 247-252.

Muck, R.E. and Steenhuis, T.H., 1981. Nitrogen losses in free stall dairy barns. In: *Livestock Wastes: Proceedings of 4th International Symposium on Livestock Wastes. A Renewable Resources*. Am. Soc. Agric. Eng., St. Joseph, MI, USA. p 163.

NRC. 1998. Nutrient Requirements of Swine (10th ed.). National Academy Press, Washington DC, USA.

Orban, J.I., Patterson, J.A., Sutton, A.L. and Richards, G.N., 1993. Effects of sucrose thermal oligosaccharide caramel on growth and intestinal microflora of broiler chickens. *Poultry Sci.* **72** (**Suppl. 1**), 132 (Abstr.).

Orban, J.I., Patterson, J.A., Sutton, A.L., Adeola, O. and Richards, G.N., 1995. Influence of sucrose thermal oligosaccharide caramel and vitamin-mineral level on growth and changes in intestinal microbial populations in broilers from day-old to four weeks of age. *Poultry Sci.* **74**, (**Suppl. 1**), 209 (Abstr.).

Orban, J.I., Patterson, J.A., Adeola, O., Sutton, A.L. and Richards, G.N., 1997. Growth performance and intestinal microbial populations of growing pigs fed diets containing sucrose thermal oligosaccharide caramal. *J. Anim. Sci.* **75**, 170-175.

Partridge, L.G., Keal, H.D. and Mitchell, K.C., 1982. The utilization of dietary cellulose by growing pigs. *Anim. Prod.* **35**, 209-214.

Patience, J.F., Austic, R.E. and Boyd, R.D., 1987. Effect of dietary electrolyte balance on growth and acid-base status in swine. *J. Anim. Sci.* **64**, 457-462.

Pettigrow, J.E., 2000. Mannan oligosaccharides' effects on performance reviewed. *Feedstuffs* **72(53)**, 12-14. Dec. 25.

Phillips, J., Muir, J.G., Birkett, A., Zhong, X.L., Jones, G.P. and O'Dea, K., 1995. Effect of resistant starch on fecal bulk and fermentable-dependent events in humans. *Am. J. Clin. Nutr.* **62**, 121-130.

Pond, W.G., Yen, J.T., Varel, V.H., 1985. Effects of level and source of dietary fiber in gestation on reproductive performance and nutrient digestibility in gilts. *Nutr. Rep. Int.* **32**, 505-511.

Potkins, Z.U., Lawrence, T.L.J. and Thomlinson, J.R., 1984. Studies on the effects of composition and physical form of the diet on gastric abnormalities and nutrient utilization in the growing pig. *Anim. Prod.* **38**, 534-539.

Potkins, Z.U., Lawrence, T.L.J. and Thomlinson, J.R., 1991. Effects on ileal apparent digestibility in the growing pig of replacing barley with bran, oatmeal by-product, guar gum and pectin. *Anim. Feed Sci. Technol.* **35**, 171-177.

Roediger, W.E.W., 1980. Role of anaerobic bacteria in the metabolic welfare of the colonic mucosa in man. *Gut* **21**, 793-798.

Rowan, A.M., Moughan, P.J. and Wilson, M.N., 1992. The flows of deoxyribonucleic acid and diaminopimelic acid and the digestibility of dietary fiber components at the terminal ileum, as indicators of microbial activity in the uppor digestive tract of ileostomised pigs. *Anim. Feed Sci. Technol.* **36**, 129-141.

Salvador, V., Cherbut, C., Barry, J., Bertrand, D., Bonnet, C., Delort-Laval, J., 1993. Sugar composition of dietary fiber and short-chain fatty acid production during *in vitro* fermentation by human bacteria. Br. J. Nutr. 70, 189-197.

Sauer, W.C., Just, A., Jorgensen, H.H., Fekadu, M. and Eggum, B.O., 1980. The influence of diet composition on the apparent digestibility of crude protein and amino acids at the terminal ileum and over all in pigs. *Acta Agric. Scand.* **30**, 449-468.

Sauer, W.C., Mosenthin, R., Ahrens, F. and den Hartog, L.A., 1991. The effect of source of fiber on ileal and fecal amino acid digestibility and bacterial nitrogen excretion in growing pigs. *J. Anim. Sci.* **69**, 4070-4079.

Schulze, H., van Leeuwen, P., Verstegen, M.W.A. and van den Berg, J.W.O., 1995. Dietary level and source of neutral detergent fiber and ileal endogenous nitrogen flow in pigs. *J. Anim. Sci.* **73**, 441-448.

Southgate, D. and Englyst, H., 1985. Dietary fiber: chemistry, physical properties and analysis. In: H. Trowell, D. Burkitt and K. Heaton (Ed.), *Dietary Fiber*. Academic Press, london, UK. P 31.

Spaeth, G., Berg, R.D., Specian, R.D., Deitch, E.A., 1990. Food without fiber promotes bacterial translocation. Surgery 108, 240-247.

Stephen, A.M., Cummings, J.H., 1980. Mechanisms of action of dietary fiber in the human colon. *Nature* 284, 283-284.

Stevens, R.J., Laughlin, R.J. and Frost, J.P., 1989. Effect of acidification with sulphuric acid on the volatilization of ammonia from cow and pig slurry. *J. Agric. Sci.* **113**, 389-393.

Strobel, H.J. and Russell, J.B., 1986. Effect of pH and energy spilling on bacterial protein synthesis by carbohydrate-limited cultures of mixed rumen bacteria. *J. Dairy Sci.* **69**, 2941-2947.

Subair, S., Fyles, J.W. and O'Halloran, I.P., 1999. Ammonia volatilization from liquid hog manure amended with paper products in the laboratory. *J. Environ. Qual.* **28**, 202-207.

Sutton, A.L., Kephart, K.B., Patterson, J.A., Mumma, R., Kelly, D.T., Bogus, E., Jones, D.D. and Heber, A., 1996a. Manipulating swine diets to reduce ammonia and odor emmissions. In: Proceedings of 1st International Conference, *Air Pollution from Agricultural Operations*, Kansas City, Mo, USA. pp 445-452.

Sutton, A.L., Kephart, K.B., Patterson, J.A., Mumma, R., Kelly, D.T., Bogus, E., Jones, D.D. and Heber, A., 1997. Dietary manipulation to reduce ammonia and odorous compounds in excreta and anaerobic manure storages. In: Proceeding International Symposium, *Ammonia and Odour Control from Animal Production Facilities*, Vinkeloord, The Netherlands.

Sutton, A.L., Mathew, A.G., Scheidt, A.B., Patterson, J.A., Kelly, D.T., 1991. Effect of carbohydrate sources and organic acids on intestinal microflora and performance of the weaning pig. In: 1991. EAAP Pub. No. 54 Pudoc., Wageningen, The Netherland. pp. 422-427.

Sutton, A., Patterson, J., Kelly, D., Kones, D. and Herber, A., 1996b. Swine diets to reduce ammonia and odor emissions. *Purdue 1996 Swine Day Report.* pp 1-6.

Sutton, A.L., Patterson, J.A., Kelly, D.T., Nielsen, J., Jones, D.D., Heber, A.J., Kephart, K.B. and Bogus, E., 1998. Addition of carbohydrates to low crude protein pig diets to reduce manure nitrogen excretion and odors. *Purdue 1998 Swine Day Report.* pp 1-7.

Tabor, C.W. and Tabor, H., 1985. Polyamines in microorganisms. *Microbiol. Rev.* **49**, 81-99.

Terada, A., Hara, H., Kato, S., Kimura, T., Fujimori, I., Hara, K., Maruyama, T. and Mitsuok, T., 1993. Effect of lactosuccrose on fecal flora and fecal putrefactive products of cats. *J. Vet. Med.* **55**, 291-295.

Terada, A., Hara, H., Oishi, T., Matsui, S., Mitsuoka, T., Nakajyo, S., Fujimori, I., and Hara, K., 1992. Effect of dietary lactosucrose on fecal flora and fecal metabolites of dogs. *Micrb. E. Coli Health Dis.* **5**, 87-92.

Terada, A., Hara, H., Sakamoto, J., Sato, N., Takagi, S., Mitsuoka, T., Mino, R., Hara, K., Fujimori, I. And Yumada, T., 1994. Effect of dietary supplementation with lactosucrose on cecal flora, cecal metabolites, and performance in broiler chickens. *Poultry Sci.* **73**, 1663-1672.

Trowell, H., Southgate, D.A.T., Wolever, T.N.S., Leeds, A.R., Gussell, M.A. and Jenkins, D.J.A., 1976. Dietary fiber redefined. *Lancet* **1**, 967-971.

Tucker, W.B., Harrison, G.A. and Hemken, R.W., 1988. Influence of dietary anion-cation balance on milk, blood, urine and rumen fluid in lactating dairy cattle. *J. Dairy Sci.* **71**, 346-351.

Varel, V.H., 1987. Activity of fiber-degrading microorganisms in the pig large intestine. *J. Anim. Sci.* **65**, 488-496.

Willard, M.D., Simpson, R.B., Delles, E.K., Coben, N.D., Fossum, T.W., Kolp, D. and Reinbart, G., 1994. Effect of dietary supplementation of fructo-oligosaccharides on small intestinal bacterial overgrowth in dogs. *Am. J. Vet. Res.* **55(5)**, 654-659.

Younes, H., Demigne, C., Behr, S. and Remesy, C., 1995. Resistant starch exerts a lowering effect on plasma urea by enhancing urea N transfer into the large intestine. *Nutr. Res.* **15**, 1199-1210.

Current Pollution and Odor Control Technologies for Poultry Production

K. H. Nahm

Feed and Nutrition Laboratory, College of Natural Resources, Taegu University, Gyong San, 712-714, South Korea. E-mail: nahmkh@daegu.ac.kr

ABSTRACT

Concentrated poultry production has resulted in pollution of water by nitrogen (N) and phosphorus (P), and air due to ammonia (NH_3), odors and dust within the poultry barns. Chemical additives containing calcium (Ca), aluminum (Al), or iron (Fe) reduce NH_3 emissions 35 to 99% and soluble P 31 to 95%, depending on the chemical and concentration used. Poultry feed manipulation methods for reducing N and P contents in poultry manure involve reducing protein contents and supplementing with synthetic amino acid to reduce N excretion up to 29.14%. Reducing soluble P contents in broiler diets (40% of NRC requirements) during the withdrawal period reduced soluble P contents in the manure. Enzyme supplements in poultry feed improve dry matter digestibility and phytic P utilization from grain diets, thereby reducing P content in manure. Litter materials increase carbon content of manure and sawdust has specifically been found to reduce the nitrogen in manure by 21%. Covers reduce odor production (impermeable covers by 70 to 85% and permeable covers by 45 to 85%) from manure storage areas. Filter systems reduce dust production and accompanying odors by 80% from poultry barns. Certain land application techniques of manure reduce odor and ammonia by 90%. Ozone lowers NH_3 levels in poultry buildings up to 25% and also eliminates pathogens. Mixing fly ash with manure reduces soluble P contents in stockpiled manure up to 85% and composted manure up to 93%. Addition of vitamin D alone to poultry feed improves phytate P retention from 31 to 68%, while use with phytase improved retention to 79%. Using combinations of the methods would maximize their effectiveness.

(Keywords: pollution, N, P, NH_3, dust, chemical, enzyme, litter, ozone, fly ash, vitamin D)

INTRODUCTION

In recent decades farmers worldwide have confined large numbers of chickens in relatively small spaces to use more enclosed and densely stocked housing, which can result in waste disposal problems. Environmental problems started to appear when confinement farming started to grow and has been related to the problems of acidification and eutrophication of water resources. The US Environmental Protection Agency (EPA) needs new tools for estimating the amounts of ammonia, nitrous oxide, methane, particulate matter and other pollutants emitted from livestock farms and for determining how these emissions are dispersed in the atmosphere (Van Kley, 2002).

Ammonia is a major concern (Reece *et al.*, 1981; Asman, 1992; Sharpe and Harper, 1997) because it can be redeposited elsewhere via rainfall, contaminating nearly soil and surface waters (van der Molen *et al.*, 1990). Atmospheric acids are primarily neutralized by ammonia and ammonia is a common component of atmospheric aerosols. Decomposing feces, hydrolysis of urea in urine to NH_4, losses during production and application of fertilizers and losses from burning biomass are all sources of atmospheric NH_3. In 1986 livestock housing and storage tanks contributed 36% (82,000 t/a) of the ammonia emissions from Dutch livestock farming (DeWinkel, 1988). Ammonia emissions from poultry houses, mainly from laying hens and broilers, were responsible for about 22% (about 19000 t/a) of the total load. For confinement housing, the air quality parameters of concern are carbon dioxide (CO_2), hydrogen sulfide (H_2S), ammonia (NH_3) and aerosolized particulates or dust. NH_3 is the most prominent contaminant from poultry layer facilities (Reece *et al.*, 1981), while under most conditions CO_2 and H_2S do not reach concentrations that are likely to create problems (McQuitty and Feddes, 1982). Sharpe and Harper (1997) reported that gaseous emissions of NH_3 and nitrous oxide (N_2O) lead to conditions detrimental to the environment. N_2O and methane (CH_4) are greenhouse gases that affect global climate change (Jungbluth *et al.*, 2001). Not only does atmospheric NH_3 can raect with acidic species and atmospheric N loading into the aquatic environment, but NH_3 emissions from manure can cause chicken production problems as well as human health problems such as respiratory ailments of poultry workers. Upper respiratory ailments are seen in up to 50% of poultry workers, suggesting that high NH_3 concentrations in poultry facilities contribute to these ailments (Donham *et al.*, 1989). An NH_3 level of 7 ppm inside livestock and poultry buildings has been suggested as a threshold concentration (Donham, 2000).

Phosphorus (P) content of animal manure is currently the primary environmental concern since it is normally the limiting nutrient for eutrophication of fresh water systems (Schindler, 1977). Eutrophication of lakes and rivers reduces their esthetic appeal and can lead to oxygen deprivation resulting in fish kills. Municipal drinking water supplies are compromised by algal blooms. Geosmin, a by-product of certain algae, can contaminate water supplies and give drinking water a muddy taste and odor (Sharpley et al., 1994; Sharpley, 1996, 1999).

In many countries, manure applications based on nitrogen (N) requirements represent phosphorus (P) surpluses. Excess P remains largely fixed in the solid phase of the soil system (Foth, 1990). It is now widely accepted that transfer of P from agricultural soils to surface waters occurs in sufficient quantities to present a major cause of eutrophication of both inland and coastal water bodies (Fay and Withers, 1995; Moss, 1996; Daniel et al., 1998). In normal poultry litter, the N to P ratio is generally two or less, whereas most cropping situations require a ratio of 7-11:1. (Smith et al., 1998).

At the local level, odor from livestock farms is the most serious concern. Odors are generally not a problem in aerobic treatment systems. However, when malfunctions or other circumstances cause aerobic systems to go anaerobic, odors will be released. Odors from livestock wastes are a result of anaerobic decomposition. More than 75 specific odorous compounds have been identified in livestock wastes (Ritter, 1989). Kreis (1978) developed one of the earliest lists of volatile compounds associated with the decomposition of livestock and poultry wastes. This research indicated that poultry, cattle and swine wastes consist of 17, 32 and 50 different compounds, respectively. O'Neill and Phillips (1992) identified 168 different compounds in both swine and poultry wastes. Odor from concentrated animal feeding operations (CAFOs) sources, as experienced by humans, may be the composite of 170 or more specific gases, present in trace concentrations either above or below their individual olfactory thresholds (Sweeten et al., 2001).

Poor odor prevention and control from animal wastes is related to a lack of knowledge of the fundamental nature of odor and its production by farm animals (Mackie et al., 1998). There is not a universally accepted definition of an objectionable odor. Thus, regulation and control of odors in the environment is difficult because of the technical difficulties of defining odor limits and their measurement and evaluation (Mackie et al., 1998). The sense of odor (smell) is highly variable (Harper et al., 1968), and, among individuals, it differs with age, smoking habits, and presence of nasal allergies or head colds (Cheremisinoff and Young, 1975; Schiffman and Gatlin, 1993). The recognition of odor threshold is often 1.5 to 10 times higher than the detection threshold (Mackie et al., 1998). Odors may originate from livestock building and feedlot, waste treatment or storage units or from land spreading (Ritter, 1989). Odors cannot be entirely eliminated but can be minimized by proper construction and management procedures.

This review describes the current understanding of the biochemical identification and biological origin of key components of pollution in poultry waste and considers ways of reducing or controlling them.

POLLUTION
Water Pollution
Nitrogen (N)

Nitrogen components such as uric acid, urea, NH_3/ammonium (NH_4^+) and undigested proteins are the potential sources for ammonia production. Uric acid and undigested protein are the two main N components in feces, representing about 70 and 30% of the total N, respectively, in poultry wastes (Preismann *et al.*, 1990; Keenstra and Pit, 1990). Their formation can be simplified as follows.

$$C_5H_4O_3N_4 + 1.5O_2 + 4H_2O \longrightarrow 5CO_2 + 4NH_3$$

(Schefferle, 1965; Carlile, 1984)

$$\text{Undigested protein (C, H, O, N, S)} \longrightarrow CO_2 + H_2O + NO_3^- + SO_4^{2-}$$

(Westerman and Zhang, 1997)

Under aerobic conditions,

$$\left.\begin{array}{l}\text{Protein} \\ \text{Peptides} \\ \text{Amino acids}\end{array}\right\} \xrightarrow{\text{heterotrophic bacteria*}} NH_4^+$$

$$\xrightarrow{\text{Autotrophic bacteria**}} \text{Nitrite } (NO_2^-) \longrightarrow \text{Nitrate } (NO_3^-) \longrightarrow \text{Nitrogen gas } (N_2)$$

* Heterotrophic bacteria require nourishment from organic substances.
** Autotrophic bacteria obtain nourishment from inorganic matter such as NH_4^+.

$$\begin{array}{l}\text{Sulfur compounds} \\ \text{(Sulfur-containing protein)}\end{array} \longrightarrow \text{Sulfate } (SO_4^{2-}) \longrightarrow H_2S$$

(Westerman and Zhang, 1997)

The combination of nitrification ($NH_4^+ \rightarrow NO_3^-$) and denitrification ($NO_3^- \rightarrow N_2$) will remove N from the livestock manure. The organic N content of the fresh broiler manure ranged from 80% of the total N for bird-rearing temperature (RT) of 26℃ to 85% for RT of 16℃. The inorganic N (mostly NH_4-N) of the fresh manure ranged from 15% to 20% of the total N (Sistani et $al.$, 2001).

Ammonia is highly water-soluble and it can largely remain in the water in the dissociated form as ammonium. Only that part which is present in the un-ionized form can become volatile. Its release is determined by the gradient of the partial pressure of the ammonia between the liquid phase and the ambient air and by the diffusion in conditions (Miner, 1974). The degradation of uric acid and proteins is influenced by temperature, pH and moisture content. The degradation of uric acid in reused broiler litter has been described quantitatively in relation to temperature and pH by Elliot and Collins (1982). Faster breakdown rates are seen with rising temperatures, with sharp increases seen between 20 and 30℃. Breakdown rates are increased with pH levels of 5.5 and higher, with an optimum pH of 9 for uricase (Vogels and Van der Drift, 1976). Optimal microbial growth in chicken manure is seen between 40 and 60% moisture (wet basis) (Elliot and Collins, 1983). When moisture values fell below this, the amount of ammonia released also decreased. At low moisture contents, ammonia release stopped.

In the atmosphere, acidic species may react with NH_3 to form ammonium sulfate, ammonium nitrate or ammonium chloride, or NH_3 may be deposited on the surface of the earth. The gas-to-particle conversion rate of NH_3 to NH_4^+ partially governs the particular NH_3 source's contribution to atmospheric N deposition (Paerl, 1997). There may be a substantial impact of NH_3 deposition since reduced N species have been found in costal and estuarine ecosystems (Paerl, 1997).

Ni (1997) clarified the definition of NH_4^+, NH_3, total ammonia (TA), ammoniacal nitrogen (AN) and total ammoniacal nitrogen (TAN). NH_3 exists in the liquid manure in the form of ammonium ions (NH_4^+) and free ammonia (NH_3). In liquid manure, NH_3 exists in the forms of ammonium ions (NH_4^+) and free ammonia (NH_3). In the NH_3 release models, the sum of NH_3 and NH_4^+ is referred to as TA. TA includes the mass of the hydrogen nuclei in NH_3 and NH_4^+, while AN or TAN are based on the mass of the N nuclei. These values are also denoted as NH_3-N or NH_4-N (TAN = NH_4-N + NH_3-N).

Phosphorus (P)

No matter what you do to treat or break down the compounds in manure or in processing plant water, you will still have elemental N and P. Historically, poultry litter application rates have been based on N needs of the crop rather than the P concentrations. Because the poultry litter is no longer incorporated in the soil by tilling, it is possible that the move to no-till farming as a soil conservation measure has increased P migration into watersheds. Concentrated poultry areas also generally produce several times more manure P than is taken up and removed by crops in these areas (Lander *et al.*, 1998). The basic reason for the P imbalances is that large quantities of P are imported into these regions in feedstuffs. The surplus P has been building up in soils in concentrated poultry areas for several years, and there is increasing concern about P runoff from these high-P soils causing surface water quality problems (Sharpley *et al.*, 1998; Sims *et al.*, 1998). Of greatest concern are ecological problems and odor and taste problems in drinking water, resulting from excess algae growth due to P enrichment of the water (Burkholder and Glasgow, 1997).

Although both N and P stimulate eutrophication, P is often the nutrient limiting algal growth (Schindler, 1977; Sharpley *et al.*, 1994). Eutrophication not only impacts lakes and rivers by reducing the esthetic appeal, it can lead to oxygen deprivation, causing fish kills. Eutrophication leads to growth of a toxic dinoflagellate, *Pfiesteria piscicida* that release toxins that cause temporary memory loss and immunosuppression (Burkholder and Glasgow, 1997). There has not been a direct cause and effect relationship established between P loading and *pfiesteria*, but the scientific consensus is that excessive nutrient loading creates an environment rich in microbial prey and organic matter that *pfiesteria* and menhaden (target fish) use as food (Sharpley, 1999).

In plant ingredients, P is present in different forms such as those attached to organic molecules like lipids, proteins or phytic acid. This P that is organically bound is called organic P. Inorganic P is the free P present in cells as phosphate ions. In plant derived ingredients, the organic P is present as phytic acid P (Nelson *et al.*, 1968). To monogastric animals, such as broilers, phytic acid P or phytic P (PP) is variably available (Simons *et al.*, 1990). PP chelates to various divalent cations found in plant ingredients and to proteins and carbohydrates (Ravindran *et al.*, 1995). The PP that is in its free form or not chelated is known as non-phytate P. Non-Phytate P (nPP) is plant P that is not present as PP, and it can be chemically determined by subtracting PP from total P (TP). Available P (aP) is the P that is available for broilers but it is not the same as nPP even though the two terms are often interchanged. AP can only be determined by conducting animal availability trials. The aP includes portions of inorganic P and organic P (including PP) that are absorbed, but the nPP excludes any available PP.

P in manure is present in inorganic and organic forms, with most as inorganic P (60-90%) (Barnett, 1994a; Leinweber, 1996; Nahm, 2002). The dissolved P fraction in runoff consists of varying amounts of organic P as well as inorganic P. Dissolved organic P is not generally used by algae, however, unless it is hydrolyzed to inorganic P (Sonzogni *et al.*, 1982). It is assumed that in most aquatic environments, inorganic P is the main P form utilized by algae and plants. Bromfield (1960) reported that crop response is directly related to the inorganic P form in manure.

Although data on manure P availability are limited, it is currently assumed that 80 to 90% of manure P is plant available (Risse *et al.*, 2001) because inorganic P commonly makes up 60 to 90% of total P (Barnett, 1994a; Leinweber, 1996). More accurate estimates of plant available P in animal manures will be needed as current concerns with P contamination of surface waters leads to manure application based on P requirements.

The total P concentration of manure can average 25 g/kg for poultry manure and 20 g/kg for poultry litter (Barnett, 1994a, b). This amount of P concentrations in animal manures typically are many times greater than in soils, which are 0.486 to 2.439 mg P/g in surface soils (0-5 cm) receiving long-term manure application (Sharpley, 1996). Hence, surface-applied manure could be a source for elevated P losses in runoff. In fields receiving surface applications of poultry litter and manure, many factors influence the form, concentration and loss of N and P. The properties and management of the soil land surface; the method, rate and timing of litter application; and rainfall intensity and duration are the most influential factors (McLead and Hegg, 1984; Edwards and Daniel, 1992).

Dou *et al.* (2000) reported that manure P release during soil analysis was not greatly affected by shaking time but decreased rapidly with increasing number of repeated extractions. They said that a one hour shaking of manure with H_2O may provide a quick measure of the relative magnitude of P that is most susceptible. This research has found that extracting manures with water may provide a rapid estimate of the manure that can potentially contaminate surface runoff and these rapid methods could provide the impact needed to assess the risk of P loss from fields receiving animal manure. Nahm (2003a) summarized the amount of P extracted using independent extraction and sequential extraction for poultry manure, poultry composite and poultry litter in one table. For manure and compost, the potential for P to be leached into the environment was most closely related to water extractable inorganic P concentration of the respective materials (Sharpley and Moyer, 2000). Therefore water extractable P concentrations of land applied manure or compost may be used to estimate P release and its ability to enrich leachate and surface runoff P.

Heavy metals

Poultry manure and litter contain relatively high concentrations of heavy metals, such as As, Co, Cu, Fe, Mn, Se and Zn (Sims and Wolf, 1994; Moore, Jr., *et al.*, 1995a). As, Co, Cu, Fe, Mn, Se, and Zn are added to poultry diets to prevent diseases, improve weight gain and feed conversion and increase egg production (Nockels, 1991). Most of the added metal pass directly to the feces, which leads to elevated levels in the manure.

Several workers have shown that soils receiving applications of poultry litter for many years have high concentrations of As, Cu, and Zn, particularly near the soil surface (van der Watt *et al.*, 1994; Kingery *et al.*, 1994). Little data is available on metal concentration in runoff water from fields fertilized with manure. Moore, Jr., *et al* (1998) found that Cu and Zn concentrations in the runoff water were 0.7 and 0.1mg/L, indicating a potential for non-point source metal pollution from fields fertilized with poultry manure and litter.

Air Quality

There is no universally accepted definition of an objectionable air quality. Thus, regulation and control of air quality in the environment is difficult because of the technical difficulties of defining air quality limits, especially odor limits and their measurement and evaluation in each country. Groot Koerkamp *et al.* (2001) reported that the three most important topics are ammonia, odor and dust of air quality of animal production (Fig. 1). Van Kley (2002) cited in his review that a list of air pollutions may be of most concern at animal feeding operations. In that list of air pollutions there are ammonia, hydrogen sulfide, methane, nitric oxide, nitrous oxide, odors, particulate matter (PM), and volatile organic compounds (VOC).

Degradation of manure releases major sources of methane and nitrogen oxides (nitrite), which along with carbon dioxide contribute to accumulation of green house gases. During the nitrification-denitrification cycle emissions of nitrous oxide (N_2O) contributes to ozone depletion (Schulte, 1997) and greenhouse gas accumulation (Groot Koerkamp *et al.*, 2001). Odors emitted from manure are also contributing factors to friction between urban and rural residents (Lowe, 1995). Worldwide CH_4 production is estimated at 400×10^6 t; animals are likely responsible for 15 to 25% of this amount, 90% of this originating from ruminants (cattle, sheep, goats and buffalos) (USEPA, 1992).

Odor

Incomplete anaerobic decomposition of stored manure results in release of malodors. Malodorous intermediate compounds are produced and accumulate during decomposition if there are insufficient populations of bacteria that degrade these compounds. If the odor substrate is completely decomposed, odorless gases, CO_2 and CH_4 are produced, along with some odorous gases, NH_3 and H_2S, which contribute minimally to the overall odor intensity (Powers *et al.*, 1999). Incomplete decomposition has been shown to result in over 200 different compounds at one time and the interaction of these compounds produces the specific nature of the odor produced (Power, 2002). These complex chemical mixtures include VFA, alcohols, aromatic compounds, amines (including NH_3) and sulfides (O'Neill and Phillips, 1992; Hartung and Phillips, 1994). Any number of compounds in manure can produce odors, including NH_3, H_2S and VOCs (Van Kley, 2002) However, these gases of interest were present at such low concentrations and direct chromatographic analysis was not possible with available apparatus (Merkel *et al.*, 1969). Hobbs *et al.* (1997) reported that four major groups of odorants were identified as sulfides, volatiles fatty acids (VFA), phenols and indoles.

In poultry operations, the housing and manure/litter storage areas are the principle source of odor (Powers, 2002) (Fig. 1). For the poultry housing system (layers and broilers) the reduction of the NH_3 emissions did not have a clear effect on the odor emissions. This again showed that NH_3 and odor come from different sources and are influenced by different processes and factors (Groot Koerkamp *et al.*, 2001). However, most offensive odors coming from poultry houses are due to poultry feces (Chavez *et al.*, 2001). Additionally, odors from the feed and from the animal will be present (Powers, 2002). The greatest concern was odors from swine producing sites. Dairy and poultry units also produce odors that have a negative impact on neighboring residences (Sweeten *et al.*, 2001).

Reliable data about CH_4 emissions are basically only available for cattle housing systems. Data about N_2O emissions from animal houses are lacking, because of the difficulties in measuring very low N_2O concentration. However, the results of existing investigations are not comparable and most of them do not meet the minimum requirements (Jungbluth *et al.*, 2001). The reported N_2O and CH_4 emissions from laying hens vary greatly and have to be judged critically, because the measured concentrations were very low (sometimes only slightly above the ambient concentration of N_2O). In general, floor systems for laying hens seem to emit more N_2O than battery cage or aviary systems. No N_2O and CH_4 emission data are available for other kinds of poultry like turkeys, broilers, ducks, etc, or for housing systems with natural ventilation (Sneath *et al.*, 1996; Neser *et al.*, 1997; Mennicken, 1999).

There must be a clear distinction between odor and pollutants since certain compounds in feces and urine contribute little to odor but contribute greatly to pollution (e.g., N and P). High levels of odor compounds reportedly reduce growth performance and increase susceptibility to disease (e.g., hogs in confinement housing; Tamminga, 1992). The health of workers is also impacted by odor, with physiological responses ranging from irritation of the eyes, nose and throat, to nausea, headache and vomiting to disturbance, annoyance and depression (NRC, 1979).

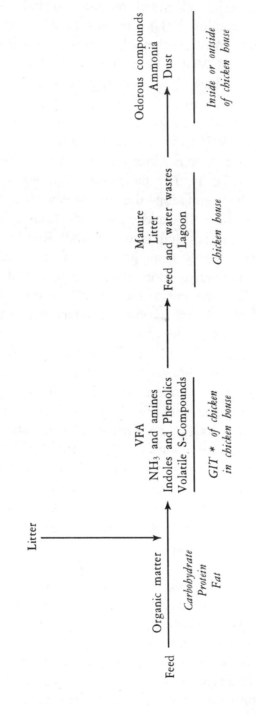

*GIT : Gastrointestinal Tract

Figure 1. Sources of air pollution and odorous compounds

Ammonia

The ammonia in manure or litter is liable to volatilization to the surrounding air. Poultry feces is one source for ammonia volatilization. Dietary N converts to animal product in an inefficient process which results in 50 to 80% of the N consumed being excreted (Arogo *et al.*, 2001). N compounds including uric acid, urea, ammonia/ammonium and undigested proteins are potential sources for ammonia volatilization. Some of the factors important for the volatilization process include dry matter content, acidity (pH), temperature and physical properties of the feces (Elliot and Collins, 1982, 1983).

As seen in equations (1) and (4), ammonia is involved in equilibria in the liquid (l) and gas (g) phases before being liberated into the air.

$$(1)\ NH_4^+\ (l) \longrightarrow NH_3\ (l) + H^+$$

Temperature and pH influence the ammonium - ammonia equilibrum (Weast *et al.*, 1986). At a pH of 7 or below, nearly all of the ammonia is bound as ammonium and does not volatilize. Ammonia concentrations increase at higher temperatures, since temperatures have a positive influence on the dissociation constant Ka. This constant is defined as:

$$(2)\ Ka = [NH_3]\ [H_3O^+]\ /\ [NH_4^+]$$

The volatilization equilibrium of ammonia to the gas phase follows Henry's law for dilute systems.

$$(3)\ NH_3\ (l) \longrightarrow NH_3\ (g)$$

$$(4)\ NH_3\ (g,\ manure) \longrightarrow NH_3\ (g,\ air)$$

There is a proportional relationship between the partial pressure of gaseous ammonia, NH_3 (g) and the NH_3 (l) concentration. The volatilization of ammonia from manure to air is called the mass flux. This flux is the product of the differences in partial pressure between the two media and a mass transfer coefficient. The flux is increased by higher partial pressure difference. Increasing air velocity increases the mass transfer coefficient (English *et al.*, 1980).

Dust

In confinement housing, the air quality parameters of primary concern include CO_2, H_2S, NH_3 and aerosolized particulates or dust. In poultry facilities, NH_3 is the most prominent contaminant (Reece *et al.*, 1981). In normal circumstances, CO_2 and H_2S concentrations are not likely to cause problems (McQuitty and Feddes, 1982). Dust has also been considered to be a serious contaminant (Lampman, 1982).

Guidelines on acceptable concentrations of dust in poultry environments have not been established. Donham (2000) introduced that threshold concentrations were as follows: 2.5 mg/m^3 total dust, 2.5 mg/m^3 respirable dust, 600 EU/m^2 endotoxin, and 12 ppm ammonia. The USEPA is concerned most about particulate matter (PM) in the sizes of ten micrometers or less (PM 10) and two and a half micrometers or less (PM 2.5). The smaller particles lodge more easily in the lungs. In agriculture, PM originates from manure particles (e.g., blown from poultry fans or stirred up in feedlots), exhaust from engines in machinery and equipment, feed particles, bedding materials, animal dander, feather particles, road dust, field dust raised by wind and equipment (Van Kley, 2002). If these particles were of a size that could reach the lungs, then they would serve as a vehicle to increase ammonia's impingement in the pulmonary region.

Hartung and Rokicki (1984) performed analyses for phenolic compounds in the dusts from pig and poultry (layer) houses. All the dusts contained phenol, p-cresol, indole and skatole. In addition, the poultry dust contained L,6-dimethyl phenol and 3,4-dimethyphenol (Hammond *et al.*, 1981). McQuitty *et al.* (1985) found out that the combination of dust and NH$_3$ concentration found in the environment in Barn B of their study in particular would appear to represent a substantial challenge to the birds respiratory system. Odor travels attached to particles and odorous compounds tend to be carried on dust particles (Powers, 2002).

Williams (1989), using olfactometry and particle analyses, has examined the relationship between dust and odor in broiler house air. He found no significant change in odor concentration when dust was filtered out and no correlation between odor concentration and dust total mass or dust total surface area. The dust production for each age group with respect to environmental temperature tends to be much the same for all temperature for the birds in cages with no litter (Koon *et al.*, 1963). They reported these broilers raised on litter did produce more dust in most instances than similar birds raised in wire cages. With the birds raised on litter, there is a distinct decline in dust production at 32 ℃.

The chemical analysis showed that dust consisted of dry matter (92%), crude protein (60%), fat (9%), cellulose (4%) and ash as well as hydrocarbons. However, chemical analysis of broiler dust from floor of broilers revealed that it was higher in protein and lower in fat as compared with dust from hens raised on wire. The chemical analysis of dust produced by laying hens revealed no significant differences in composition because of environmental temperature (Koon *et al.*, 1963).

MINIMIZING POLLUTION AND ODOR IN THE POULTRY INDUSTRY

Reducing pollution from the poultry industry must concentrate on lowering N and P levels released into surface and ground waters, controlling odor by reducing release of ammonia gases and VFA, and eliminating the dust found in poultry houses. Much research has been done to attain these goals. There is no single method, however, to reduce the pollutants released from poultry farms and improve air and water quality in these areas. Research has concentrated on use of additives (Chemicals, enzymes, ash and vitamin D), diet manipulation, different types of litter, storage covers for manure, filter systems for removing dust and odor from poultry barns, ozone utilization and different manure land application techniques.

Chemicals

Additives are chemicals that are mixed with livestock waste to alleviate one or more of the problems previously discussed in this paper. Several types of additives have been investigated in the past three decades, but their effectiveness, especially those available as commercial products, has been debated (Ritter, 1989; Zhu et al., 1997a). Unfortunately information on the composition of commercial products, or their mode of action is not available because of confidentiality and is limited to the marketing literature supplied.

Ammonia volatilization from poultry litter is extremely dependent on litter pH. The pH of normal poultry litter is basic (8.0 to 8.5), and by adding acids to the litter, ammonia volatilization can be reduced (Groot Koerkamp, 1994). Many different acidifying agents have been studied to determine their effectiveness in reducing ammonia volatilization. And also precipitation of soluble P in manure and reducing P runoff are goals of adding chemical reagents to poultry manure. Many scientists have hypothesized that aluminum (Al), calcium (Ca) or iron (Fe) amendments would reduce ammonia volatilization and soluble P in manure and litter after mixing in these chemicals thoroughly (Table 1). Cooke et al. (1986) stated that aluminum sulfate (alum) removes phosphate from solutions by two different mechanisms, depending on the pH. Under acidic conditions (pH < 6), they indicated that $AlPO_4$ forms, whereas at pH 6 to 8 an $Al(OH)_3$ forms, which removes P from solution by sorption of inorganic phosphate and entrapment of organic particles containing P. Possible mechanisms (Ripley, 1974) for the reduction in soluble P with Al, Ca and Fe chemicals are:

1. $Al_2(SO_4)_3 \cdot 14H_2O + 2H_2PO_4 \longrightarrow 2AlPO_4 + 6H^+ + 3SO_4^{2-} + 14H_2O$

2. $Fe_2(SO_4)_3 \cdot 2H_2O + 2P_4^{3-} \longrightarrow 2FePO_4 + 3SO_4^{2-} + 2H_2O$

3. $5Ca(OH)_2 + 3H_2PO_4^- + 3H^+ \longrightarrow Ca_5(PO_4)_3OH + 9H_2O$

4. $Al(OH)_3 + H_3PO_4 \longrightarrow Al(OH)_3\text{-}H_3PO_4$

Table 1. Summary of the effectiveness of additives in reducing NH_3 emission and soluble P in chicken manure.

Name of Chemical	Amount to be Added	Pollutant to be reduced		Types of Waste	Authors	Comments
		NH_3 emission	Soluble P			
Thipectin Zinc bacitracin	100mg/kg manure 100mg/kg manure	84% (50µl/l) 49% (160µl/l)		Poultry manure	Kitai and Arakawa(1979)	The amount of NH_3 emission in basal diet was 30µl/l at 5 wks
Clinoptilolite	5kg m^{-3} (as adsorbents)	35%		Broiler litter	Nakau et al. (1981)	Application directly to the litter appears to be more effective in reducing NH_3 emission than feed
Aluminum sulfate Aluminum sulfate Ferrous sulfate	100g/kg litter 200g/kg litter 200g/kg litter	36% 99% 58%	77% (467mg P/kg) 95% (111mg P/kg) 74% (529mg P/kg)	Poultry litter	Moore, Jr., et al. (1995b)	Control group showed 14g N/kg litter and 2022mg P/kg litter
Aluminum sulfate Ferrous sulfate	1 : 5 (Both) = amendment : litter	87% (first runoff) 63% (second runoff) 77% (first runoff) 48% (second runoff)		Broiler litter	Shreve et al. (1995)	In the first runoff soluble content of litter alone was 83.0mgL^{-1}, while in second year runoff soluble P content of litter alone was 17.3mgL^{-1}
Aluminum sulfate Ferrous sulfate	130g/kg litter 130g/kg litter	95% (0.7g N/kg litter) 77% (3.31g N/kg litter)	31% (1.17g/kg) 56% (0.75g/kg)	Broiler litter	Moore, Jr., et al. (1996)	The amount of NH_3 emission and soluble P in control group was 14.4g N/kg litter and 1.70g/kg, respectively
Zeolites Acidified zeolites	38% (w/w) 38% (w/w)	37.5% (25g N/kg manure) 50% (20g N/kg manure)				The amount of NH_3 emission in control group was 40g N/kg manure.
Coir (mesocarp or coconut fruit)	20% (w/w)	5.7% (33g N/kg manure)		Poultry manure	Kithome et al. (1999)	35g N/kg manure
Coir	33% (w/w)	57% (15g N/kg manure)				
Calcium Carbonate (CaCl$_2$)	20% (w/w)	35% (26g N/kg manure)				40g N/kg manure
Aluminum sulfate	20% (w/w)	25% (30g N/kg manure)				
Aluminum sulfate	100lb/1000ft^{-2} (45.4kg/92.8m^2)	50% (both)		Broiler litter	Taylor (1999)	NH_3 emission of control group was 60 ppm, while NH_3 emission of chemical treatment group was 30 ppm.
Sodium bisulfate	93lb/1000ft^{-2} (42.2kg/92.8m^2)					
Aluminum sulfate	0.091kg/bird	75% (Ave. for 3yr)	73% (Ave. for 3yr)	Broiler litter	Moore, Jr., et al. (2000)	The NH_3 fluxes for 3yrs were about 75% lower for alum treated litter than for normal litter (2.14 vs. 8.27mg NH_3-N m^{-2} h^{-1}). 1st yr. -0.75 and 3.91mg P/l, 2nd yr. -2.04 and 7.94mg P/l, and 3rd yr. -1.70 and 7.69mg P/l for alum treated and control, respectively.

Oxidizing agents act to reduce odorant concentrations in livestock slurry and to disinfect, thereby inhibiting microorganisms from forming odorants. The oxidizing agents that have been most widely investigated are potassium permanganate ($KMnO_4$), hydrogen peroxide (H_2O_2) and ozone (O_3). The first report of an oxidizing agent reducing livestock odor was a 1% solution of $KMnO_4$ being highly effective for odor control on a cattle feedlot (Faith, 1964). During short-time tests (72 hours), Cole et al. (1976) found that $KMnO_4$ at concentrations of 500mg L^{-1} controlled pig slurry odor effectively. H_2O_2 was found to be effective at concentration of 50 and 100 mg L^{-1} in reducing H_2S and odor emissions from cattle slurry (Hollenbeck, 1971). Cole et al. (1976) reported that when H_2O_2 was applied at 500 mg L^{-1} to liquid pig slurry there were reductions in odor offensiveness (by 93%) and H_2S emissions (by 96%). Sodium hydroxide (NaOH) was found to be effective for controlling odors from poultry slurry, with 0.9% NaOH (w/v) controlling odor for 28 days (Burnett and Dondero, 1970).

Diet Manipulation

Since manure is a combination of urine and feces excreted from animals, the amount and composition of this manure varies with the original composition of the diet. The sources, forms and levels of dietary ingredients influence nutrient availability, excretion levels and forms. The efficiency of nutrient utilization in livestock and poultry operations are also influenced by feeding management practices.

Microbial metabolism in the digestive tract of the animal is responsible for odorous and gaseous compounds emitted immediately after excretion. More pronounced odors are produced during storage due to further decomposition and these odors majorly impact air quality. Dietary manipulation is a practical and economical method to control the initial point of source of nutrient excretion with reductions of N excretion of 28 to 29.14% seen (Gate, 2001; Jacob et al., 1994) and this would have a major effect on minimizing pollution of water, soil and air. Hobbes et al. (1996) demonstrated that reducing dietary protein concentration reduced several of the odorous compounds. Modifying gut pH and the use of agents which modify gut bacterial populations could prove to be helpful in reducing odors (van Heugten and van Kempen, 1999).

Reduction in nitrogen excreted in poultry waste may be achieved by lowering the amount of crude protein (CP) fed by supplementing diets with synthetic amino acids (AA). Nitrogen retention by the bird may be made more efficient by reducing the non-essential amino acid pool along with supplying a more "ideal" amino acid profile in the diet. As the crude portein levels were reduced from 22.5% to 16.6% (Waldroup, 2000), the body weigh gains, carcass N and fecal N concentrations were decreased. Addition of potassium sulfate to increase the dietary electrolyte balance did not affect performance of the birds fed the low CP diet. When synthetic AA were added to lower CP diets within (% units), there was no difference in performance. In addition, the tryptophan: large neutral amino acid (LNAA) did not affect any of the performance parameters. Increasing the AA level improved feed conversion, Waldroup (2000) concluded that there are still limitations to reducing the CP level of diets with the addition of synthetic AA for broilers. Gates (2001) indicated that pens with birds fed the high CP diet exhibited significantly greater equilibrium NH_3 gas (69.6, 36.5, 20.6 and 7.4 ppm for the high, medium high, medium low and low, respectively). When dietary treatments consisted of for levels of CP: a conventional high CP diet (23% CP), a very low CP diet (16.3% CP) with supplemental essential amino acid (EAA), and two intermediate CP diets (20.77% CP for medium high and 18.53% CP for medium low) obtained by mixing the high and low CP diets in a 2:1 and 1:2 ratio, respectively. However, research has suggested that the ratio of essential AA (EAA) to non-essential AA (NEAA) in the diets may be important. Thirty-three to 45% of EAA to NEAA would be required with low CP diets to maintain bird performance (Bedford and Summers, 1988).

There is insufficient research with turkeys, ducks and layers on the reduction of crude protein and the addition of synthetic AA to reduce nitrogen excretion. Genetics are ever changing within individual poultry species and requirements for individual strain and yield-types are uncertain. Variations also exist in the feeding programs (ages or number of phases) used at different operations. Variability also exists in the availability of amino acids from different grain or feed byproducts, feed mixing uniformity and ingredient separation during feed handling. The additional amounts of N fed and subsequently excreted are mainly due to uncertainty of the bird's needs, ingredient pricing, ingredient variability and feed manufacturing constraints (Nahm, 2002). Also the main driving force behind the level of CP and supplemental AA fed to poultry in commercial operations has been feed nutrient availability and cost (Nahm, 2002).

Data for the P requirements of the broilers of today are very limited (NRC, 1994; Waldroup *et al.*, 2000a). The values proposed by the NRC (1994) do not reflect the changes in genetic make-up of current bird nor data from commercial situations. Angel *et al.* (2001) have emphasized a four-phase feeding system for broilers, which are starter, hatch to 18 d of age; grower, 18 to 32 d of age; finisher, 32 to 42 d of age; and withdrawal, 42 to 49 d of age. A series of three experiments (Angel *et al.*, 2000) were done using Ross 308 male broilers. These research projects showed that the nPP level in starter was 0.45%, in grower 0.36%, in finisher 0.18% and in withdrawal 0.14%. These represent a 5% reduction for growers, 15% reduction for finishers and an 40% reduction for the withdrawal period (40% of NRC requirement). The commercial levels tested were 0.43, 0.36. 0.32 and 0.28% in the starter, grower, finisher and withdrawal phases, respectively.

Excess dietary levels of P can be decreased by ingredient selection and variability. The bioavailability of monocalcium phosphate is relatively higher than dicalcium phosphate, while deflourinated phosphate has the lowest availability regardless of the reference (DeGroote and Huyghebaert, 1996). It has been shown that nPP and available P (aP) are not the same (Angel *et al.*, 2001). In corn, the nPP was 24% of the total P, but 29% was available for broilers (Van Der Klis and Versteegh, 1996). For soybean meal, 39% of the total P was nPP but 61% was available for broilers. P contents and availabilities are greatly affected by these variations among different sources of grain (Angel *et al.*, 2001).

New plant genotypes, such as high aP (HAP) corn, are being developed to lower the phytate P content (Angel and Applegate, 2001). HAP corn contains the same total P content as other corn, but only 35% of total P is phytase P versus 75 to 80% in other corn varieties. Studies in chicks have shown the P in HAP corn to be more available (Waldroup *et al.*, 2000a). The phytic acid content of soybeans can be reduced (Raboy and Dickinson, 1993), resulting in a concomitant decrease in phytic phosphorus from 70 to 24% of total P by breeding programs (Raboy *et al.*, 1985).

Many different factors influence the P requirement of broilers. Concentrations of calcium (Ca), Ca:total P, levels of P, vitamin D_3 and its metabolites, energy and protein concentrations are some of the dietary factors affecting P requirements. Other factors that should be considered include the P standard used (aP vs. nPP vs. total P) and the criteria used to determine the requirement (e.g., growth, bone mineralization, bone breakage strength, fecal P concentration or processing P plant losses). Requirements are also impacted by carry-over effects from earlier phases, age, sex, health status, environmental condition and breed of the broiler (Angel *et al.*, 2001).

Enzyme Addition

Enzymes are widely used in European pig and poultry diets. Feed enzymes are used in four major areas: 1) removal of anti-nutritional factors, 2) increasing digestibility of existing nutrients, 3) increasing digestibility of non-starch polysaccharides (NSP's) and 4) supplementing host endogenous enzymes (Classen, 2000). These four areas are related to ensure minimal nutrient output into the environment.

The addition of a specific enzyme (VegPro) alone or in combination with phytase has been found to improve the ideal digestibility of dry matter, protein

Table 2. The effect of enzyme supplementation on apparent ileal digestibility coefficient (%) (Rostango *et al.*, 2000)

Enzyme	Dry Matter	Crude Protein	Energy
Control	69.88	77.55	72.20
VegPro [*]	71.59	79.86	73.11
VegPro + phytase	72.73	80.36	73.66

[*] VegPro: a specific enzyme

and energy of corn/soya diets fed to chicks (Table 2). Phytase has long been known to improve the availability of phosphorus, but phytic acid also helps bird utilize many minerals and amino acids.

Worldwide enzyme supplements are utilized with wheat- and barley based diets for broilers and layers. N retention is enhanced by enzyme supplementation since the enzyme free up carbohydrate and fiber portions of many cereals and byproduct ingredients (Patterson, 2001). Soybean and canola meal, peas, beans and sunflower seeds are added to diets for their protein and energy levels. In these oilseeds and legumes, complex NPS are an integral part of the cell wall and protein remains encapsulated in this matrix, unavailable to birds. Selective enzymatic additions release these proteins and this results in increased amino acid availability. Enzymes also regulate ingredient anti-nutritional factors which improve protein digestibility and reduce N excretion (Patterson, 2001). These anti-nutritional factors include trypsin inhibitors in soybeans, lectin in legumes, tannins in sorghum, NSP and phytate phosphorus which can negatively effect digestion and use of amino acids. Strategic use of dietary enzymes improves nutrient digestibility and reduces N excretion (Patterson, 2001). When N excretion is reduced, this can contribute to reduce ammonia losses in air, ammonia-N in surface water and formation of nitric acid which is one of the principle components of acid rain.

Most of the P (more than 60%) in plant ingredients of seed origin is in the form of phytate phosphorus (PP) (Nelson *et al.*, 1968; Reddy *et al.*, 1982). Absorption of phytate bound P by poultry involves the hydrolysis of the phytate bound P to inorganic P by a phosphatase enzyme (Table 3 & 4). Since the phytate P has low P availability, P requirements for poultry are met by addition of inorganic P sources. A wide variety of seeds such as rice, wheat, barley, corn, soybean and rye have phytase activity, but this activity is so low that it is not significant (Reddy *et al.*, 1982).

Using combinations of phytase, high available P corn and reductions in nPP for broilers reduced total P to 58%, soluble P to 17% and the soluble P to total P ratio to 12% of the values in normal diets (Sims *et al.*, 1999). Less total P needs to be fed to poultry and excretion of unabsorbed P can be reduced by improving

Table 3. Some recent research results on phytase addition and phosphorus requirements

References	Species	Amounts of phytase added	Types of phytase[1]	Amounts of P to be added	Reduced rates of P in excreted manure	Comments
Perney et al. (1993)	Broiler	750U/kg	Dry	0.38% aP[2] 0.44% aP	20% 16%	1. Each diet was fed to 4 groups of 8 chicks from 4 to 10 days of age. All excreta were collected from 3 groups during days 7 to 19. 2. 1 unit of phytase activity was the amount of enzyme liberating 1 μmol of inorganic P per min at 37.5°C.
Um and Paik (1999)	Hen (21 wks age)	500U/kg	Dry	0.37% TP[3]	41%	1. The quantity of enzyme required to produce 1 μ inorganic P/min from 5.1 mmol/L of sodium phytase at a pH of 5.5 and a water bath temp. of 37°C.
Kwon et al. (1999)	Broiler	300PU/kg (for starter) 500PU/kg (for finisher)	Dry	0.36% aP	Starter period : 17% Finisher period : 10%	1.1 PU of phytase is the quantity of enzyme which sets free 1 μ mol of inorganic P/min from 0.0015 mol/L sodium at pH 5.5 at 37°C.
Waldroup et al. (2000)	Broiler (0-3 wks age)	800U/kg	Dry	HAPC[4] in diet 0.45% nPP YDC[5] in diet 0.45% nPP	47% (HAPC in diet) 28% (YDC in diet)	1. The diets of HAPC and YDC were compared to the diet which was mixed with NRC (1994) diet as control.
Keshavarz (2000)	Pullets (0-18 wks age)	phytase 300U/kg	Dry	Levels of nPP in diet : 0-6 wks age 0.20% 6-12 wks age 0.15% 12-18 wks age 0.10%		1. The level of control group nPP was same nPP requirement of NRC (1994) for 0-6 wks age (0.4%), 6-12 wks (0.35%), and 12-18 wks age (0.30%). 2. The author wrote that did not help increase percentage or daily total P retention during phase 1 (wk 5) or phase 3 (wk 18). He wrote that beneficial effects of phytase on performance could have been due to increasing the digestibility and availability of other nutrients that might have been limiting in other diets.

Table 4 (Continued). Some recent results on phytase addition and phosphorus requirements

References Species	Amounts of phytase added	Types of phytase	Amounts of P to be added	Reduced rates of P in excreted manure	Comments
Zyla et al. (2001) Broiler	750FTU/kg (phytase) 3156U/kg (acid phosphatase) 1900U/kg (pectinase) 20g/kg (citric acid)	Dry	1.7g nPP[6]/kg 4.1g TP/kg 8.0g Ca/kg	56%	1.1 unit of phytase activity (FTU) was the amount of enzyme required to liberate 1 μM of inorganic phosphorus from 2mM sodium phytase in 1 min. under 40℃, pH 4.5. 2.1 unit of acid phosphatase (ACPU) was equal to 1 μM/min of p-nitrophenol liberated from 5.5mM disodium p-nitrophenol at 40℃, pH 4.5. 3.1 unit of pectinase (PGU) was the amount of enzyme which released 1.0 μM of reducing sugars from 0.7% apple pectin (degree of methylation 60%) per min under the above conditions.
Yan et al. (2001) Broiler (3-6 wks age)	800U/kg	Dry	Levels in nPP in the diets were increased from 0.10% through 0.45% with ratio of increase, 0.05%		1. At the lower P levels (> 0.25%), birds fed diets with phytase excreted less P than those fed diets without phytase. At higher P levels (< 0.25% nPP), little difference in fecal P was noted between birds fed diets with or without phytase. Thus, they wrote that addition of phytase alone, without commensurate reduction in dietary P, will not ameliorate P excretion.
Keshavarz (2003) Laying hen (20-63 wks age)	300U/kg	Dry	Levels of nPP in the diet were 0.25 (20-30 wk age), 0.2 (36-51 wk age), 0.15% (52-63 wk age) plus 300U/kg diet with control 0.45% (20-63 wk age)	55.6%	1. Natuphos 600 (BASF Corp., Mt. Olive, NJ) was used as the source of microbial phytase.

[1] All phytase were microbial; [2] aP: available phosphorus; [3] TP: total phosphorus; [4] HAPC: high available P corn; [5] YDC: yellow dent corn; [6] nPP: non-phytate phosphorus

the availability of phytate P. P availability and the effectiveness of phytase are also influenced by enzymes that break down structural components in plant materials (Zyla et al., 1995), feed particle size, intestinal pH, vitamin D metabolites and use of organic acids (Jongbloed and Jongbloed, 1996; Qian et al., 1997; Boling-Frankenbach et al., 2001). These factors are also known to interact.

There is a variety of sensitivity seen with the phytase sources on digestive activity. The most common source of phytase, Aspergillus niger phytase, is more resistant to proteolytic digestion than enzymes from plants such as wheat (Phillippy, 1999). Phytase A (a phosphotase with two pH optima of 2.5 and 5.0) resists trypsin digestion more but is more susceptible to pepsin than phytase B (with a pH optima of 2.5) (Zyla, 2000). A peptide with high phytase activity is produced by Escherichia coli (Rodriguez et al., 1999). Aspergillus fumigatus synthesizes a phytase shown by substrate specificity studies to be of a different type (Wyss et al., 1999).

Using Litter Materials in Manure

Poultry litter is a mixture of excreta, feed, feathers and bedding material. There are 4 different litter materials including wood products (pine shavings, sawdust, wood chips, wood by-product and tree bark), plant residues (rice hulls, bagasse, straw, corncobs and miscellaneous plant by-products), paper products and earth products (sand and miscellaneous earth products). Sawdust has replaced pine shavings in some areas. Regionally, rice hulls, straw, and peanut hulls can be found in use by poultry producers for litter. Sand and re-cycled paper products have received much research attention and development.

Snyder et al. (1958) reported on the different litters used as poultry bedding. Suitability as a bedding material varied by region, management system or type of poultry production. The bedding materials need to be very absorbent, have a reasonable drying time, and not be toxic to poultry or poultry growers. The material must also be cost competitive.

Concentrations of N (Gordillo and Cabrera, 1997), carbon (Reinertsen et al., 1999), hemicellulose (Lupway and Haque, 1998), and lignin (Melillo and Aber, 1982; Mueller et al., 1998), and ratios of chemical components such as C to N (Barbarika et al., 1985; Gordillo and Cabrera, 1997; Mueller et al., 1998), lignin to N (Mueller et al., 1998) and hemicellulose to N (Lupway and Haque, 1998) have all been shown to be correlated with rates of organic C or N mineralization. Composting of poultry manure results in a high potential for NH_3 volatilization since poultry waste has high N concentrations and low C/N ratios (Nahm, 2003b).

Ammonia emissions have been successfully minimized by some adsorbents, especially during the first few days of composting. Since poultry manure is a low C/N ratio material, it may be beneficial to add C to it when composting in order to immobilize some of the N. In poultry manure the N is readily decomposable and there are immediate losses of NH_3. The carbon sources are not as readily available so the adsorbents help to tie up some of the NH_4^+ and allow microbial populations to develop before NH_4^+ is inmobilized (Kithome *et al.*, 1999). However, factors have been found to affect the extent or occurrence of biological denitrification. Mature oat straw constitutes a less favorable substrate for denitrification than alfalfa hay and there was loss of N in decomposition of alfalfa, but not in decomposition of oat straw with plant material in shallow (3mm) layers and at two-thirds moisture saturation (Jansson and Clark, 1952). Kirchmann and Witter (1989) reported that increasing straw additions reduced N volatilization during aerobic decomposition. Straw caused no immobilization of N under anaerobic conditions. In aerobic manure, N was mainly bound in organic forms whereas in anaerobic manure about two-thirds of the N was in ammonium form. C/N ratios in the organic matter of anaerobic manure were higher (33.1-87.5) than in the aerobic manure (9.5-18.0) (Kirchmann and Witter, 1989).

The N to P ratio required by plants is 5:1 or greater but the ratios found in livestock or poultry manure is often 2:1 or less after substantial amounts of N are lost. This is the reason that N is no longer available to crops after application of the manure. Addition of carbon sources such as sawdust to manure on pen surfaces or during composting widens the carbon to N ratio and improves N retention. Lory *et al.*, (2002) reported that sawdust application resulted in the most N retention [9.6 kg N per steer vs. 5.5 kg for the control or 6.2 kg for the acid group (sulfuric acid)] from the pen surface in manure. They said the sawdust treatment reduced N loss 21% compared to the control without affecting animal performance and carcass characteristics. They hypothesized that most of the N lost during this trial was through volatilization of NH_3. However, Elwinger and Svensson (1996) reported that there were no differences concerning ammonia emission or N losses between litter beds in broiler houses based on straw or wood shavings and nor did the amount of litter type have any influence.

Total N losses from all types of manure during storage could be predicted from the C : N ratio of the manure (Kulling *et al.*, 2001). In this study, deep litter manure with the highest C : N ratio had the lowest emission rates of total N, ammonia and methane with intermediate values of nitrous oxide. Conditions found to be favorable for low N losses include C : N ratios above 25, temperatures below 50 C, dry matter contents of 250 g/kg, oxygen contents between 10 to 15% and air contents above 50% (Schucdardt, 1990; Maeda and Matsuda, 1997).

Manure Storage Covers

One of methods for controlling odors is by physical confinement. There are two types of covers, impermeable covers and permeable covers. The emission-reducing effect of the individual covers depends on the season and the type of slurry (de Bode, 1990).

Use of impermeable covers over manure storage areas prevents the release of odorous gases into the atmosphere by decoupling the air and solution interfaces. Emission rates are also unaffected by wind and radiation. Polyethylene covers range in price from $ 4.43 to $ 8.37 per sq. m, with the average of approximately $ 4.92 (Freese, 1997). Installation usually costs approximately $ 5.91 per sq. m. (Lorimor, 1998). These impermeable covers have been shown to have odor reduction efficiencies of 70 to 85% (Manneback, 1986). Covering manure storage areas with an impermeable plastic cover reduced dilution-to-threshold concentrations from 340 to 30; meaning that without the cover an odorous air sample requires 340 dilutions with odor-free air to be imperceptible, but with the cover only 30 dilutions are required (Lorimor, 1998).

Permeable covers or biocovers control odor by acting as biofilters on top of manure storage areas. Materials used as these covers include straw, corn stalks, peat moss, foam and Leka rock. Odor reduction occurs because the radiation onto the surface of the manure storage area is reduced and the wind velocity over the surface is also reduced. The cover allows the humidity at the surface/air interface to remain high and this creates a stabilized boundary that slows the emission rate of odorous volatiles. In the biocover an aerobic zone exists that allows the growth of aerobic microorganisms that utilize carbon, N and sulfur from the manure emissions. The odors emitted above the biocover are reduced by further degrading and making use of these compounds prior to use as a biocover. Odor was reduced 40 to 50% when straw was used as a biocover, 45 to 55% when foam pellets were used and up to 85% when a floating mat or corrugated material was used (Mannebeck, 1986). The cost of biocovers varies greatly depending on the material used and the method it is applied. The costs for straws or cornstalks is $ 0.10 per sq. m; for peat moss and foam it costs $ 2.56 per sq. m; and for Leka rock it costs $ 8.87 sq. m (Freese, 1997).

Filters for Dust and Odor Removal

The two main activities involving air emissions (air quality) are the poultry house and waste management processes. From the poultry house particulate matter, especially particulate matter 10 microns in diameter (PM10), are primarily emitted. From the waste management processes emission of NH_3, H_2S, N_2O and PM10 are the major pollutants (Saito, 2002).

Although filtering devices of dust in poultry houses have been proved to be ineffective or uneconomical (Koon et al., 1963), the effects of dust must also be considered. Odorous compounds in livestock building air can be adsorbed on to particles of dust (Hammond et al., 1979). Many odorous compounds attach to dust particles and by removing dust from the airstream, likewise, odor and gases may be removed (Wheeler, 2002). He said that gases may adsorb to filter materials. Biomass (inexpensive materials), like chopped straw, can be used as a biomass filter. They are a simple dust and gas traps that offers up to 80% reduction of dust and odor at low ventilation rates used during cold weather conditions (Hoff et al., 1997).

Dust particles carry odorous compounds (Powers, 2002). Housekeeping measures in poultry houses that reduce dust emissions are a strategy to reduce odors (Hartung and Rokicki, 1984). Practices that are used to reduce dust include filtration of exhaust air when it leaves the poultry housing, filtration of odorous air before it leaves the property line, use of impermeable barriers that arrest particle transport and reduction of odorous compounds with in the housing environment. When 65% of particles between 5 and 10 um and 80% of particles larger that 10 um are trapped from animal housing areas, the odor dilution threshold is reduced 40-70% (Hoff et al., 1997).

In poultry houses, dust concentrations varied from 0.02 to 81.33 mg/m^3 for inhalable dust, and from 0.01 to 6.5 mg/m^3 for respirable dust (Ellen et al., 2000). Poultry houses with caged laying hens showed the lowest dust concentrations (less then 2 mg/m^3) while concentrations in perchery or aviary systems were often four to five times higher. A 50 to 65% reduction in inhalable dust concentrations was achieved in an aviary system by spraying water with 10% oil (Ellen et al., 2000).

A safe maximum threshold value for inhalable and respirable dust concentrations in poultry houses for working people is difficult to establish. There are limited direct and acute effects of dust, while severe effects in the long run are known for poultry farmers. There are no regulations yet, but they are expected in the future.

Ozone to Reduce Odor and Pathogen

Ozone is a very powerful oxidizing agent and biocide that has been used to treat drinking water for almost 100 years (Debevec, Jr., 1990). Ozone generally is used to freshen the air in offices and industrial facilities but due to the toxic nature of ozone, there is opposition to its use indoors (Watkins et al., 1997; Wu et al., 1998). Because of its strong oxidizing properties, ozone has the potential to break numerous chemical bonds of toxic compounds (Wu et al., 1998), steroidal compounds (Shore et al., 1993), drug residues (Shore et al., 1993) and odorous metabolites (Wu *et al.*, 1999).

Ozonation of stored swine manure slurry at dose levels ranging from 0.25-1.00 g/L effectively reduced the concentrations of the volatile phenolic and indolic metabolites, commensurating with a significant reduction of the malodor (Wu *et al.*, 1999). While the volatile phenolic and indolic metabolites in air dried caged layer manure was not determined, the volatile fatty acid concentrations were not affected with ozonation over 15, 30 and 60 minutes (Kim-Yang *et al.*, 1999). There was also no appreciable change in the ammonium ion concentration in the ozonated caged layer manure in comparison to the control untreated manure (19.33 mg/g vs. 22.2 mg/g, respectively) (Kim-Yang *et al.*, 1999).

Data from studies on reducing the number of E. coli and controlling malodors in ozonated poultry houses is not yet available. Since dust particles are major carriers of odorants from poultry facilities (Hartung and Rokicki, 1984), it may be beneficial to control odors through ozonation since reductions in dust particles and *E. coli* have been observed in swine facilities with ozonation of air. Yokoyama and Masten (2000) reported interesting results about ozonation for layers and broilers. Increases in feed and water consumption compared to the control, a slight improvement in gain to feed ratio, a 25% decrease in ammonia levels in the chicken house, and increases in total egg production and improved hatch were all noted. Treating poultry manure potentially eliminates steroidal compounds and drug residues in ground water and surface run-off water. There are few studies, however, which have examined the actual effectiveness and dose rates necessary for such remediation (Yokoyama and Masten, 2000). Currently high installation and energy cost inhibit installation of equipment for ozonation.

Land Application

Manure is an excellent source of major plant nutrients, such as N, P, an potassium (K). Land-applied poultry manure can be a valuable source of nutrients and is know to increase yields of fescue grass (Vandepopuliere *et al.*, 1975; Quisenberry *et al.*, 1980) and corn (Wengel and Kolega, 1972; Weil *et al.*, 1979).

Broiler and layer data presented in Asman (1992) indicated that the ammonia emissions, in kg/animal/year, is at least double during conventional spreading events than it is for the combined emissions from housing and manure storage. However, ammonia losses were consistently reduced with slurry applied by different techniques compared to the conventional methods. Frost (1994) demonstrated large reductions in NH_3 emission from careful placement of slurry in narrow bands (60% reduction), compared with conventional surface application, in small scale plot experiments. Field research has shown 90% reduction of odor and ammonia volatilization with shallow or deep injected manure versus surface application (Phillips *et al.*, 1988). The limited data available from experiments carried out under UK conditions suggest that shallow injection abatement methods may not be so effective (Misselbrook *et al.*, 1996; Pane and Misselbrook, 1997). Smith *et al.* (2000) reported that the overall reduction in NH_3 emissions provided by the band-spread, trailing shoe and shallow injection techniques was 39, 43, and 57% relatively to conventional surface broadcast application. Generally, solid or treated manure is less offensive than liquid application. Additionally, solid manure incorporation has not traditionally been done since it requires tillage equipment to follow manure application (Wheeler, 2002).

Slurry land application techniques offer great potential for cost-effective abatement. Also land application of poultry manures like other animal manures can help mitigate potentially negative consequences of rising atmospheric CO_2 on the global climate by contributing to greater sequestration of carbon in the soil. Methane is a significant contributor to global warming and animal agriculture is a significant contributor of methane emissions globally.

There are environmental risks associated with land application of animal manures including potential pollution from the organic materials, nutrients and pathogenic microorganisms. Soluble contaminants in runoff or insoluble pollutants carried on soil particles during soil erosion events are the primary sources of surface water contamination. Ground water is contaminated with nitrates by percolation, seepage and direct infiltration. The most common pollutant associated with animal wastes are nutrients. These nutrients are responsible for eutrophication and low dissolved oxygen levels, especially in estuaries where N is more limiting than P for algal growth (Sharpley *et al.*, 1994). High concentrations of ammonia may be toxic to fish (Daniel *et al.*, 1994).

In normal poultry manure and litter, the N to P ratio is generally 2 or less. Plants use roughly 8 times more N than P. Therefore, when annual applications of manures are applied on an N basis, the level of P build up in the soil to cause harmful levels in fields that receive repeated applications (Huneycuttet *et al.*, 1988; Soil Conservation Service, 1992).

Fly Ash

"Fly ash" is the residue of coal combustion in power plant and may be an alternative for use in reducing the solubility of P in manure. The composition of this material depends on coal and combustion conditions (Roy and Griffin, 1982), and it is produced in large quantities due to increased use of coal in power production.

Treated manure having reduced soluble P concentrations would have N and P nutrient ratios more in balance with plant nutritional needs than untreated manures when land-applied (Stout *et al.*, 1998). According to the report of Dao (1999), caliche, alum and fly ash reduced water-extractable P in stockpiled manure by 21, 60 and 85% and by 50, 83 and 93% in composted manure at the 0.1 kg/kg rate. Mixing these amendments with feedlot manure widened the effective manure N/P ratio by a factor ranging from 1.5 to 18. And applying fly ash-treated stockpiled or composted manure reduced all extractable P fractions from amended soils although alum and calithe consistently reduced the water-extractable P fraction only. In the above research (Dao, 1999), appropriate amount of alum [$AL_2(SO_4)_3$ · 18 H_2O, reagent grade, Fisher Scientific], powdered caliche and class C fly ash obtained from a local power generation plant were added (0, 0.10, 0.25 or 0.50 kg/kg) to the manures and redistributed uniformly by stirring and shaking. Little research has been done about fly ash and P solubility in poultry manure, while different responses for fly ash and P solubility in dairy and swine manure may still be found. Future research should address fly ash and P solubility in poultry manure.

Vitamin D and its Metabolites

Phosphorus transport mechanisms in the intestine are stimulated by vitamin D (Mohammed *et al*, 1991; Biehl and Baker, 1997) and vitamin D also enhances phytase activity. Phytase activity has also been shown to be enhanced by vitamin D and its metabolites, 25 OH D_3 and 1,25-dehydroxycholecalciferol [1,25 (OH)$_2$ D_3].

Addition of 5ug of 1,25 (OH)$_2$ D_3/kg to a corn-soybean meal diet deficient in P increased phytate P retention from 31 to 68% (Edwards, Jr., 1993). The phytate P retention was further increased to 79% by the additional supplementation of 75 units phytase/kg of diet. Applying these results to poultry, swine and cattle may provide considerable relief to the problem of environmental contamination with phosphorus.

CONCLUSION

The poultry industry needs to reduce the N and P content of poultry wastes in order to reduce contamination of ground and surface waters, improve the air quality through odor and ammonia control and reduce the dust in poultry houses. Chemical additives containing Ca, Al or Fe are applied to reduce N and P contents in waters. Dietary manipulation reduces the amount of N and P excreted into manure. Enzyme supplementation improves digestibility and inhibits factors that reduce digestibility. Manure additives with high carbon contents such as sawdust alter the C : N ratio of the manure and reduce NH_3 emissions. Covers are used over liquid manure storage area to reduce odors. Utilization of filter systems in poultry barns reduces dust and NH_3 levels. Ozone in poultry barns results in lowered odor levels and eliminates pathogens. Mixing fly ash with manure prior to land application decreases the soluble P content in runoff. Addition of vitamin D improves phytate P availability in grain and phytase activity which enhances phosphorus utilization from the feed and decreases P content in manure. Although research with these methods is ongoing, combinations of these methods would maximize their effectiveness.

ACKNOWLEDGMENTS

This research was supported by the Taegu University Research Grant, 2003. The author thanks them for their partial financial support.

REFERENCES

Angel, R. and Applegate, T.J. 2001. Feeding strategies to reduce phosphorus output in broilers. In *Proceedings of Midwest Poultry Federation*, Minneapolis, MN, USA. pp. 149-157.

Angel, R., Applegate, T.J. and Christman, M. 2000. Effect of dietary non-phytate phosphorus (nPP) on performance and bone measurements in broilers fed on a four-phase feeding system. Poultry Sci. 79 (Suppl. 1), 21.

Angel, R., Dhandu, S.D., Applegate, T.J. and Christman, M. 2001. Non-phytin phosphorus requirement of broilers fed on a four-phase feeding program. In *Addressing Animal Production and Environmental Issues*, Oct.3-5, 2001. Sheraton Imperial, Research Triangle Park, NC, USA pp. 416-427.

Arogo, J., Westerman, P.W., Heber, A.J., Robarge, W.P. and Classen, J.J. 2001. Ammonia produced by animal operations. In *Addressing Animal Production and Environmental Issues*, Oct. 3-5, Sheraton Imperial, Research Triangle Park, NC, USA. pp. 278-293.

Asman, W.A.H. 1992. Ammonia emission in Europe updated emission and emission variation. Report 228471008, National Institute of Public Health and Environmental Protection (RIVM), Bilthoven, The Netherlands.

Barbarika, A., Jr., Sikora, L.J. and Colacicco, D. 1985. Factors affecting the mineralization of nitrogen of sewage sludge applied to soils. Soil Sci. Soc. Am. J. 49, 1403.

Barnett, G.M. 1994a. Phosphorus forms in animal manure. Bioresour. Technol. 19, 139.

Barnett, G.M. 1994b. Manure P fraction. Bioresour. Technol. 19, 149.

Bedford, M.R. and Summers, J.D. 1988. The effect of the essential to nonessential amino acid ratio on turkey performance and carcass composition. Can. J. Anim.

Sci. 68, 899.

Biehl, R.R. and Baker, D.H. 1997. 1 Alfa - hydroxychole-calciferol does not increase the specific activity of intestinal phytase but does improve phosphorus utilization in both cacectomized and sham operated chicks fed cholecalciferol-adequate diets. J. Nutr. 127, 2054.

Boling-Frankenbach, J.L., Snow, S.D., Parsons, C.M. and Baker, D.H. 2001. The effect of citric acid on the calcium and phosphorus requirements for chicks fed corn-soybean meal diets. Poultry Sci. 80, 783.

Bromfield, S.M. 1960. Sheep faeces in relation to the phosphorus cycle under pastures. Aust. J. Agric. Res. 12, 111.

Burkholder, J.A. and Glasgow, H.B. Jr., 1997. *Pfiesteria piscicidia* and other *pfiesteria-dinoflagellates* behaviors, impacts, and environmental controls. Limnol. Ocean. 42, 1052.

Burnett, W.E. and Dondero, N.C. 1970. Control odor from animal wastes. Transactions of the ASAE. pp. 221-224.

Carlile, F.S. 1984. Ammonia in poultry houses: A literature review. World's Poultry Sci. J. 40(20), 99.

Chavez, C., Niemeyer, T.P., Reynolds, P.L., Russo, R.A., Lacey, R.E. and Carey, J.B. 2001. The impact of methionine source on poultry fecal matter odor volatiles. In: Addressing Animal Production and Environmental Issues, Oct. 3-5, Sheraton Imperial, Research Triangle Park, NC, USA pp. 54-58.

Cheremisinoff, P.E. and Young, R.A. 1975. *Industrial Odor Technology Assessment.* Ann. Arbor Science Publishers, Ann Arbor, MI, USA.

Classen, H.L. 2000. *Exogenous Enzyme Use in Animal Feeding.* 2000-01 Direct-Fed Microbial, Enzyme and Forage Additive Compendium. The Miller Publishing company.

Cole, C.A., Bartlett, H.D., Buckner, D.H. and Younkin, D.E. 1976. Efficacy of certain chemical and biological compounds for control of odor from anaerobic liquid swine manure. J. Anim. Sci. 42, 1.

Cooke, G.D., Welch, E.B., Peterson, S.A. and Newroth, P.R. 1986. *Lake and Reservoir Restoration.* Butterworths, Ann Arbor Science Book, Boston, MA, USA.

Daniel, T.C., Sharpley, A.N. Edwards, D., Wedepohl, R. and Lemunyon, J.L. 1994. Minimizing surface water entrophication from agriculture by phosphorus management. J. Soil Water Conserv. 49, 30.

Daniel, T.C., Sharpley, A.N. and Lemunyon, J.L. 1998. Agricultural phosphorus and eutrophication: A symposium overview. J. Environ. Qual., 27, 251.

Dao, T.H. 1999. Coamendments to modify phosphorus extractability and nitrogen/phosphorus ration in feedlot manure and composted manure. J. Environ. Qual. 28, 1114.

Debevec, L., Jr. 1990. A review of ozone generating facilities in some US water and waste water treatment plants. Ozone: Science and Engineering. J. Inter. Ozone Assn. 5, 103.

de Bode, M.J.C. 1990. A comparison of ammonia emission from different types of liquid slurry storage system. In *Ammoniak in der Umwelt*. eds Hartung, J., Paduch, M., Schirz, S., Dohler, H. and van den Weghe, H.. Landwirtschaftsverlag GmbH, Munster, Germany. pp. 43. 1-13.

De Goote, G. and Huyghebaert, G. 1996. The bio-availability of phosphate from feed phosphates for broilers as influenced by bio-assay methods, dietary calcium level, and feed form. Anim. Feed Sci. and Tech. 69, 329.

De Winkel, K. 1988. *Emission Factors of Ammonia for Livestock Farming*. Publicatiereeks Lucht 76, Ministerie van VROM, Leidschendam, The Netherlands. pp. 59.

Doham, K.J. 2000. Occupational health hazards and recommended exposure limits for workers in poultry buildings. In *Proceedings 2000 National Waste Management Symposium*. eds Blake, J.P. and Patterson, P.H., Auburn University Press, Auburn, AL, USA. PP. 92-109.

Donham, D., Haglind, P., Peterson, Y., Rylander, R. and Belin, L. 1989. Environmental and health studies of farm workers in Swedish confinement buildings. Br. J. Ind. Med. 46, 31.

Dou, Z., Toth, J.D., Galligan, D.T., Ramberg, Jr., C.F. and Ferguson, J.D. 2000. Laboratory procedures for characterizing manure phosphorus. J. Environ. Qual. 29, 508.

Edwards, H.M., Jr. 1993. Dietary 1,25-dihydroxycholecalciferol supplementation increases natural phytate phosphrus utilization in chickens. J. Nutr. 123, 567.

Edwards, D.R. and Daniel, T.C. 1992. Environmental impacts of on-farm poultry waste disposal- A Review. Bioresour. Technol. 41, 9.

Ellen, H.H., Bottcher, R.W., von Wachenfelt, E. and Takai, H. 2000. Dust levels and control methods in poultry houses. J. Anim. Sci. and Health 45, 33.

Elliot, H.A, and Collins, N.E. 1982. Factors affecting ammonia release in broiler houses. Transactions of the ASAE 25, 413.

Elliot, H.A. and Collins, N.E. 1983. Chemical methods for controlling ammonia release from poultry manure. ASAE, paper 83-4521. pp. 17.

Elwinger, K. and Svensson, L. 1996. Effect of dietary protein content, litter and drink type on ammonia emission from broiler houses. J. Agric. Engng. Res. 64, 197.

English, C.J., Miner, J.R. and Koelliker, J.K. 1980. Volatile ammonia losses from surface-applied sludge. J. Water Poll. Con. Fed. 52(9), 2340.

Faith, W.L. 1964. Odor control in cattle feed yards. J. Air. Pollut. Control Assoc. 1411, 459.

Foth, H.D. 1990. *Fundamentals of Soil Science*, 8th ed., John Wiley & Sons, Toronto, Canada. pp. 360.

Foy, R. H. and Withers, P.J.A. 1995. The contribution of agricultural phosphorus to eutrophication. The Hort. Soc. Proc., 365, 1.

Freese, B. 1997. Side by side: Manure storage covers. Successful Farming, Setpember. pp. 40-42.

Frost, J.P. 1994. Effect of spreading method application rate and dilution on ammonia volatilization from cattle slurry. Grass and Forage Sci. 49, 391.

Gates, R.S. 2001. Ammonia volatilization as affected by broiler litter rewetting and dietary manipulation. In *Addressing Animal Production and Environmental Issues*, Oct. 3-5, 2001. Sheraton Imperial, Research Triangle Park, NC, USA. pp. 372-383.

Gordillo, R.M. and Cabrera, M.L. 1997. Mineralizable nitrogen in broiler litter. I. Effect of selected litter chemical characteristics. J. Environ. Qual. 26, 1672.

Groot Koerkamp, P.W.G. 1994. Review on emissions of ammonia from housing systems for laying hens in relation to sources, processes, building design and manure handling. J. Agric. Engng. Res. 59, 73.

Groot Koerkamp, P.W.G., Metz, J.H.W., Uenk, G.H., Phillips, V.R., Holden, M.R., Sneath, R.W., Short, J.L., White, R.P., Hartung, J., Seedorf, J., Schroder, M., Linkert, K.H., Pedersen, S., Takai, H., Johnsen, J.O. and Wathes, C.M. 1998. Concentrations and emissions of ammonia in livestock buildings in Northern Europe. J. Agric. Engng. Res. 70, 79.

Groot Koerkamp, P.W.G., van Middelkoop, J.H. and Ellen, H.H. 2001. Air quality management and requirements in Europe. In *Addressing Animal Production and Environmental Issues*, Oct. 3-5, Sheraton Imperial, Research Triangle Park, NC, USA. pp. 72-79.

Hammond, E.G., Fedler, C. and Junk, G. 1979. Identification of dust-borne odours in swine confinement facilities. Transactions of the ASAE 22(5), 1186.

Hammond, E.G., Fedler, C. and Smith, R.J. 1981. Analysis of particle-borne swine house odours. Agric. and Environ. 6, 395.

Harper, R., Bate Smith, E,C. and Land, D.G. 1968. *Odour Detection and Odour Classification*. American Elsevier Science Publication Co., New York, NY, USA.

Hartung, J. and Phillips, V.R. 1994. Control of gaseous emissions from livestock buildings and manure stores. J. Agric. Eng. Res. 57, 173.

Hartung, J. and Rokicki, E. 1984. The occurrence of phenolic compounds in the dust of pig and hen houses. Zbl. Bakt. Hyg., I. Abt. Orig B179. pp. 431-439.

Hobbs, P.J., Misselbrook, T.H. and Pain, B.F. 1997. Characterization of odorous compounds and emissions from slurries produced from weaner pigs fed dry feed and liquid diets. J. Sci. Food Agric. 73, 437.

Hobbs, P.J., Pain, B.F., Kay, R.M. and Lee, P.A. 1996. Reduction of odorous compounds in fresh pig slurry by dietary control of crude protein. J. Sci. Food and Agric. 71, 508.

Hoff, S.J., Dong, L., Bundy, D.S., Xin, H., Harmon, J. and Li, X. 1997. Odor removal using biomass filters. In *Livestock Environment V, Proceedings of the Fifth International Symposium*, Vol. 1. ASAE, St. Joseph, MI, USA. pp. 101-108.

Hollenback, R.C. 1971. Manure odour abatement using hydrogen peroxide. Rep. No. 5638-R. Food Machinery Corp., Princeton, NJ, USA.

Huneycutt, H.G., West. C.P. and Phillips, J.H. 1988. Response of Bermuda grass, tall fescue, and toll fescue-clover to broiler litter and commercial fertilizer. Bull. 913. Arkansas Agric. Exp. Stn., University of Arkansas, Fayetteville, Ar., USA.

Jacob, J.P., Blair, R., Bennett, D.C. Scott, T. A., and Newberry, R. C., 1994. The effect of dietary protein and amino acid levels during the grower phase on nitrogen excretion of broiler chickens. In Proceedings of Canadian Animal Science Meetings, Univ of Saskatchewan, Saskatoon, SK, Canada. p. 307.

Jansson, S.L. and Clark, F.E. 1952. Losses of nitrogen during decomposition of plant material in the presence of inorganic nitrogen. Soil Sci. Soc. Am. Proc. 16, 330.

Jongbloed, A.W. and Jongbloed, R. 1996. The effect of organic acids in diets for growing pigs on enhancement of microbial phytase efficacy. *Report ID-DLO No. 96009*. Lelystad, The Netherlands.

Jungbluth, T., Hartung, E. and Erose, G. 2001. Green house gas emissions from animal houses and manure stores. Nut. Cycling in Agrocosystems 60, 133.

Keshavarz, K. 2000. Reevaluation of nonphytate phosphorus requirement of growing pullets with and without phytate. Poultry Sci. 79, 1143.

Keshavarz, K. 2003. The effect of different levels of non-phytate phosphorus with and without phytase on the performance of four strains of laying hens. Poultry Sci. 82, 71.

Kim-Yang, H., Raman, H., Yokoyama, M.T. and Masten, S.J. 1999. The effect of ozonation on the formation of toxic by-products in swine manure. In *Proceedings of the 14th IOA World Congress*, Dearborn, MI, USA. Aug. 22-26. pp. 581-584.

Kingery, W.L. Wood, C. W., Delaney, D.P., Willians, J.C. and Mullins, G.L. 1994. Impact of long-term application of broiler litter on environmentally related soil properties. J. Environ. Qual. 23, 139.

Kirchmann, H. and Witter, E. 1989. Ammonia volatilization during aerobic and anaerobic manure decomposition. Plant and Soil 115, 35.

Kitai, K. and Arakawa, A. 1979. Effect of antibiotics and caprylohydroxamic acid on ammonia gas from chicken excreta. Br. Poult. Sci. 20, 50.

Kithome, M., Paul, J.W. and Bomke, A.A. 1999. Reducing nitrogen losses during simulated composting of poultry manure using adsorbents or chemical amendments. J. Environ. Qual. 28, 194.

Koon, J., Howes, J.R., Grub, W. and Rollo, C.A. 1963. Poultry Dust: Origin and composition. Agric. Engineering (November). pp. 608-609.

Kreis, R.D. 1978. *Control of animal production odors: the State-of-the-Art. EPA Environment Protection Technology Series*; EPA-600/2078-083. Ada, OK, USA. Environmental Protection Agency, Office of Research and Department.

Kulling, D.R., Menzi, H., Krober, T.F., Neftel, A., Sutter, F., Lischer, P. and Kreuzer, M. 2001. Emissions of ammonia, nitrous oxide and methane from different types of dairy manure during storage as affected by dietary protein content. J. Agric. Sci. 137, 235.

Kwon, K., Han, I.K., Sohn, K.S., Kwon, C.H., and Kwack, J.H. 1999. Effects of microbial phytse on performanceof broiler chicks fed corn-wheat-soy diets. Kor. J. Anim. Sci. 41(5), 519.

Lampman, W.P. 1982. *Analysis of Dust Particles and their Influence in a Livestock Environment*. Bull. 1-1982, Dept. of Agricultural Engineering, Univ. of Saskatchewan, Saskatoon, Sask., Canada. pp. 69.

Lander, C.H., Moffitt, D. and Alt, K. 1998. Nutrients available from livestock manure relative to crop growth requirements. USDA/NRCS. In *Proceedings 2000 National Poultry Waste Management Symposium*. ed. Bock, B.R.. Economic and technical feasibility of energy production from poultry litter. Auburn University Printing Service, Auburn University, AL 36849, USA. pp. 133-148.

Leinweber, P., 1996. Phosphorus fractions in soils from an area with high density of livestock production. Z. Pflanzeneraehr. Bodenkd. 159, 251.

Lorimor, J. 1998. *Iowa Odor Control Demonstration Project*: Synthetic Covers. Iowa State University Extention, Publication Pm-1754a, Ames, Iowa, USA.

Lory, J., Adams, J., Eghball, B., Klopfenstein, T. and Powers, J.F. 2002. Effects of adding sawdust and acidification for steers production. In *Sawdust Application May Reduce Nitrogen Losses from Dirt Feedlots*. ed. Lundeen, T.. 74(5), 9 & 11.

Lowe, P.D. 1995. Social issues and animal wastes: A European perspective: In *Proceedings of International Livestock Odor Conference*. Iowa State University, College of Agric., Ames, IA, USA.

Lupway, N.Z. and Haque, Z. 1998. Mineralization of N, P, K, Ca and Mg from sesbania and leucaena leaves varying in chemical composition. Soil Biol. Biochem. 30, 337.

Mackie, R.I., Stroot, P.G. and Varel, V.H.1998. Biochemical identification and biological origin of key odor components in livestock waste. J. Anim. Sci. 76, 1331.

Maeda, T. and Matsuda, J. 1997. Ammonia emissions from composting livestock manure. In *Ammonia and Odour Emissions from Animal Production Facilities, International Conference Proceedings.* eds Voermans, J.A.M. and Monteny, G.J.. Vinkeloord, the Netherlands. pp. 145-153.

Mannebeck, H. 1986. Covering manure storing tanks to control odour. In *Odour Prevention and Control of Organic Sludge and Livestock Control.* eds Nielson, V.V., Voorburg, J.H. and L'Hermite, P.. Elsevier Applier Science Publishers, London, UK. pp. 188-193.

McLeod, R.V. and Hegg, R.O. 1984. Pasture runoff quality from application of inorganic and organic nitrogen sources. J. Environ. Qual. 13, 122.

McQuitty, J.B. and Feddes, J.J.R. 1982. *Manure Gases and the Animal Environment Paper* presented at Joint Session, CSAE/CSA/CSAS, AIC Annual Conference, Vancouver, BC, Canada.

McQuitty, J.D., Feddes, J.J.R. and Leonard, J.J. 1985. Air quality in commercial laying barns. Can. Agric. Eng. 27, 13.

Melillo, J.M. and Aber, J.D. 1982. Nitrogen and lignin control of hardwood leaf litter decomposition dynamics. Ecology 63, 621.

Mennicken, L. 1999. Biobeds for laying hens - A contribution to environmental production. 1DG8 13, 12.

Merkel, J.A., Hazen, T.E., Miner, J.R. 1969. Identification of gases in a confinement swine building atmosphere. Transactions of the ASAE 12, 310.

Miner, J.R. 1974. Odors from confined livestock production. Environ. Prot. Technol. Ser. EPA-660/2-74-023 US Environmental Protection Agency, Washington, DC, 20460, USA.

Misselbrook, T.H., Laws, J.A. and Pain, B.F. 1996. Surface application and shallow injection of cattle slurry on grassland nitrogen losses, herbage yields and nitrogen recoveries. Grass and Forage Sci. 51, 270.

Mohammed, A., Gibney, M.J. and Taylor, T.C. 1991. The effect of dietary levels of inorganic P, calcium and cholecalciferol on the digestibility of phytate phosphorus by the chick. Br. J. Nutr. 66, 215.

Moore, P.A., Jr., Daniel, T.C., Edwards, D.R. and Miller, D.M. 1995b. Effect of chemical amendments ammonia volatilization from poultry litter. J. Environ. Qual. 24, 293.

Moore, P.A., Jr., Daniel, T.C., Gilmour, J.T., Shreve, B.R., Edwards, D.R. and Wood, B.H. 1998. Decreasing metal runoff from poultry litter with aluminum sulfate. J. Environ. Qual. 27, 92.

Moore, P.A., Jr., Daniel, T.C. and Edwards, D.R. 2000. Reducing phosphorus runoff and inhibiting ammonia loss from poultry manure with aluminum sulfate. J. Environ. Qual. 29, 37.

Moore, P.A., Jr., Daniel, T.C., Edwards, D.R. and Miller, D.M. 1996. Evaluating chemical amendments to reduce ammonia volatilization from poultry litter.

Poultry Sci. 75, 315.

Moore, P.A., Jr., Daniel, T.C., Wood, C.W. and Sharpley, A.N. 1995a. Poultry manure management. J. Soil Water Conserv. 50, 29.

Moss, B.A. 1996. A land awash with nutrients-the problem of eutrophication. Chem. Ind. 11, 407.

Mueller, T., Jensen, L.S., Nielsen, N.E. and Magid, J. 1998. Turnover of carbon and nitrogen in a sandy loam soil following incorporation of chopped maize plants, barley straw and blue grass in the field. Soil Boil. Biochem. 30, 561.

Nahm, K.H. 2002. Efficient feed nutrient utilization to reduce pollutants in poultry and swine manure. Crit. Review in Environ. Sci. Tech. 32(1), 1.

Nahm, K.H. 2003a. Bioavailability of phophorus in poultry manure. Avian and Poultry Biol. Reviews. (accepted). June.

Nahm, K.H. 2003b. Evaluation of the nitrogen content in poultry manure. World's Poultry Sci. J. 59, 73.

Nakau, H.S., Koelliker, J.K. and Pierson, M.L. 1981. Studies with clinoptilolite in poultry: II. Effect of feeding broilers and the direct application of clinoptilolite Zeolite on clean and reused broiler litter on broiler performance and house environment. Poultry Sci. 60, 1221.

National Research Council. 1994. Nutrient requirements of poultry. 9th revised edition. National Academy Press, Washington DC, USA.

Nelson, T.S., Ferrara, L.W. and Storer, N.L. 1968. Phytate phosphorus content of feed ingredients derived from plants. Poultry Sci. 47, 1372.

Neser, S., Depta, G., Stegbauer, B., Groaauer, A. and Schon, H. 1997. Mass balance of the compounds nitrogen and carbon in housing systems for laying hens. In *Proceedings International Symposium Ammonia and Odor Control from Animal Facilities.* eds Voermanus, J.A.M., Monteny, G.J., Rosmalen, 6.10-6.13, Vinkeloord. Eds Voermanus, J.A.M., Monteny, G.J., Rosmalen, The Netherlands. NVTL pp. 129-137.

Ni, J. 1997. Mechanistic models of ammonia release from liquid manure: A Review. J. Agric. Engng. Res. 72, 1.

NRC. 1979. Committee on odors from stationary and mobile sources. National Research Council, National Academy of Science, Washington, DC., USA.

O'Neill, D.H. and Phillips, V.R. 1992. A review of the control of odour nuisance from livestock buildings. 3. Properties of the odours substances which have identified in livestock wastes or in the air around them. J. Agric. Engng. Res. 53(1), 23.

Paerl, H.W. 1997. Coastal eutrophication and harmful algal blooms: Importance of atmospheric deposition and groundwater as "new" N and other nutrient sources. Limnol. Ocean Ogr. 42, 1154.

Pain, BF. And Misselbrook, T.H. 1997. Sources of variation in ammonia emission factors for manure applications to grassland. In *Nitrogen Emissions from Grasslands*. eds Jarvis, S.C. and Pain, B.F.. CAB International, UK. pp. 239-301.

Patterson, P.h. 2001. Greater scruting of poultry feeding and management practices. In *The 48th Maryland Nutrition Conference*, May 1-2. University of Maryland, College Park, Maryland 20742, USA. pp. 13-21.

Perney, K.M., Cantor, A.H., Straw, M.L. and Herkelman, K.L. 1993. The effect of dietary phytase on growth performance and phosphorus utilization of broiler chicks. Poultry Sci. 72, 2106.

Phillips, V.R., Pain, B.F. and Klarenbeek, J.V. 1988. Factors influencing the odour and ammonia emission during and after the land spreading of animal slurries. In *Volatile Emissions from Livestock Farming and Sewage Operation*. eds Nielsen, V.D., Voorburg, J.H. and Hermite, P.L.. Elsevier Applied Science, London, UK. pp. 123-145.

Phillippy, B.Q. 1999. Susceptibility of wheat and *Aspergillus nigar* phytases to inactivation by gastrointestinal enzymes. J. Agric. and Food Chem. 47, 1385.

Powers, W.J. 2002. Odor mechanisms and mitigation. In *Proceeding 2002 National Poultry Waste Management Symposium*. eds Patterson, P.H., Blake, J.P. and Roberson, K.D. Auburn University Printing Service, Auburn University, AL 36849, USA. pp. 11-17.

Powers, W.J., Van Horn, H.H., Wilkie, A.C., Wilcox, C.J. and Nordstedt, R.A. 1999. Effects of anaerobic digestion and additives to effluent or cattle feed odors and odorant concentrations. J. Anim. Sci. 77(6), 1412.

Preismann, T., Petersen, J., Frenken, A. and Schmitz, W. 1990. Nitrogen losses from chicken manure in different housing system. In *Ammoniak in der Umweit* eds Dohler, H. and Van der Wefhe, H., Proceedings Symposium, 10-12 October, Bundesforschungsan-stalt fur Landwirtschaft, Braunschweig Volkenrode, Germany. pp. 38.1-38.23.

Qian, H., Kornegay, E.T. and Denbow, D.W. 1997. Utilization of phytate phosphorus and calcium as influence by microbial phytase, cholecalciferol and calcium: total phosphorus ratio in broiler diets. Poultry Sci. 76, 37.

Quisenberry, V.L., Hegg, R.O., Reese, L.E., Rice, J.S. and Torrence, A.K. 1980. Management aspects of applying poultry or dairy manures to grasslands in the Piedmont region. In *Livestock Waste: A Renewable Resource. Proceedings of Fourth International Symposium on Livestock Wastes*. 177. St. Joseph, MI, USA: ASAE. pp. 170-173.

Raboy, V. and Dickinson, D.B. 1993. Phytic acid levels in seed of *Glycine max* and *G. Sojo* as influenced by phosphorus status. Crop Sci. 33, 1300.

Raboy, V., Hudson, S.J. and Dickinson, D.B. 1985. Reduced phytic acid content does not have an adverse effect on germination of soybean seeds. Plant Physiol. 79, 323.

Ravindran, V., Bryden, W.L. and Kornegay, E.T. 1995. Phytase: Occurences, bioavailability and implication in poultry nutrition. Poultry and Avian Bio. Rev. 6, 125.

Reddy, N.R., Sathe, S.K. and Salunkhe, D.K. 1982. Phytase in legumes and cereals. In Chichester Co. eds Mrak, E.M. and Stewart, G.F.. Academic Press, New York, NY, USA. pp. 1-19.

Reece, F.N., Lott, B.D.and Deaton, J.W. 1981. Low concentrations of ammonia during brooding decrease broiler weight. Poultry Sci. 60, 937.

Risse, M., Gaskin, J., Zhang, H., Gilley, J., Franzluebbers, A., Phil Campbell, J., Sr., Radcliffe, D. and Tollner, B. 2001. Land application of manure provides numerous benefits. In *Addressing Animal Production and Environmental Issues*, Oct. 3-5, Sheraton Imperial, Research Triangle Park, NC, USA. pp. 145-148.

Reinertsen, S.A., Elliott, L.F., Cochran, V.L. and Campbell, G.S. 1999. Role of available carbon and nitrogen in determining the rate of wheat straw decomposition. Soil Biol. Biochem. 16, 459.

Ritter, W.F. 1989. Odor control of livestock wastes: State-of-the-art in North America. J. Agric. Engng. Res. 42, 51.

Rodriguez, E., Porres, J.M., Han, Y. and Lei, X.G. 1999. Different sensitivity of recombinant *Aspergillus niger* phytase (r-phy A) and *Escherichia coli* pH 2.5 acid phosphatase to trypsin and pepsin in vitro. Ach. Biochem. Biophys. 365, 262.

Rostango, H.S., Tejedor, A.A., Albino, L.F.T. and Silva, J.H.V. 2000. Enzyme supplementation of corn/soya diets improves ileal digestibility of nutrients in broiler chicks. In *Biotechnology in the Feed Industry*. eds Lyons, T.P. and Jacques, K.A.. Nottingham Press, Nottingham, UK. pp. 175-182.

Roy, W.R. and Griffin, R.A. 1982. A proposed classification system for coal fly ash in multidisciplinary research. J. Environ. Qual. 11, 563.

Saito, M. 2002. Air permitting issues for livestock waste management. In *Proceedings 2002 National Poultry Waste Management Symposium*. eds Patterson, P.H., Blake, J.P. and Roberson, K.D.. Auburn University Printing Service, Auburn University, AL 36849, USA. pp. 153-159.

Schefferle, H.E. 1965. The decomposition of uric acid in built up poultry manure. J. App. Bact. 28, 412.

Schiffman, S.S. and Gatlin, C.A. 1993. Clinical physiology of taste and smell. Annu. Rev. Nutr. 13, 405.

Schindler, D.W. 1977. The evolution of phosphorus limitation in lakes. Science 195, 260.

Schulte, D.D. 1997. Critical parameters for emissions. In *Proceedings Ammonia and Odor Emissions from Animal Production Facilities*. eds Voermans, J.A.M. and Monteny, G.J., NVTL Publishing, Rosmalen, The Netherland. pp. 23-24.

Schuchardt, F. 1990. Ammoniakverluste bei der Kompostierung tierischer Exkremente. In *Ammoniak in der Umwelt*. Kreislaufe, Wirkungen, Minderung, Conference Proceedings, eds Hartung, J., Paduch, M., Schirz, S., Dohler, H. and Weghe, Van den. Darmstadt, Germany: KTBL. pp. 37.1-37.14.

Sharpe, R.R. and Harper, L.A. 1997. Ammonia and nitrous oxide emissions from sprinkler irrigation applications of swine effluent. J. Environ. Qual. 26, 1703.

Sharpley, A.N. 1996. Availability of residual phosphorus in manure soils. Soils Sci. Soc. Am. J. 60, 1459.

Sharpley, A.N. 1999. *Agriculture and Phosphorus Management: The Chesapeake Bay*. Lewis Publishers. Boca Roton, Fl., USA.

Sharpley, A.N., Chapra, S.C., Wedepohl, R., Sims, J.T., Daniel, T.C. and Reddy, K.R. 1994. Managing agricultural phosphorus for protection of surface waters: Issues and options. J. Environ. Oual. 23, 437.

Sharpley, A.N., Meisinger, J.J., Breeuwsma, A., Sims, T., Daniel, T.C. and Schepers, J.S. 1998. Impacts of animal manure management on ground and surface water quality. In *Effective management of animal wastes as a soil resource*. ed Hatfield, J.. Ann Arbor Press, Chelsea, MI, USA.

Sharpley, A.N. and Moyer, B. 2000. Phosphorus forms in manure and compost their release during stimulated rainfall. J. Environ. Qual. 29, 1462.

Shore, L.S., Harel-Markowitz, E., Gurevich, M. and Shemesh, M. 1993. Factors affecting the concentration of testosterone in poultry litter. J. Environ. Sci. Health A28(8), 1749.

Shreve, B.R., Moore, Jr., P.A., Daniel, T.C., Edwards, D.R. and Miller, D.M. 1995. Reduction of phosphorus in runoff from field-applied poultry litter using chemical amendments. J. Environ. Qual. 24, 106.

Simons, P.C.M., Versteegh, H.A.J., Jongbloed, A.W., Kemme, P.A., Slump, P., Bos, K.D., Wolters, M.G.E., Beudeker, R.F. and Verschoor, G.J. 1990. Improvement of phosphorus availability by microbial phytase in broilers and pigs. Br. J. Nutr. 64, 525.

Sims, J.T., Lavahum, M.F., Malone, G.W., Saylor, W.M. and Raboy, V. 1999. Effects of microbial phytase, high available phosphorus corn and dietary phosphorus level on broiler performance. 3. Effect on broiler litter composition. Poultry Sci. 78(Suppl. 1), 102.

Sims, J.T., Simgrd, R.R. and Joern, B.C. 1998. P losses in agricultural drainage: Historical perspective and current research. J. Environ. Qual. 27, 277.

Sims, J.T. and Wolf, D.C. 1994. Poultry manure management: Agricultural and environmental issues. Adv. Agron. 52, 1.

Sistani, K.R., Rowe, D.E., McGowen, S.L., Brink, G.E. and Miles, D.M. 2001. Impact of drying method, rearing temperature and dietary phosphorus level on broiler manure nutrient composition. In *Addressing Animal Production and*

Environmental Issues, Oct. 3-5, Sheraton Imperial, Research Triangle Park, NC, USA.

Smith, K.A., Chalmers, A.G., chambers, B.J. and Christie, P. 1998. Organic manure phosphorus accumulation, mobility and management. Soil Use Manage 14, 1.

Smith, K.A., Jackson, D.R., Misselbrook, T.H., Pain, B.F. and Johnson, R.A. 2000. Reduction of ammonia emission by slurry application techniques. J. Agric. Engng. Res. 77(3), 277.

Sneath, R.W., Holden, M.R., Phillips, V.R., White, R.R. and Wathes, C.M. 1996. An inventory of emissions of aerial pollutants from poultry buildings in the UK. In *International Conference on Air Pollution from Agricultural Operations*. Kansas City, Missouri, USA. pp. 45-61.

Snyder, J.M., Rowoth, O.A., Scholes, J.C. and Lee, C.E. 1958. *Profitable Poultry Management*. 23ed. 79-83.

Soil Conservation Service. 1992. Agricultural Waste Management Handbook. US Gov. Print. Office, Washington DC, USA.

Sonzogni, W.C., Chaora, S.C., Armstrong, D.E. and Logan, T.J. 1982. Bioavailability of phosphorus inputs to lakes. J. Environ. Qual. 11, 555.

Stout, W.L., Sharpley, A.N. and Pionke, H.B. 1998. Reducing soil phosphorus solubility with coal combustin by-products. J. Environ. Qual. 27, 111.

Sweeten, J.M., Jacobson, L., Heber, A.J., Schmidt, D., Lorimor, J., Westerman, P., Miner, J.R., Zhang, R., Williams, C.M., Auvermann, B.W. and Koziel, J. 2001. Odor mitigation for concentrated animal feeding operations: White paper and recommendations. In *Addressing Animal Production and Environmental Issues*, Oct. 3-5, Sheraton Imperial, Research Triangle Park, NC, USA. pp. 48-53.

Tamminga, S. 1992. Gaseous pollutants by farm animal enterprises. In *Farm Animals and the Environment*. eds Phillips, C. and Piggins, D. CAB International, Wallingford, UK. pp. 345-357.

Tayer, D. 1999. The litter treatment, litter management and the effects on ammonia release, performance, litter weight and number of darling beetles and flies. In *Litter Treatment, Composting May Provide Benefits to Broilers, Layers*, ed Dudley-Cash, W.A. Feedstuffs 71, 14 & 26.

Tufft, L.S. and Nockels, C.F. 1991. The effects of stress, *Escherichia Coli*, dietary EDTA and their interaction on tissue trace elements in chicks. Poultry Sci. 70, 2439.

Um, K.Y. and Paik, I.K. 1999. Effects of microbial phytase on performance, nutrient digestibility and phosphorus excretion in hens fed corn-soy diets. Kor. J. Anim. Sci. 41(5), 329.

USEPA. 1992. Anthropogenic methane emissions in the United States. Office of Air and Radiation, US Environmental Protection Agency, WashingtonDC, USA.

Vandepopuliere, j.M., Johannsen, C.J. and Wheaton, H.N. 1975. Manure from caged hens evaluated on fescue pasture. In Managing Livestock Wastes. Proceedings Third International Symposium on Livestock Wastes. St. Joseph, MI, USA: ASAE. pp. 269-270.

Van Der Klis, J.D. and Versteegh, H.A.J. 1996. Phosphorus nutrition in broilers. In *Recent Advances in Animal Nutrition*. eds Garnsworty, P.C., Wiseman, J. and Haresign, W.. Nottingham University Press, Nottingham, UK.

van der Molen, J., Beljaars, A.C.M., Chardon, W.J., Jury, W.A., and van Faassen, H.G. 1990. Ammonia volatilization from arable land after application of cattle slurry. II. Derivation of a transfer model. Neth. J. Agric. Sci. 38, 239.

van der Watt, H.V.H., Summer, M.E. and Cabrera, M.L. 1994. Bioavailability of copper, manganese and zinc in poultry litter. J. Environ. Qual. 23, 43.

van Heugten, E. and van Kempen, T. 1999. Methods may exist to reduce nutrient excretion. Feedstuffs 71(15), 12. April 26.

Van Kley, J.A. 2002. Air pollution issues for animal feeding. In *Proceeding 2002 National Poultry Waste Management Symposium*. eds Patterson, P.H., Blake, J.P. and Roberson, K.D. Auburn University Printing Service, Auburn University, AL 36849, USA. pp. 89-97.

Vogels, G.D. and Van der Drift, C. 1976. Degradation of purines and pyrimidines by microorganisms. Bacteriol. Reviews 40, 403.

Waldroup, P.W. 2000a. Feeding programs for broilers: the challenge of low protein diets. Feed Management 47, 119.

Waldroup, P.W., Kersey, J.H., Saleh, E.A., Fritts, C.A., Yan, F., Stillborn, H.L., Crum, R.C., Jr. and Raboy, V. 2000. Nonphytate phosphrus requirements and phosphorus excretion of broiler chicks fed diets composed of normal or high available phosphate corn with and without microbial phytase. Poultry Sci. 79, 1451.

Water Environment Federation. 1978. *Odor Control for Wastewater Facilities*. Manual of Practice No. 22. Water Pollution Control Federation, Washington DC, USA.

Watkins, B.D., Hengemuehle, S.M., Person, H.L., Yokoyama, M.T. and Masten, S.T. 1997. Ozonation of swine manure wastes to control odors and reduce the concentrations of pathogens and toxic fermentation metabolites. Ozone: Science and Engineering. J. Inter. Ozone Assn. 19, 425.

Weast, R.C., Astle, M.J. and Beyer, W.H. 1986. *Handbook of Chemistry and Physics*. 67th Edition. Florida: CRC Press, USA. pp. D-163.

Weil, R.R., Kroontje, W. and Jones, G.D. 1979. Inorganic nitrogen and soluble salts in a Davidson clay loam used for poultry manure disposal. J. Environ. Qual. 8, 86.

Wengel, R.W. and Kolega, J.J. 1972. Land disposal of poultry manure in relations to soil water quality and silage corn yield. Paper No. 72-957. ST. Joseph, MO, USA: ASAE. pp. 72-957.

Westerman, P.W. and Zhang, R.H. 1997. Aeration of livestock manure slurry and lagoon liquid for odor control: A review. App. Engin. Agric. 13(2), 245.

Wheeler, E.F. 2002. Overview of strategies to reduce emissions. In *Proceedings 2002 National Poultry Waste Management Symposium*. eds Patterson, P.H., Blake, J.P. and Roberson, K.D.. Auburn University Printing Service, Auburn University, AL 36849, USA. pp. 99-104.

Williams, A.G. 1989. Dust and odour relationships in broiler house air. J. Agric. Engng. Res. 44, 175.

Wu, J.J., Park, S., Hengemuehle, S.M., Yokoyama, M.T., Person, H.L., Gerrish, J.B. and Masten, S.J. 1999. The use of ozone to reduce the concentration of malodorous metabolites in swine manure slurry. J. Agric. Eng. Res. 72, 317.

Wu, J.J., Park, S., Hengemuehle, S.M., Yokoyama, M.T., Person, H.L. and Masten, S.J. 1998. The effect of storage and ozonation on the physical, chemical and biological characteristics of swine manure slurries. Ozone: Science and Engineering. J. Inter. Ozone Assn. 20, 35.

Wyss, M., Brugger, R., Kronenberger, A., Remy, R., Fimbel, R., Qesterhelt, G., Lehman, M. and van Loon, A.P.G.M. 1999. Biochemical characterization of fungal phytases (myo-inositol hexakisphosphate phosphohydrolases): Catalytic properties. App. Environ Microb. 65, 367.

Yan, F., Kersey, J.H. and Waldroup, P.W. 2001. Phosphorus requirements of broiler chicks three to six weeks of age as influenced by phytase supplementation. Poultry Sci. 80, 455.

Yokoyama, M.T. and Masten, S.J. 2000. Effectiveness of ozonation as a manure treatment. In *Proceedings 2000 National Poultry Waste Management System*. eds Blake, J.P. and Patterson, P.H., Auburn University Printing Service, Auburn University, AL 36849, USA. pp. 85-91.

Zhu, J., Bundy, D.S., Xiwei, L. and Rashid, N. 1997a. The hindrance in the development of additive products for swine manure odor control A review. J. Environ. Sci. Health. A. 32, 2429.

Zyla, K. 2000. Phytase applications in poultry feeding: Selected issues. XX World's Poultry Congress, Montreal, Canada. Aug. 20-24.

Zyla, K., Koreleski, J., Swiatkiewicz, S., Ledoux, D.R. and Piironen, J. 2001. Influence of supplemental enzymes on the performance and phosphorus excretion of broilers fed wheat-based diets to 6 weeks of age. Anim. Feed Sci. Tech. 89, 113.

Zyla, K., Ledoux, D.R., Garcia, A. and Veum, T. 1995. An in vitro procedure for studying enzymatic dephosphorilation of phytate in maise-soybean feeds for turkey poults. Poultry Sci. 74, 3.

Additives to reduce P excretion and P solubility in poultry and swine manure

*K. H. Nahm**

Feed and Nutrition Laboratory, College of Natural Resources, Taegu University Gyong San, 712-714, South Korea. E-mail: NahmKH@Daegu.ac.kr

Abstract: In the past 20 years, scientists have realized that environmental contamination by non-point source nutrients is a significant problem and its control is not easily managed. Manure phosphorus (P) was found to be a primary pollutant of surface water, so methods to reduce manure P runoff have been a research focus. This review concentrates on approaches developed to reduce the excretion of manure P and to reduce the soluble P content of manure by poultry and swine. Addition of phytase to poultry and swine diets reduces P excretion dramatically. For example, phytase addition lowered broiler manure P by 10-56%, hen manure P by 41%, growing-finishing pig manure P by 21-51%, and weaning-growing pig manure P by 20-25%. Phytase also improves the availability of other nutrients. Addition of vitamin D and its metabolites increases P retention by 31 to 79%, while use of this vitamin and its metabolites with phytase improved P retention by 79%. Further research is needed in the use of organic acids, probiotics and starch and their impact on manure P reduction. Dietary Ca: total P ratios in the range of 1.1:1 to 1.4:1 appear to provide the best efficiency of supplemental phytase and D_3 in broilers. Determination of dietary P requirements for each growth phase is vital, as well as accurate and quick measurement of P contents in feeds. Certain chemical reagents containing aluminum (Al), calcium (Ca) or iron (Fe) have been found effective in reducing the solubility of P when added to manure or litter. Research reports have shown that reagents containing aluminum reduced P solubility in manure by 39-100%. Compounds containing iron decreased P solubility by 48-95%, while calcium compounds reduced soluble P by 65%. Fly ash containing Al, Fe and Ca may also be used to lower soluble P content in manures.

(*Additional keywords*: manure phosphorus; poultry; swine; aluminum; calcium; iron; phytase; growth phase)

*Corresponding author. Present address: 25001 Cashel Bay Rd., Manhattan, IL 60442, USA. E-mail: KHNahm1@cs.com

Introduction

Rapid and concentrated growth of the animal industry has caused concerns in many countries with respect to water quality. Large amount of nutrients including phosphorus (P) in feeds were imported to a relatively small land area, creating an imbalance in nutrient distribution (CAST, 1996). Most of the P contained in feeds and consumed by animals is excreted in manure, which is then land applied locally. As a result of long term manure application at rates exceeding crop requirements for P, manure P accumulates in soils, contributing to elevated run off and leaching losses to waters (Kingery et al. 1994).

Phosphorus runoff losses are enhanced by increased manure application rate as well as higher rainfall intensity (McLeod and Hegg 1984; Edwards and Daniel 1993). High concentrations of P (14-76 mg P/L) were reported in runoff from pastures receiving poultry litter, most of which was dissolved inorganic P ($\approx$ 85%), with only a small amount of particulate P (Edwards and Daniel 1993). Dissolved inorganic P is directly available to algae (Sonzogni et al. 1982) and management practices used to decrease P runoff should focus on the bioavailable-P (BAP) load instead of the total P (tP) load.

A number of approaches have been undertaken to reduce potential P losses and the negative environmental impact. These methods may be subdivided into methods: (i) that reduce P excretions through feed management including utilization of phytase, addition of vitamin D metabolites and organic acids, maintaining proper Ca:P ratios with phytase and D_3, and dietary manipulation; (ii) methods that reduce P solubility in manure with chemical amendments and fly-ash. While some of these methods have been proven effective, their use is limited, primarily due to the cost and expertise required. In recent years, attention has focused on treatment methods as well as practical and economically viable to the farmers.

REDUCTION OF P EXCRETION THROUGH FEEDING MANAGEMENTS
Phytase
1. Definition of phytin and types of phytase
Phytic acid is a phosphorylated cyclic sugar alcohol (phosphorylated inositol). Phytate is the anion form of phytic acid, while phytin is the chelated form of phytate. Phytin is the primary storage form of phosphorus in plants (mainly in the seed), and this P is called phytin phosphorus (Angel 2003). The storage location

of phytin in the seed varies among species of plants. The P of phytin is not available to monogastric animals until released by a phytase enzyme. And phytin is complexed with proteins in legumes such as soybeans and is not located within a certain area of the seed (deBoland *et al.* 1975).

Absorption of phytate bound P by poultry and swine requires first the hydrolysis of the phytate bound P to inorganic P by a phosphatase enzyme (Table 1). Since the phytate P (PP) is largely unavailable, P requirements of poultry and swine are met by addition of inorganic P minerals. A wide variety of seeds such as rice, wheat, barley, corn, soybean and rye have phytase activity, but this activity is so low that it is not significant (Reddy *et al.* 1982). Improved availability of phytin P in corn-soybean meal diets fed to pigs was reported when exogenous microbial phytase was added to the diets (Cromwell *et al.* 1995). Using combinations of phytase, high available P (aP) corn and reductions in non-phytate P (nPP) for broilers reduced tP by 58%, soluble P by 17% and the soluble P to tP ratio by 12% as compared to control diets (Sims *et al.* 1999). Less total P needs to be fed to poultry and pigs, and excretion of unabsorbed P can be reduced by improving the availability of phytate P.

Worldwide, extensive work has been done to increase P availability in poultry and swine production (Cromwell *et al.* 1995; Kwon *et al.* 1995b; Van Der Klis and Versteegh 1996; Woldroup *et al.* 2000). Reduction of P excretion through adjusting Ca levels, available P, and Ca to available P ratios has been shown to be effective. When phytin chelates with Ca and other cations, it may form soluble complexes, especially at a low pH. The hydrolysis of phytin by phytase occurs when phytin is in solution (Van Der Klis and Versteegh 1996). Phosphorus availability and the effectiveness of phytase are influenced by enzymes that break down structural components in plant materials (Zyla *et al.* 1995), feed particle size, intestinal pH, vitamin D metabolites and use of organic acids (Jongbloed and Jongbloed 1996; Qian *et al.* 1997; Boling-Frankenbach *et al.* 2001). PP utilization by chicken can be as low as zero to 15% (Nelson 1976; Carlos and Edwards 1998) or as high as 70-75% (Mohammed *et al.* 1991; Mitchell and Edwards 1996).

The phytases have different specific activities; vary in additional activities such as acid protease, acid phosphatase, and pectinase; and reveal different abilities for feed dephosphorylation (Zyla *et al.* 1995). Acid phosphatase was shown to have a key role in feed dephosphorylation, while fungal acid protease enhanced dephosphorylation by stimulating gastric digestion (Zyla *et al.* 1995). Phillippy (1999) revealed that *Aspergillus nigar*, which is the most common source of phytase, is more resistant to proteolytic digestion than the enzymes from plant sources such as wheat, and it appears that phytase A (a phosphatase with two pH optima of 2.5 and 5.0) is more resistant to trypsin digestion and less resistant to pepsin than phytase B (with a pH optima of 2.5). The peptic digestion of pH 2.5 acid phosphatase from *Escherichia coli* yields a peptide with high phytase activity (Rodriguez *et al.* 1999).

2. Characteristics of phytase

Characteristics of an enzyme suitable for seed dephosphorylation in the poultry and swine should include high specific catalytic activity expressed in units per mg of protein, broad substrate specificity, adequate thermostability, high residual activity at 37℃, high activity in the pH range of 2.5 to 7.5, resistance to proteolysis, good stability at ambient temperatures and low production costs (Zyla 2000). To be effective, these conditions are required when phytases are added to poultry and swine feed. Van Der Klis *et al.* (1997) mixed in a poultry diet a phytase which had one phytase unit (FTU) equal to 1 μ mol of ortho-phosphate liberated from 5.1mmol of sodium phytate within 1min at 37℃ and pH 5.5. Punna and Roland (1999) defined a phytase unit or FTU/kg as the amount that liberates 1 μ mol of inorganic P/min from 0.0015mol sodium phytate at 37℃ and pH 5.5. Similarly, several others (Biehl and Baker 1997b; Qian *et al.* 1996a; and Sebastian *et al.* 1996) defined phytate unit (PU) as the quantity of enzyme required to produce 1 μ mol of inorganic P/min from 5.1mmol/L of sodium phytate at a pH of 5.5 and a water bath temperature of 37℃.

Supplemental dietary microbial phytase has been shown to increase the availability of phytate P for poultry and pigs fed a commercial corn-soybean meal diet. The P equivalency of microbial phytase for 1 g of nPP is reported to be 650 to 750 U of phytase in broilers (Schoner *et al.*, 1991; Kornegay *et al.*, 1996), 520 to 700 U of phytase in turkey poults (Ravindran *et al.*, 1995; Qian *et al.*, 1996b) and 500 U of phytase in growing-finishing pigs (Kwon *et al.*, 1995a; Harper *et al.*, 1997).

Scientists (Waldroup *et al.* 2000; Yan *et al.* 2001; Yan *et al.* 2003) showed that a diet with reduced P but added 800 units of phytate per kilogram of diet markedly reduced excreta excretion of P by broilers at ages 0-3 wk, 3-6 wk and 6-9 wk (Table 1). Phytase in pullet chicks did not have a beneficial effect in increasing daily tP retention during phase 1 (wk 5) or phase 3 (wk 18) of the experiment (Keshavarz 2000) (Table 1). The study concluded that beneficial effects of phytase on performance could have been due to increasing the digestibility and availability of nutrients, other than PP, that might have been limiting in the diet. Determination of nPP requirement of laying hens was also performed by Keshvarz (2003). A control diet was fed that contained with 0.45% nPP for the entire experiment (20 to 63 wk of age). The birds in experimental groups were fed an nPP regimen of 0.25% for phase 1 (20 to 35 wk of age), 0.2% for phase 2 (36 to 51 wk of age), and 0.15% for phase 3 (52 to 63 wk of age) plus 150 or 300 units phytase/kg diet. The results showed that the higher level of phytase was more effective than the lower level in restoring the performance of birds fed the low-P diets when compared to the control (Table 1). Rutherfurd *et al.*(2002) showed that supplementation with microbial phytase to the broiler chicken diet resulted in a significantly greater phytate P disappearance from the terminal ileum for rice bran diets (17% units), but not for soybean meal, maize, wheat or rapeseed meal diets. Supplemental phytase caused improvements in weight gain and food efficiency of broilers but the magnitude of the response was greater in low nPP diets, resulting in significant nPP x phytase interactions (Cabahug *et al.* 1999).

Supplemental phyase from *Aspergillus nigar* improves PP bioavilability and reduces fecal P excretion (up to 30%) in pigs fed corn-soybean meal-based diets (Cromwell *et al.* 1993; Lei *et al.* 1993; Heindl 2000). Matsui *et al.* (2000) showed that yeast phytase improves bioavilability of P in the diet for growing pigs but the efficacy of yeast phytase is less than that of *Aspergillus nigar* phytase. Stahl *et al.* (2000) also claimed that a new phytase enzyme from a yeast system was as effective as Natuphos, at the inclusion level of 700 or 1200 U/kg of a P-deficient, corn-soybean meal diet, in improving PP utilization by young pigs. These researchers helped solve the problems of the cost and other limitation of the currently available commercial phytase (Wodzinski and Ullah 1996).

To lower the cost and address other limitations associated with currently available commercial phytases such as *Aspergillus nigar*, researchers (Robbins *et al.* 2000; Zhang *et al.* 2000; Lei 2002) started to investigate the efficiency of phytaseed (phytase produced from canola seed genetically modified with *Aspergillus ficuum* phytase gene, BASF Corp., Offenbach, Germany). As a new source of phytase, phytaseed was produced in canola seed by expressing the same phytase gene that was expressed in *Aspergillus nigar* for the production of Natuphos (Microbial phytase: Natuphos 5000, produced by *Aspergillus nigar* genetically modified with *Aspergillus ficuum* phytase gene. BASF Corp., Mt. Olive, NJ, USA) compared with the conventional microbial phytase. The efficiency of phytaseed was similar to that of Natuphos for enhancing the utilization of phytase P in corn-soybean meal-based weanling pigs diets (Zhang *et al.* 2000).

There are numerous reports on the beneficial effects of phytase on increasing the digestibility and availability of other nutrients such as amino acids and trace minerals in addition to increasing the availability of PP for poultry and swine (Lei *et al.* 1993; Biehl and Baker 1996, 1997a; Sebastian *et al.* 1996; Namkung and Leeson 1999). Although Peter and Baker (2001) reported that the addition of phytase improved nitrogen retention, these effects were independent of dietary phytic acid and aP levels. Many intriguing and perplexing questions about the potential

Table 1. Recent research on phytase addition and phosphorus requirements

References	Species	Amounts of phytase added	Types of phytase[1]	Amounts of P to be added	Reduced rates of P in excreted manure (%)	Comments
Perney et al. (1993)	Broiler	750U/kg	Dry	0.38% aP[2] / 0.44% aP	20 / 16	1. Each diet was fed to 4 groups of 8 chicks from 4 to 10 days of age. All excreta were collected from 3 groups during days 7 to 19. 2. 1 unit of phytase activity was the amount of enzyme liberating 1 μmol of inorganic P per min at 37.5°C.
Um and Paik (1999)	Hen (ISA Brown, 21 wks age)	500U/kg	Dry	0.37% TP[3]	41	1. The quantity of enzyme required to produce 1 μ inorganic P/min from 5.1mmol/L of sodium phytase at a pH of 5.5 and a water bath temp. of 37°C.
Kwon et al. (1999)	Broiler	300PU/kg (for starter) / 500PU/kg (for finisher)	Dry	0.36% aP	Starter period : 17 / Finisher period : 10	1. 1PU of phytase is the quantity of enzyme which sets free 1 μmol of inorganic P/min from 0.0015mol/L sodium at pH 5.5 at 37°C.
Waldroup et al. (2000)	Broiler (0-3 wks age)	800U/kg	Dry	HAPC[4] in diet / 0.45% nPP[5] / YDC[3] in diet / 0.45% nPP	47 (HAPC in diet) / 28 (YDC in diet)	1. The diets of HAPC and YDC were compared to the diet which was mixed with NRC (1994) diet as control.
Keshavarz (2000)	Pullets (0-18 wks age)	300U/kg	Dry	Levels of nPP in diet: 0-6 wks age 0.20% / 6-12 wks age 0.15% / 12-18 wks age 0.10%		1. The level of control group nPP was same nPP requirement of NRC (1994) for 0-6 wks age (0.4%), 6-12 wks (0.35%), and 12-18 wks age (0.30%). 2. The author wrote that phytase did not help increase percentage or daily total P retention during phase 1 (wk 5) or phase 3 (wk 18). He wrote that beneficial effects of phytase on performance could have been due to increasing the digestibility and availability of other nutrients that might have been limiting in other diets.
Zyla et al. (2001)	Broiler	750FTU/kg (phytase) / 3156U/kg (acid phospharase) / 1900U/kg (pectinase) / 20g/kg (citric acid)	Dry	1.7g nPP[6]/kg / 4.1g TP/kg / 8.0g Ca/kg	56	1. 1 unit of phytase activity (FTU) was the amount of enzyme required to liberate 1 μM of inorganic phosphorus from 2mM sodium phytate in 1 min. under 40°C, pH 4.5. 2. 1 unit of acid phosphatase activity was equal to 1 μM/min of p-nitrophenol liberated from 5.5mM disodium p-nitrophenol at 40°C, pH 4.5. 3. 1 unit of pectinase (PGU) was the amount of enzyme which released 1.0 μM of reducing sugars from 0.7% apple pectin (degree of methylation 60%) per min under the above conditions.

Table 1(contiued). Recent research on phytase addition and phosphorus requirements

References	Species	Amounts of phytase added	Types of phytase[1]	Amounts of P to be added	Reduced rates of P in excreted manure (%)	Comments
Yan et al. (2001)	Broiler	800U/kg	Dry	Levels in nPP in the diets were increased from 0.10% through 0.45% with ratio of increase, 0.05%.		1. At the lower P level (> 0.25%), birds fed diets with phytase excreted less P than those fed diets without phytase. At higher P levels (< 0.25% nPP), little difference in fecal P was noted between birds fed diets with or without phytase. Thus, they wrote that addition of phytase alone, without commensurate reduction in dietary P, will not ameliorate P excretion.
Yan et al. (2003)	Broiler (3-6 wks age)	800U/kg	Dry	0.1% through 0.35% with 0.05% increments (nPP)	39-52	1. The diets of HAPC and YDC were compared to the diet which was mixed with NRC (1994) diet as control.
Lim et al. (2003)	Lay hen (21 wks age)	300U/kg	Dry	0.15 and 0.25% of nPP	Up to 19	Novo Nordisk Crop, Novo Alle 2880 Bagsvaerd, Denmark, phytase activity
Kwon et al. (1995a)	Swine (Growing - Finishing)	500FTU/kg	Dry	0.17% aP : Grower 0.10% aP : Finisher	51	1.1 phytase FTU/kg unit is the amount that liberates $1 \mu mol$ inorganic P/min from 0.0015mol sodium phytate at 37°C, pH 5.5. 2. Control was 0.26% aP. 3. Starting weight was 18 ± 2kg. 4. Experimental length was 12 wks with 42 days for grower and 42 days for finisher.
Kwon et al. (1995b)	Swine (Winning and Growing)	500FTU/kg	Dry	0.26% aP : Winner 0.19% aP : Grower	20-25	1.1 phytase FTU/kg unit is defined as above. 2. The aP level of control was 0.33% for weaning period and 0.23% for growing period. 3. Starting weight was 16 ± 2kg. 4. Experimental length was 10 wks for weaning and growing period.
Harper et al. (1997)	Swine (Growing - Finishing)	500U/Kg	Dry	P Grower : Finisher = 0.40% : 0.35% Ca Grower : Finisher = 0.53% : 0.43%	21	Control Group P - Grower : Finisher = 0.50 : 0.40 Ca - Grower : Finisher = 0.58 : 0.48

[1] All phytase were microbial; [2] aP: available phosphorus; [3] TP: total phosphorus; [4] HAPC: high available P corn; [5] YDC: yellow dent corn; [6] nPP: non-phytate phosphorus

efficacy of microbial phytase for improving protein utilization were presented here. If phytase does truly improve protein and/or amino acid digestibility, why don't these improvements also consistently manifest in improvements in growth performance for non-ruminant animals fed amino acid-deficient diets?

According to Zyla et al. (1995, 2001), phytase alone could not release 100% of the PP present in a corn-soybean diet. These reports indicated that phytase preparations (commercial and laboratory derived sources) are not pure phytase but that they contain acid phosphotases, acid proteases and pectinase. A negative correlation was found between the purity of the phytase preparation and its ability to release PP. An exact balance between the different components of the enzymatic "cocktail" was needed for 100% release of PP from the corn-soybean diet to occur.

Vitamin D, its metabolites and organic acids

Vitamin D stimulates P transport mechanisms in the intestine (Mohammed *et al.* 1991; Biehl and Baker 1997a), and it also appears to enhance phytase activity. Phytase activity has been enhanced by vitamin D, as well as its metabolites, 25 OH D_3 and 1, 25-dehydroxycholecalciferol (1, 25 $(OH)_2$ D_3). The addition of 5 μg 1, 25 $(OH)_2D_3$/kg to corn-soybean meal diets deficient in P increased the retention PP from 31 to 68% (Edwards 1993). Supplementation of 75 units of phytase/kg of diet in addition to the 1, 25 $(OH)_2$ D_3 further increased the retention of PP to 79%. Application of these results to poultry and other animals (mainly swine and rats) may provide considerable relief to the phosphate dilemma.

Increasing the level of cholecalciferol (D_3) in the diet of broiler chickens may increase the utilization of PP (Mohammed *et al.* 1991). High levels of D_3 (110 μg and 220 μg/kg of diet) increased PP utilization, but the increase was not as much as that obtained from 1,25-$(OH)_2D_3$ supplementation. 1,25-$(OH)_2D_3$, D_3 and 1 α -OHD_3 were consistently effective in increasing PP utilization as measured by plasma Ca & P, incidence of P rickets, bone ash and retention of Ca, P and phytate P (Edwards 2002). Edwards *et al.*(2002) reported that 1- α -hydroxycholecalciferol (1 α -OHD_3) was approximately eight times as effective as D_3 for satisfying the requirements of several criteria (body weight, plasma Ca, rickets, and bone ash). These researchers believed that percentage bone ash gave the most precise values in experiments.

Organic acids (C_1-C_7) that are widely distributed in nature and are normal plant and animal constituent have been used as food and feed preservatives for their antimicrobial action. These acids inhibit or delay certain strains of bacteria through their effect on diet and intestinal pH. Propionic, formic, citric, lactic and ascorbic acids may positively affect utilization of nutrients in swine and poultry without adversely affecting animal performance. Boling-Frankenbath *et al.* (2001) included 6% citric acid in a corn-soybean meal diet for 8 to 22 day old broiler chicks. This spared 0.15% P for growth and 0.1% P when bone ash was measured. On the other hand, 500U/kg of supplemental phytase plus 0.35% Nutri-acid may completely replace inorganic P, while reducing fecal P excretion by approximately 20% (Omogbenigun *et al.* 2003). However, Boling *et al.* (2000) suggested that use of citric acid at level of 2 to 6% of the diet for improving PP utilization would not be economical for either pigs or poultry. They also said that dietary citric acid effectively improved phytate P utilization in chicks, but has a much smaller effect in pigs.

There are still limited number of publications on organic acids, probiotics, starches and other additives and their impact on P utilization efficiency. Further research should address these additives.

Maintaining proper Ca:P ratios with phytase and D_3

The equivalence of phytate for nPP (1 g of nPP / 650-750 U of phytase in broilers, Korengay *et al.* 1996; Yi *et al.* 1996) was influenced by dietary Ca:tP ratios and nPP levels because these two factors affect not only phytate P release and P absorption in the small intestine, but also phytase activity in broiler and pigs (Schoner *et al.* 1993; Qian *et al.* 1995). Mohammed *et al.* (1991) reported that supplemental D_3 dramatically increased PP digestibility and the retention of P and Ca of the chick. However, this improvement by D_3 addition was also influenced by dietary Ca because the addition of D_3 could not totally overcome the P depletion unless dietary Ca was lowered simultaneously.

Qian *et al.* (1997) demonstrated that dietary Ca:tP ratios formulated in the range of 1.1:1 to 1.4:1 appear to provide the maximum efficiency of supplemental phytase and D_3 in broilers. They reported that maximum responses when broiler chicks were fed with diets containing 600 to 900 U of phytase/kg diet, a D_3 level of 660 μg/kg diet, and a dietary Ca:tP ratios ranging from 1.1:1 to 1.4:1. D_3 supplementation increased the level of phytase activity in pigs, which led to an improvement in PP utilization when diets were low or devoid of D_3 (Pointillart *et al.* 1986, 1989). In laying hens the effect of phytase supplementation was significantly modified by the levels of Ca and nPP (Lim *et al.* 2003). High Ca:tP ratios (1.5:1 to 2.0:1) in low-P corn-soybean meal diets supplemented with microbial phytase decrease the utilization of P for weanling pigs (Lei *et al.* 1994; Qian *et al.* 1996b) and growing-finishing pigs (Liu *et al.* 1998).

The specific regions of P absorption in the digestive tract is also of interest to researchers. Lowing the dietary Ca:tP ratios to 1.0:1 in a low-P diet containing phytase increased the apparent absorption of P in the small intestine. And a significant amount of P was absorbed in the cecum (Liu *et al.* 2000).

Dietary manipulation to lower P requirements

Insufficiencies associated with digestion and metabolism results in nutrient excretion. On average 20-60% of the P consumed is retained in the body (Table 2). This illustrates the importance of using nutritional means to reduce nutrient excretion and diet cost.

As animals grow, nutrient requirements change in the maintenance requirement, the composition of growth and production, which results in increased feed consumption. The time period which poultry and pigs are fed an over- or under-supply of nutrients may be reduced by phase feeding diets with specific nutrient composition that match growth and production stages of the livestock. Angel *et al.* (2000a, 2000b) analyzed the nPP requirements of broilers in a four phase feeding system. The four phases were: starter (hatch to 18 d of age), grower (18 to 32 d of age), finisher (32 to 42 d of age) and withdrawal (42 to 49 d of age). The four individual phases had 0.45, 0.36, 0.18 and 0.14% nPP compared to commercial diets of 0.63, 0.36, 0.32 and 0.28% nPP for the same periods. There were no increases in the numbers of birds that had broken wings or legs at processing. The researchers conclude that nPP can be reduced (compared to commercial usage levels) by 5% in the grower and 15% in the finisher diets without affecting bone strength or performance, and withdrawal phase nPP can be reduced by 40% as well.

Often, commercial diets are formulated with the consideration of several factors including the variability of ingredients, nutrient availability within an ingredient for each animal, changes in nutrient availability due to processing, growing season or soil where ingredients were grown, specific genotype of the plant, livestock status, physiological factors of the poultry, swine or cattle such as sex and age, environmental factors such as heat or animal density, and accuracy of the feed mill in mixing the ingredients. Deficiencies are prevented by using safety margins in formulations and these safety margins may be decreased (Nahm 2002).

To minimize formulation safety margins, formulators need improved knowledge on ingredient nutrient content and its variability for poultry and swine. Analytical techniques such as near infrared reflectance (NIR) technology at the feed mill allows for rapid ingredient analysis, resulting in "real time" formulation and decreased safety margins. Other methods to lower these safety margins include changes in

Table 2. Digestion and retention of phosphorus by different classes of swine

Phosphorus	Nursery	Finishing	Gestating	Lactating
Digested (%)	20-70	20-50	30-45	10-35
Retained (%)	20-80	20-45	20-45	20

(Kornegay and Harper, 1997)

ingredient delivery systems, seasonal formulations, and diet formulation for specific poultry or swine individuals. The use of new technologies to minimize safety margins has been hindered by implementation costs, information and technology availability, and previous lack of economic or legislative incentives (Nahm 2003).

A logical and cost effective approach to reduce nutrient excretion in pig production is to improve feed efficiency. By improving feed efficiency 0.1 points (for example, from 3.0 to 2.9) a 33% reduction in nutrient excretion can result while maintaining animal growth and nutrient retention (Heugton and Kempen 1999). One study (Koch 1990) estimated, based on theoretical calculations that nitrogen and phosphorus excretion could be reduced 13% by using two feeds during the grower-finisher period rather than just one. It has been estimated that phosphorus excretion can be reduced by 10-25% through precision feeding, the formulation of dietary nutrients to meet an animals exact needs. Excretion of excess nutrients can also be reduced with the knowledge on the content and availability of nutrients in feedstuffs and accuracy in feed manufacturing (Nahm 2002).

The major components of pig diets are cereal grains and oilseed meals. In feedstuffs of vegetable origin, the bioavailability of P ranges from 14 to 50% (NRC 1998). P excretion can be reduced by formulation of diets based on available P and selection of ingredients with high P availability. Table 3 shows the calculated total and aP levels in diets formulated to contain 0.5% total P using different ingredients (Cromwell 1990). According to this table, when corn-soybean meal was used, the diet contained 0.23% available P, but when it was actually fed, the available P was greater than the growing pigs requirements. This would result in higher P excretion because the amount of available P exceeds the requirement.

Table 3. Available phosphorus levels in diets formulated to contain 0.5% total phosphorus

Diet	Total phosphate, %	Available phosphorus, %	Added dicalcium phosphorus, %
Corn - soybean meal	0.50	0.23	0.96
Wheat - soybean meal	0.50	0.28	0.57
Corn - canola meal	0.50	0.10	0.09
Corn - soybean meal - wheat midds	0.50	0.20	0.68
Growing pig requirement (NRC, 1998)	0.50	0.23	

(Cromwell, 1990)

There is limited information on the P requirements of today's poultry and swine (NRC 1994; NRC 1998; Cromwell and Lindemann 2002). No conclusive values have been established apart from those published by NRC (1994), NRC (1998) and research papers. It is clear that the research is highly variable between researchers. Strain, weights at the end of the phase studied, criteria used for requirement determination (bone ash, growth etc.), age, sex, Ca level, Ca:tP ratio, Ca:aP ratio, tP and aP values in feed vary between research reports and this leads to difficulties in determining what the actual requirements may be. Further research is needed in this area.

REDUCTION OF PHOSPHORUS SOLUBILITY USING MANURE AMENDMENTS

Chemicals containing Al, Ca and Fe

Soluble P is the most vulnerable and the most common form of P in runoff from pastures receiving animal manure (Edwards and Daniel 1993), Thus, reducing the potential for P loss in runoff could be achieved by converting manure P to less-soluble forms.

Many scientists have hypothesized that Al, Ca or Fe amendments would lower soluble P and consequently decrease runoff potential. Chemical reagents that have been used for reducing P solubility in animal manure are listed in Table 4. Shreve *et al.* (1995) reported that aluminum sulfate (alum) $[Al_2(SO_4)_3 \cdot 14H_2O]$ treated poultry litter lowered P concentrations in runoff by 87 and 63% as compared to untreated litter for the first and second runoff events. Ferrous sulfate ($FeSO_4 \cdot 7H_2O$) treatment also decreased runoff P concentration by 77 and 48%. Alum amendment of poultry manure may become a management tool to reduce P loading to surface water, increase forage yields, improve the fertilizer value of litter, and economically benefit poultry products (Shreve *et al.* 1995). Moore and Miller (1994) tested 20 different chemicals for their capacity on lowering soluble P in poultry litter. Water soluble P in the poultry litter was reduced from > 2000 mg P/kg litter to < 1 mg P/kg when treated with the addition of alum, quick lime, slaked lime, ferrous chloride, ferric chloride, ferrous sulfate, or ferric sulfate under favorable pH conditions. Gypsum and sodium aluminate reduced water soluble P by 50 to 60%. Calcitic and dolomitic limestone were less effective. The results of this study suggest that treating litter prior to field application with some of these compounds could significantly reduce the amount of soluble P in runoff from litter-amended pastures.

Metal salts including alum, slaked lime $[Ca(OH)_2]$, ferric chloride ($FeCl_3$) and ferrous chloride ($FeCl_2$) are reagents commonly used to promote the precipitation of P solids that accumulate as a flocculent and are filtered from the agricultural (mainly animal manure) waste stream. Use of reagents can achieve 75 to 95% P

Table 4. Summary of the effectiveness of chemicals in reducing soluble P in manure

Name of Chemicals	Amount to be added	Reduced P Solubility (%)	Types of waste	Authors	Comments
$CaSO_4 \cdot 2H_2O$	100g/kg (litter)	65	Broiler litter		When $CaCO_3$ was added with alum to buffer the pH, virtually 100% of the soluble was removed from the solution.
$Al_2(SO_4)_3 \cdot 18H_2O$+ $CaCO_3$	from 100g to 500g/kg (litter) +100g $CaCO_3$/kg (litter)	≈ 100	Broiler litter		
$Al_2(SO_4)_3 \cdot 18H_2O$	from 200g to 500g/kg (litter)	≈ 95	Broiler litter	Moore and Miller (1994)	100g/kg - 77% reduced
$FeCl_3$	250g/kg (litter)	≈ 95	Broiler litter		Not significantly different when $Fe(SO_4) \cdot 7H_2O$ was amended with $CaCO_3$. 100g/kg - 63% reduced. 200g/kg - 74% reduced.
$FeSO_4 \cdot 7H_2O$	450g/kg (litter)	≈ 95	Broiler litter		
$FeCl_2 \cdot 4H_2O$	300g/kg (litter)	≈ 95	Broiler litter		Addition of $CaCO_3$ in conjunction with $FeCl_2 \cdot 4H_2O$ resulted in more efficient P removal at lower rates alone.
$Al_2(SO_4)_3 \cdot 14H_2O$	1 : 5 = chemical : litter	87 (first runoff) 63 (second runoff)	Broiler litter	Shreve et al. (1995)	
$FeSO_4 \cdot 7H_2O$	1 : 5 = chemical : litter	77 (first runoff) 48 (second runoff)	Broiler litter		
$Al_2(SO_4)_3 \cdot 18H_2O$	65g/kg (litter)	56	Broiler litter		
$FeSO_4 \cdot 7H_2O$	130g/kg (litter)	56	Broiler litter	Moore (1995)	
$FeCl_3$ (liquid)	100g/kg (litter)	57	Broiler litter		
Fe - rich by-product	20-50g/kg (manure)	40	Poultry manure	Codling et al. (2000)	
Al - rich by-product	590g/kg (manure)	39	Poultry manure	Dao et al. (2001)	
Fe - rich by-product	200g/kg (manure)	48	Poultry manure		
$Al_2(SO_4)_3 \cdot 14H_2O$	430mg/L (liquid manure)	84	Swine manure	Smith et al. (2001a)	
$AlCl_3$	0.75% (of final manure volume)	76	Swine manure	Smith et al. (2001b)	

removal under favorable conditions (Tomson and Vignona 1984; Bowker *et al.* 1987).

When alum was used to precipitate P, the pH had to be below 6.4 to achieve P concentrations of 0.8 mg P/L, but with lime usage the pH needed to achieve this same level was 11.5 (Ulmgren 1975). This study indicated that aluminum phosphate ($AlPO_4$) solubility reaches a minimum of 0.01 mg P/L at a pH of 6.0. In the precipitates, the Al/P mole ratios were 1.5 to 2.5. In the Swedish study, 33 plants wastewater treatments used alum, 9 used quick lime (CaO) and 1 used ferric chloride. These treatments reduced P content in effluent water as well as decreased suspended solids, BOD, heavy metals, worm eggs and parasites (Ulmgren, 1975).

According to Ripley (1974), principle chemical reactions involving the precipitation of P by Al, Ca and Fe may included:

1. $Al_2(SO_4)_3 \cdot 14H_2O + 2H_2PO_4 \rightarrow 2AlPO_4 + 6H^+ + 3SO_4^{2-} + 14H_2O$

2. $Fe_2(SO_4)_3 \cdot 2H_2O + 2PO_4^{3-} \rightarrow 2FePO_4 + 3SO_4^{2-} + 2H_2O$

3. $5Ca(OH)_2 + 3H_2PO_4^- + 3H^+ \rightarrow Ca_5(PO_4)_3OH + 9H_2O$

4. $Al(OH)_3 + H_3PO_4 \rightarrow Al(OH)_3\text{-}H_3PO_4$

Lime can be added as quick lime or slaked lime. In a similar manner, ferric chloride or ferric sulfate seem to be equally effective. In place of alum, sodium alumicate ($Na_2Al_2O_4$) has also been used. The optimum pH level for P removal with Al and Fe has been proposed to be dependent on the metal/P mole ratio (Hsu 1976). When the metal/P mole ratio was two to five, a pH range of 5.5 to 8.0 was optimal for P removal by Al, while a pH range of 4.7 to 7.1 was optimal for Fe. Fe is present as Fe (III) solids, which react with carbon in sewage. This results in Fe (III) being reduced to Fe (II) and then solubilized (reductive iron dissolution) (Freeze and Cherry 1979):

$$CH_2O + 4Fe(OH)_3 + 7H^+ \rightarrow 4Fe^{2+} + HCO_3^- + 10H_2O$$

The PO_4 can then be attenuated by the ferrous iron in solution in two ways: the first is by precipitation of Fe(II)-P solids, such as vivianite:

$$3Fe^{2+} + 2PO_4^{3-} + 8H_2O \rightarrow Fe_3(PO_4)_2 \cdot 8H_2O$$

and the second occurs if the effluent is subsequently oxidized, by the precipitation of Fe(III)-P solids like strengite:

$$Fe^{3+} + PO_4^{3-} + 2H_2O \rightarrow FePO_4 \cdot 2H_2O$$

Further research is needed on the application of alum and aluminum treated manure to the soil. Although Al, Ca and Fe have been shown to be effective in decreasing the solubility of P under certain soil conditions, Ca and Fe phosphorus minerals may dissolve. Under mildly acidic soil conditions calcium phosphate minerals may dissolve (Moore et al. 1998), so use of Ca to precipitate P in manure is not likely to be a long-term solution to the P problem. Bacteria present in saturated or flooded soils utilize the Fe (III) in ferric phosphate as a terminal electron acceptor for respiration, resulting in the formation of more soluble ferrous phosphates (Moore and Miller 1994; Shreve et al. 1995). Aluminum phosphate minerals are stable for longer periods of time because they are stable under a wide range of physico-chemical conditions such as pH and other conditions. Aluminum phosphate mineral dissolution under normal soil conditions would only occur under extremely low levels of P in the soil solution, and the release of P from aluminum phosphate would be beneficial in preventing P deficiency (Moore and Miller 1994; Moore et al. 1999). It has also been reported that fescue plots receiving alum-treated litter had significantly higher yields and N contents than plots receiving untreated litter, indicating increased availability of N in the litter when treated with alum (Shreve et al. 1995). In conclusion, the use of Al to precipitate P in manures is preferable to use of Ca or Fe. Long-term trials should be undertaken with examining potential operational problems that could result, such as permeability reduction from mineral accumulations or biomass buildup (Robertson 2000).

There has been a report, however, that high rates of alum addition to swine manure resulted in H_2S odor (Smith et al. 2001). Also application of alum sludge at rates up to 10 g/kg has been reported to increase plant yield, but higher rates decrease it (Heil and Barbarick 1989). This decreased yield was most likely due to P fixation by the sludge. Plants grown in alum sludge-amended soils (Bugbee and Frink 1985) and iron-sludge amended media (Elliott and Singer 1988) have been shown to have less P available for growth through leaf tissue analysis. In a study using costal plain sandy loam, Geertsema et al. (1994) reported no long-term (30 months) effects of alum sludge application on plant-available P or loblolly pine (Ponus rigida) growth. Alum appears to have promise as a best management practice for poultry production (Sims and Luka-McCafferty 2002) and swine production (Smith et al. 2001a).

There has been a negative relation between aluminum-P and the P availability indices with the applied P in alum sludge affected soils being immobilized mainly as Al-P (Cox et al., 1997). The relative abundance of inorganic forms of P in soils may be affected by the components of water treatment sludges, which would also influence P availability. Codling et al. (2000) reported that water quality has been affected by runoff and leaching of phosphorus from poultry litter amended fields. These scientists said that water-soluble P in poultry litter and long-term litter-amended soils can be substantially reduced by incorporating residues rich in Al and Fe. These residues may be useful for reducing P runoff and leaching from poultry litter and litter amended fields. Further studies should focus on possible benefits of the use of aluminum in the types of manure and soil application.

Fly-ash (coal) usage

Although fly ash (FA) has been used throughout the world (Wong and Wong 1989; Sims *et al.* 1995) as a soil amendment to improve soil physical and chemical properties, research on its use for reducing soluble P in animal manure is relatively recent. FA is a heterogeneous mixture of amorphous and crystalline phases and is generally considered to be a ferroaluminosilicate mineral with Al, Ca, Fe, K, Na and Si as predominant elements (Andriano *et al.* 1980; Mattigod *et al.* 1990). Particle size greatly influences chemical composition of FA and how it may affect physical properties of soil. The pH of FA can vary from 4.5 to 12.0 depending largely on the S content of the parent coal (Plank and Martens 1974).

Coal FA is the residue of coal combustion in power plants and may be an alternative for use in reducing the solubility of P in manure (Billski *et al.* 1999; Dao 1999; Dou *et al.* 2003). The composition of this material depends on coal and combustion conditions (Roy and Griffin 1982), and is produced in large quantities due to increased use of coal in power production. Coal combustion by-products are produced at a rate of 18 million Mg annually but only 20% of the ash produced is being used (Bilski *et al.* 1999).

Animal manure P solubility may be reduced by Ca, Al or Fe-rich amendments and they may reduce risk of off site movement from uncovered manure storage areas and land application of stockpiled or composted manures. Treated manure having reduced soluble P concentrations would have N and P nutrients ratios more in balance with plant nutritional needs than untreated manures when land-applied (Stout *et al.* 1998). According to the reported of Dao (1999), caliche, alum and FA reduced water-extractable P in stockpiled manure by 21, 60 and 85% and by 50, 83 and 93% in composted manure at the 0.1 kg/kg rate. Mixing these amendments with feedlot manure widened the effective manure N/P ratio by a factor of 1.5 to 18. And applying fly ash-treated stockpiled or composted manure reduced all extractable P fractions from amended soils although alum and calithe consistently reduced the water-extractable P fraction only.

Vincini *et al.* (1994) reported that a marked mobilization of inorganic P compounds of FA, not correlated with the gradual acidification of the mixtures during the experimental period, occurred in the amended manure, possibly as a consequence of the microbial activity. The fermentation bottles in their research contained 1500 ML of swine manure or 1500 ML of swine manure and 150 g of FA (fly ash/manure ratio of 10% w/v) or 1500 ML of swine manure and 300 g of FA (20 w/v). Toth *et al.* (2001) reported interesting research results. They found that fluidized bed combustion FA was effective in reducing readily soluble P in the treated dairy manure, although at higher amendment rates than the alum. However, anthracite refuse FA did not significantly reduce soluble-P in the dairy manure and this amendment was ineffective in the swine samples. They said that reasons for the differential response to the amendments in P solubility between the dairy and swine manure are unclear. Dou *et al.* (2003) reported more progressively that the fluidized bed combustion fly ash (FBC) reduced readily soluble P by 50 to 60% at a rate of 400g/kg for dairy, swine, or broiler litter manure. They also said that flue gas desulfurization by-product (FGD) reduced readily soluble P by nearly 80% when added to swine manure and broiler litter at 150 and 250g/kg, and another by-product, anthracite refuse fly ash (ANT), was ineffective for all three manures. Further research should be addressed.

CONCLUSION

There are 2 methods currently used to reduce the phosphorus content of manure. One is to reduce the amount of P excreted into the manure and the other is to reduce the P solubility in manure. Reduction of P excretion in manure may be achieved by feeding management techniques such as use of phytase, vitamin D metabolites and organic acids, proper Ca:P ratios and diet manipulation. Research is still needed for use of organic acids, probiotics or starch to reduce phosphorus excretion in manure. To reduce the P solubility in manure, certain amounts of chemical reagents containing Al, Fe or Ca must be added to the manure or litter. Use of FA in manure or litter to reduce P solubility has had questionable research results so far, but more research is needed.

ACKNOWLEDGMENT

Nickolas Nahm of Duke University (Biomedical Engineering Department) helped with library work and typed this manuscript. The author appreciates his assistance.

REFERENCES

Adriano DC, Page AL, Elseewi AA, Chang AC, Straughan I. (1980) Utilization and disposal of fly ash and other coal residues in terrestial ecosystems: A review. *Journal of Environmental Quality* **9**, 333-344.

Angel CR. (2003) Nutrient management to meet environmental challenges in poultry. In *The Proceedings of the California Animal Nutrition Conference*, Radisson Hotel, Presno, CA 93721, USA. pp. 23-37.

Angel R, Applegate TJ, Christman M. (2000a) Effect of dietary non-phytate phosphorus (nPP) on performance and bone measurements in broilers fed on a four-phase feeding system. *Poultry Science* **79** (**Suppl. 1**), 21.

Angel R, Applegate TJ, Christman M. (2000b) Effect of dietary non-phytate phosphorus (nPP) on performance and bone measurements in the starter and grower phase. *Poultry Science* **79** (**Suppl. 1**), 22.

Biehl RR, Baker DH. (1996) Efficacy of supplemental 1a-hydroxycholecalciferol and microbial phytase for young pigs fed phosphorus- or amino acid-deficient corn-soybean meal diets. *Journal of Animal Science* **74**, 2960-2966.

Biehl RR, Baker DH. (1997a) 1 α -Hydroxycholecalciferol does not increase the specific activity of intestinal phytase but does improve phosphorus utilization in both cacectomized and sham-operated chicks fed cholecalciferol-adequate diets. *Journal of Nutrition* **127**, 2054-2059.

Biehl RR, Baker DH. (1997b) Microbial phytase improves amino acid utilization in young chicks fed diets based on soybean meal but not diets based on peanut meal. *Poultry Science* **76**, 355-360.

Bilski JJ, Alva AK, Sajwan KS. (1999) Fly ash. In: Rechcigl JE, editor. *Soil Amendments and Environmental Quality*. CRC Press, Lewis Publ., Boca Ration, FL, USA.

Boling-Frankenbach JL, Snow SD, Parsons CM, Baker DH. (2001) The effect of citric acid on the calcium and phosphorus requirements for chicks fed corn-soybean meal diets. *Poultry Science* **80**, 783-788.

Boling SD, Webel DM, Mavromichalis I, Parsons CM, Baker DH. (2000) The effects of citric acid on phytate-phosphorus utilization in young chicks and pigs. *Journal of Animal Science* **78**, 682-689.

Bowker RPW, Stensel HD, Hartmann GL, Smith JM. (1987) Process design manual for phosphorus removal. *USEPA 625/1-87/01 USEPA*, Cincinnati, OH, USA.

Bugbee CJ, Frink CR. (1985) Alum sludge as a soil amendment: Effect on soil properties and plant growth. *Connecticut Agricultural Experiment Station Bulletin* p. 827.

Cabahug S, Ravindran V, Selle PH, Bryden WL. (1999) Response of broiler chickens to microbial phytase supplementation as influenced by dietary phytic acid and non-phytate phosphorus contents. I. Effects on bird performance and toe ash. *British Poultry Science* **40**, 660-666.

Carlos AB, Edwards HM, Jr.. (1998) The effects of 1,25-Dihydroxycholecalciferol and phytase on the natural phytase phosphorus utilization by laying hens. *Poultry Science* **77**, 850-858.

Codling EE, Chaney RL, Mulchi CL. (2000) Use of aluminum and iron-rich residues to immobilize phosphorus in poultry litter and litter-amended soils. *Journal of Environmental Quality* **29**, 1924-1931.

Council for Agricultural Science and Technology. (1996) *Integrated animal waste management. Task Force Rep 128.* CAST, Ames, IA, USA.

Cox AE, Camberato JJ, Smith BR. (1997) Phosphate availability and inorganic transformation in an alum sludge-affected soil. *Journal of Environmental Quality* **26**, 1393-1398.

Cromwell GL. (1990) Application of phosphorus availability data to practical diet formulation. *Carolina Swine Nutrition Conference.* Proceedings, November 7-8, pp. 55-75.

Cromwell GL, Coffey RD, Paker GR, Monegue HJ, Randolph JH. (1995) Efficacy of recombinant-derived phytase in improving the bioavailability of phosphorus in corn-soybean meal diets for pigs. *Journal of Animal Science* **73(7)**, 2000-2008.

Cromwell GL, Coffey RD, Paker GR, Monegue HJ, Randolph JH. (1995) Efficacy of phytase in improving the bioavailability of phosphorus in soybean meal and corn-soybean meal diets for pigs. *Journal of Animal Science* **71**, 1831-1840.

Cromwell GL, Lindemann MD. (2002) Taking a closer look at calcium and phosphorus. *Feed Management* **53(5)**, 19-23.

Dao TH. (1999) Coamendments to modify phosphorus extractability and nitrogen/phosphorus ratio in feedlot manure and composted manure. *Journal of Environmental Quality* **28**, 1114-1121.

Dao TH, Sikora IJ, Hamasaki A, Chaney RL. (2001) Manure phosphorus extractability as affected by aluminum- and iron by-products and aerobic composting. *Journal of Environmental Quality* **30**, 1693-1698.

deBoland AR, Garner GB, O'Dell BL. (1975) Identification and properties of phytate in cereal grains and oilseed products. *Journal of Agriculture and Food Chemistry* **23**, 1186-1192.

Dou Z, Zhang GY, Stout WL, Toth JD, Ferguson JD. (2003) Effecacy of Alum and coal combustion by-products in stabilizing manure phosphorus. *Journal of Environmental Quality* **32(4)**, 1490-1497.

Edwards HM, Jr.. (1993) Dietary 1,25-Dihydroxycholecalciferol supplementation increases natural phytate phosphorus utilization in chickens. *Journal of Nutrition* **123**, 567-577.

Edwards HM, Jr.. (2002) Studies on the efficacy of cholecalciferol and derivatives for stimulating phytate utilization of broilers. *Poultry Science* **81**, 1026-1031.

Edwards DR, Daniel TC. (1993) Effects of poultry litter application rate and rainfall intensity on quality of runoff from fescue grass plots. *Journal of Environmental Quality* **22**, 361-365.

Edwards HM, Jr., Shirley RB, Escoe WB, Pesti GM. (2002) Quantitative evaluation of 1-α-hydroxycholecalciferol as a cholecalciferol substitute for broilers. *Poultry Science* **81**, 664-669.

Elliott HA, Singer LM. (1988) Effect of water treatment sludge on growth and elemental composition of tomato (*Lycopersicon esculentum*) shoots. *Communications in Soil Science and Plant Analysis* **19**, 345-354.

Freeze RA, Cherry JA. (1979) Groundwater. Prentice-Hall, Englewood Cliffs, NJ, USA.

Geertsema WS, Knooke JT, Dove D. (1994) Long-term effects of sludge application to land. *Journal of American Water Works Association* **86(11)**, 64-74.

Harper AF, Kornegay ET, Schell TC. (1997) Phytase supplementation of low-phosphorus growing-finishing pig diets improves performance, phosphorus digestibility and bone mineralization and reduces phosphorus excretion. *Journal of Animal Science* **75**, 3174-3186.

Heil DM, Barbarick KA. (1989) Water treatment sludge influence on the growth of sorghum-sudangrass. *Journal of Environmental Quality* **18**, 292-298.

Heindl U. (2000) The effect of microbial phytase on amino acid digestibility and energy utilization in broilers. *XX World's Poultry Congress*, Montreal, Canada. August 20-24. p. 171.

Heugten EV, Kempen TV. (1999) Methods may exist to reduce nutrient excretion. *Feedstuffs* **71**, 12-13, 16-19. April 26.

Hsu PH. (1976) Comparison of iron (III) and aluminum in precipitation of phosphorus from solutions. *Water Research* **10**, 903-907.

Jongbloed AW, Jongbloed R. (1996) The effect of organic acids in diets for growing pigs on enhancement of microbial phytase efficacy. *Report ID-DLO No. 96009*, Lelystad, The Netherlands.

Keshavarz K, (2000) Reevaluation of nonphytate phosphorus requirement of growing pullets with and without phytate. *Poultry Science* **79**, 1143-1153.

Keshavarz K. (2003) The effect of different levels of nonphytate phosphorus with and without phytase on the performance of four strains of laying hens. *Poultry Science* **82**, 71-91.

Kingery WL, Wood CW, Delaney, DP, Williams JC, Mullins C. (1994) Impact of long-term land application of broiler litter on environmentally related soil properties. *Journal of Environmental Quality* **23**, 139-147.

Koch F. (1990) Amino acid formulation to improve carcass quality and limit nitrogen load in waste. *Carolina Swine Nutrition Conference*. Proceedings, November. pp. 76-99.

Kornegay ET, Denbow DM, Yi Z, Ravindran V. (1996) Response of broilers to graded levels of microbial phytase added to maize-soybean meal based diets containing three levels of nonphytate phosphorus. *British Journal of Nutrition*

75, 839-852.

Kornegay ET, Harper AF. (1997) Environmental nutrient: nutrient management strategies to reduce nutrient excretion of swine. *Professional Animal Scientist* **13**, 99-111.

Kwon K, Han IK, Sohn KS, Kwon CH. (1995a) Effects of microbial phytase on performance, nutrient digestibility and phosphorus excretion in growing-finishing pigs fed corn-soy diets. *Korean Journal of Animal Science* **37**(4), 341-352.

Kwon K, Han IK, Sohn KS, Kwon CH, Kwack JH. (1995b) Effects of microbial phytase on performance, nutrient digestibility and phosphorus excretion in weaning-growing pigs fed corn-wheat-soy diets. *Korean Journal of Animal Science* **37**(4), 353-362.

Kwon K, Han IK, Sohn KS, Kwon CH, Kwack JH. (1999) Effects of microbial phytase on performance of broiler chicks fed corn-wheat-soy diets. *Korean Journal of Animal Science* **41**(5), 519-525.

Lei XG. (2002) Expression, engineering, and testing of phytases. *Journal of Animal Science* **80**(Suppl. 1), 54.

Lei XG, Ku PK, Miller ER, Ulrey DE, Yokoyama MT. (1993) Supplemental microbial phytase improves bioavailability of dietary zinc to weanling pigs. *Journal of Nutrition* **123**, 1117-1123.

Lei XG, Ku PK, Miller ER, Ulrey DE, Yokoyama MT, Ullrey DE. (1994) Calcium level affects the efficacy of supplemental microbial phytase in corn-soybean meal diets of wealing pigs. *Journal of Animal Science* **72**, 139-143.

Lim HS, Namkung H, Paik IK. (2003) Effects of phytase supplementation on the performance, egg quality, and phosphorus excretion of lay hens fed different levels of dietary calcium and nonphytate phosphorus. *Poultry Science* **82**, 92-99.

Liu J, Bollinger DW, Ledoux DR, Veum TL. (1998) Lowering the dietary calcium to total phosphorus ratio increases phosphorus utilization in low-phosphorus corn-soybean meal diets supplemented with microbial phytase for growing-finishing pigs. *Journal of Animal Science* **76**, 808-813.

Liu J, Bollinger DW, Ledoux DR, Veum TL. (2000) Effects of dietary calcium: phosphrus ratios on apparent absorption of calcium and phosphorus in the small intestine, cecum, and colon of pigs. *Journal of Animal Science* **78**, 106-109.

Matsui T, Nakagawa Y, Tamura A, Watanabe C, Fujita K, Nakajima T, Yano H. (2000) Efficacy of yeast phytase in improving phosphorus bioavailability in a corn-soybean meal-based diet for growing pigs. *Journal of Animal Science* **78**, 94-99.

Mattigod SV, Rai D, Eary LE, Ainsworth CC. (1990) Geochemical factors controlling the modilization of inorganic constituents from fossil fuel residues. I. Review of the major elements. *Journal of Environmental Quality* **19**, 188-201.

McLeod RV, Hegg RD. (1984) Pasture runoff quality from application of inorganic and organic nitrogen sources. *Journal of Environmental Quality* **13**, 122-126.

Mitchell RD, Edwards HM, Jr.. (1996) Effects of phytase and 1,25-dihydroxycholecalciferol on phytate utilization and the quantitative requirement for calcium and phosphorus in young broiler chickens. *Poultry Science* **75**, 95-110.

Mohammed A, Gibney MJ, Taylor TC. (1991) The effect of dietary levels of inorganic P, calcium and cholecalciferol on the digestibility of PP by the chick. *British Journal of Nutrition* **66**, 251-259.

Moore PA, Jr., Daniel TC, Edwards DR. (1999) Reducing phosphorus runoff and improving poultry production with alum. *Poultry Science* **78**, 692-698.

Moore PA, Jr., Daniel TC, Edwards DR, Miller DM. (1995) Effect of chemical amendments on ammonia volatilization from poultry litter. *Journal of Environmental Quality* **24**, 293-300.

Moore PA, Jr., Jaunes WF, Miller DM. (1998) Effect of pH on the solubility of phosphate minerals. In: Blake JP, Patterson PH, editors. *Proceedings, National Poultry Waste Management Symposium*, Springdale, AR. Arburn University Print Service, Auburn, AL, USA. 19-20 Oct. 1998. pp. 328-333.

Moore PA, Jr., Miller DM. (1994) Decreasing phosphorus solubility in poultry litter with aluminum, calcium and iron amendments. *Journal of Environmental Quality* **23**, 325-330.

Nahm KH. (2002) Efficient feed nutrient utilization to reduce pollutants in poultry and swine manure. *Critical Reviews of Environmental Science and Technology* **32(1)**, 1-16.

Nahm KH. (2003) Bioavailability of phosphorus in poultry manure. *Avian and Poultry Biology Reviews* **14(2)**, 53-62.

Namkung H, Leeson S. (1999) Effect of phytase on dietary nitrogen-corrected apparent metabolizable energy and the ileal digestibility of nitrogen and amino acids in broiler chicks. *Poultry Science* **78**, 1317-1319.

Nelson TS. (1976) The hydrolysis of phytin phosphorus by chicks and laying hens. *Poultry Science* **55**, 2262-2264.

NRC. (1994) Nutrient Requirements of Poultry (9th ed.). National Academy Press, Washington DC, USA.

NRC. (1998) Nutrient Requirements of Swine (10th ed.). National Academy Press, Washington DC, USA.

Omogbenigum FO, Nyachoti CM, Slominski BA. (2003) The effect of supplementing microbial phytase and organic acids to a corn-soybean based diet fed to early-weaned pigs. *Journal of Animal Science* **81**, 1806-1813.

Perney KM, Cantor AH, Straw ML, Herkelman KL (1993) The effect of dietary phytase on growth performance and phosphorus utilization of broiler chicks. *Poultry Science* **72**, 2106-2114.

Peter CM, Baker DH. (2001) Microbial phytase may not effect protein utilization.

Feedstuffs **73**(**4**), 11-13, 15, 20 (January 22.)

Phillippy BQ. (1999). Susceptibility of wheat and *Aspergillus nigar* phytases to inactivation by gastrointestinal enzymes. *Journal of Agriculture and Food Chemistry* **47**, 1385-1388.

Plank CD, Martens DC. (1974) Boron availability as influenced by applications of fly ash to soil. *Soil Science Society of America Proceeedings* **38**, 974-977.

Pointillart A, Fontaine N. (1986) Effects of vitamin D on calcium regulation in vitamin D deficient pigs given a phytate-phosphorus diet. *British Journal of Nutrition* **56**, 661-669.

Pointillart A, Fourdin A, Bourdeau A, Thomasset M. (1989) Phosphorus utilization and hormonal control of calcium metabolism in pigs fed phytic phosphorus diets containing normal or high calcium levels. *Nutrition Reports International* **40**(**3**), 517-527.

Punna S, Roland DA, Sr.. (1999) Influence of supplemental microbial phytase on first cycle laying hens fed phosphorus-deficient diets from day one of age. *Poultry Science* **78**, 1407-1411.

Qian H, Kornegay ET. (1995) Characterization of the effects of varying Ca:P ratio on efficacy of phytase for replacing inorganic phosphorus in pig and poultry diets. *Journal of Animal Science* **73**(**Suppl. 2**), 17.

Qian H, Kornegay ET, Denbow DM. (1997) Utilization of phytate phosphorus and calcium as influence by microbial phytase, cholecalciferol and calcium: total phosphorus ratio in broiler diets. *Poultry Science* **76**, 37-46.

Qian H, Kornegay ET, Denbow DM. (1996b) Phosphorus equivalence of microbial phytase in turkey diets as influenced by Ca: P ratios and P levels. *Poultry Science* **75**, 69-81.

Qian H, Veit HP, Kornegay ET, Ravindran V, Denbow DM. (1996a) Effects of supplemental phytase and phosphorus on histological and other tibial bone characteristics and performances of broilers fed semi-purified diets. *Poultry Science* **75**, 618-626.

Ravindran V, Kornegay ET, Denbow DM, Yi Z, Hulet RM. (1995) Response of turkey poults to the levels of Natuphos phytase added to soybean meal based semipurified diets containing three levels of nonphytate phosphorus. *Poultry Science* **74**, 1843-1854.

Ripley PG. (1974) Nutrient removal - An american experience. *Journal of Water Pollution and Control Federation* **46**, 406-416.

Robbins BC, Radcliffe JS, Veum TL, Rice JP, Kornegay ET. (2000) Comparison of two genetically modified phytase sources fed to grower pigs. *Journal of Animal Science* **78**(**Suppl. 1**), 170.

Roberton WD. (2000) Treatment of wastewater phosphate by reductive dissolution of iron. *Journal of Environmental Quality* **29**, 1678-1685.

Rodriguez E, Porres JM, Han Y, Lei XG. (1999) Different sensitivity of recombinant *Aspergillus niger phytase* (r-phy A) and Escherichia coli pH 2.5 acid phosphatase to trypsin and pepsin *in vitro*. *Archives of Biochemistry and Biophysics* **365**, 262-267.

Roy WR, Griffin RA. (1982) A proposed classification system for coal fly ash in multidisciplinary research. *Journal of Environmental Quality* **11**, 563-568.

Rutherford SM, Chung TK, Moughan PJ. (2002) The effect of microbial phytase on ileal phosphrus and amino acid digestibility in the broiler chicken. *British Poultry Science* **44**, 598-606.

Schoner FT, Hoppe PP, Schwarz G. (1991) Comparative effects of microbial phytase and inorganic phosphorus on performance and retention of phosphorus, calcium and crude ash in broilers. *Journal Animal Physiology and Animal Nutrition* **66**, 248-255.

Schoner FT, Hoppe PP, Schwarz G, Wiesche H. (1993) Effects of microbial phytase and inorganic phosphate in broiler chicken: Performance and mineral retention at various calcium levels. *Journal of Animal Physiology and Animal Nutrition* **69**, 735-744.

Sebastian S, Touchburn SP, Chavez ER, Lague PC. (1996) The effect of supplemental microbial phytase on the performance and utilization of dietary calcium, phosphorus, copper and zinc in broiler chickens fed corn-soybean diets. *Poultry Science* **75**, 729-736.

Shreve BR, Moore PA, Jr., Daniel TC, Edwards DR, Miller DM. (1995) Reduction of phosphorus in runoff from field-applied poultry litter using chemical amendments. *Journal of Environmental Quality* **24**, 106-111.

Sims JT, Lavahum MF, Malone GW, Saylor WM, Raboy V. (1999) Effects of microbial phytase, high available phosphorus corn and dietary phosphorus level on broiler performance. 3. Effect on broiler litter composition. *Poultry Science* **78(Suppl.)**, 102.

Sims JT, Luka-McCafferty NJ. (2002) On-farm evaluations of Aluminum Sulfate (alum) as a poultry litter amendment: Effects on litter properties. *Journal of Environmental Quality* **31**, 2066-2073.

Smith DR, Moore PA, Jr., Griffis CL, Daniel TC, Edwards DR, Boothe DL. (2001a) Effects of alum and aluminum chloride on phosphorus runoff from swine manure. *Journal of Environmental Quality* **30**, 992-998.

Smith DR, Moore PA, Jr., Maxwell CV, Daniel TC. (2001b) Dietary phytase and aluminum chloride manure amendments to reduce phosphorus and ammonia volatilization from swine manure. In *International Symposium*, Addressing Animal Production and Environmental Issues, Oct. 3-5. Sheraton Imperial, Research Triangle Park, NC, USA. pp. 502-507.

Sims JT, Vasilas BL, Ghodrati M. (1995) Development and evaluation of management strategies for the use of coal ash as a soil amendment. In *Proceedings of the*

11ᵗʰ International Ash Utilization Symposium, Washington, DC. January 1985. American Coal Ash Association, Washington, DC, USA. pp. 8-1 to 8-18.

Sonzogni WC, Chapra SC, Armstrong DE, Logan TJ. (1982) Bioavailability of phosphorus inputs to lakes. *Journal of Environmental Quality* **11**, 555-563.

Stahl CH, Roneker KR, Thornton JR, Lei XG. (2000) A new phytase expressed in yeast effectively improves the bioavailability of phytate phosphorus to weaning pigs. *Journal of Animal Science* **78**, 668-674.

Stout WL, Sharpley AN, Pionke HB. (1998) Reducing soil phosphorus solubility with coal combustion by-products. *Journal of Environmental Quality* **27**, 111-118.

Tomson MB, Vignona L. (1984) Precipitation of phosphate minerals in waste water treatment systems. In: Nriagu JO and Moore PB, editors. *Phosphate minerals*. Springer-Verlag, New york, NY, USA. pp. 386-399.

Toth JD, Zhang G, Dou Z, Ferguson JD. (2001) Reducing readily soluble phosphorus forms in animal manures using chemicals. In: *International Symposium, Addressing Animal Production and Environmental Issues*. Sheraton Imperial, Research Triangle Park, NC, USA. Oct. 3-5, pp. 800-803.

Ulmgren L. (1975) Swedish experiences in chemical treatment of waste-water. *Journal of the Water Pollution Control Federation* **47**, 696-703.

Um KY, Paik IK. (1999) Effects of microbial phytase on performance, nutrient digestibility and phosphorus excretion in hens fed corn-soy diets. *Korean Journal of Animal Science* **41(5)**, 329-335.

Van Der Klis JD, Versteegh HAJ. (1996) Phosphorus nutrition of poultry. In: *Recent Advances* In: *Animal Nutrition*, Nottingham University Press, Nottingham, UK. pp. 71-83.

Van Der Klis JD, Versteegh HAJ, Simons PCM, Kies AK. (1997) The efficacy of phytase in corn-soybean meal-based diets for laying hens. *Poultry Science* **76**, 1535-1542.

Vincini M, Carini F, Silva S. (1994) Use of alkaline fly ash as an amendment for swine manure. *Bioresource Techolology* **49**, 213-222.

Waldroup PW, Kersey JH, Saleh EA, Fritts CA, Yan F, Stilborn HL, Crum RC, Jr., Raboy V. (2000) Nonphytate phosphorus requirement and phosphorus excretion of broiler chicks fed diets composed of normal or high available phosphorus corn with and without microbial phytase. *Poultry Science* **79**, 1451-1459.

Wodzinsk RJ, Ullah AHJ. (1996) Phytase. *Advanced Applied Microbiology* **42**, 263-302.

Wong MH, Wong JWC. (1989) Germination and sending growth of vegetable crops in fly ash-amended soils. *Agricultural Ecosystem and Environment* **26**, 23-35.

Yan F, Kersey JH, Waldroup PW. (2001) Phosphorus requirements of broiler chicks three to six weeks of age as influenced by phytase supplementation. *Poultry*

Science **80**, 455-459.

Yan F, Kersey JH, Frittis CA, Waldroup PW. (2003) Phosphorus requirements of broiler chicks six to nine weeks of age as influenced by phytase supplementation. *Poultry Science* **82**, 294-300.

Yi Z, Kornegay ET, Ravindran V, Denbow DM. (1996) Improving phytate phosphorus availability in corn and soybean meal for broilers using microbial phytase and calculation of phosphorus equivalency values for phytase. *Poultry Science* **75**, 240-249.

Zhang ZB, Kornegay ET, Radoliffe JS, Wilson JH, Veit HP. (2000) Comparison of phytase from genetically engineered *Asergillus* and canola in weanling pig diets. *Journal of Animal Science* **78**, 2868-2878.

Zyla K. (2000) Phytase applications in poultry feeding: Selected issues. *XX World's Poultry Congress*, Montreal, Canada. Aug. 20-24.

Zyla K, Koreleski J, Swiatkiewicz S, Ledoux DR, Piironen J. (2001) Influence of supplemental enzymes on the performance and phosphorus excretion of broilers fed wheat-based diets to 6 weeks of age. *Animal Feed Science and Technology* **89**, 113-118.

Zyla K, Ledoux DR, Garcia A, Veum T. (1995) An in vitro procedure for studying enzymatic dephosphorilation of phytate in maise-soybean feeds for turkey poults. *Poultry Science* **74**, 3-17.

Index

Poultry Production and
Waste Management

2004년 1월 10일 초판 인쇄
2004년 1월 14일 초판 발행

저 자 **K. H. Nahm & B. A. Nahm**

발행자 천 승 배

발행처 둻섧 **유한문화사**

주 소   157-801 서울시 강서구 가양1동 146-63
전 화   (02) 2668 - 2055~6   2668-2561
팩 스   (02) 2668 - 2565
E-mail   yuhansa@kornet.net

등 록   1979년 3월 6일   제 5-31호

ISBN 89-7722-623-6   93520